P9-DXO-011

The Cellular Functions
of Membrane Transport

PRENTICE-HALL INTERNATIONAL, INC., *London*
PRENTICE-HALL OF AUSTRALIA, PTY., LTD., *Sydney*
PRENTICE-HALL OF CANADA, LTD., *Toronto*
PRENTICE-HALL OF INDIA (PRIVATE) LTD., *New Delhi*
PRENTICE-HALL OF JAPAN, INC., *Tokyo*
PRENTICE-HALL DE MEXICO, S.A., *Mexico City*

The Cellular Functions
of Membrane Transport

A symposium held under the auspices of
The Society of General Physiologists
at its annual meeting at
The Marine Biological Laboratory,
Woods Hole, Massachusetts, September 4–7, 1963

Joseph F. Hoffman, *Editor*

Prentice-Hall, Inc.
Englewood Cliffs, New Jersey

Preface

This volume on the cellular functions of membrane transport contains the papers presented at the annual symposium of the Society of General Physiologists held September 4–7, 1963 at the Marine Biological Laboratory, Woods Hole, Massachusetts. This symposium is based on the concept that membrane transport is as much a characteristic of a cell as is metabolism, replication, or excitability. As such, it follows that transport phenomena have an integral role in cellular activity. The purpose of this symposium was to explore the interrelationships between membrane transport and other discrete cellular functions, utilizing, as far as possible, a multidisciplined approach. While previous symposia have been concerned with detailed descriptions of the characteristics of solute and solvent movement across a variety of living membranes, little emphasis has been given to the interdependence of transport and other cellular processes. However, the groundwork has been laid, and the field of transport has developed, if not matured, to the point where it is now possible and profitable to consider its cellular consequences. Thus, the hope is that this orientation will encourage workers to broaden the scope of their observations, to fit their particular results into the over-all physiological framework rather than limiting their interests to a specific process itself. As evidenced by the contents of this volume, the symposium was successful in elaborating many of these newly emerging aspects of the field and in emphasizing the need for new information to provide greater insight into the various processes involved.

I would like to express my appreciation to Drs. P. F. Curran, W. H. Freygang, and G. M. Tomkins for having served as session chairmen during the symposium. It is a pleasure to acknowledge my indebtedness to Drs. D. W. Bishop, I. S. Edelman, W. H. Freygang, E. Heinz, A. Leaf, J. Orloff, A. Rothstein, A. M. Shanes, G. M. Tomkins, and D. C. Tosteson, for their advice and counsel in the planning and organization of this symposium. On behalf of the Society of General Physiologists, I would like to thank the Corporation of the Marine Biological Laboratory for the use of their facilities and the staff for their contribution in making the meeting a success. My appreciation is also extended to Mrs. Sally Hayashi for her superior and careful editing of the manuscripts and to Prentice-Hall, Inc., for their efforts in the publication of this volume.

This symposium as well as its publication was made possible through the generous support of a research grant (GM 11274-01) kindly provided by the National Institutes of Health, United States Public Health Service.

Bethesda, Maryland   J. F. HOFFMAN

Contents

General Aspects

of Cellular Functions

of Membrane Transport

Regulation of Cell Volume by Sodium and Potassium Transport

D. C. Tosteson

Department of Physiology and Pharmacology
Duke University Medical Center
Durham, North Carolina

Most of the numerous symposia on the subject of active transport during the past decade have been directed toward the fascinating question of the molecular mechanism of this fundamental cellular process. To my knowledge, this is the first symposium to address explicitly the problem of the cellular functions of active transport. The distinction between these two aspects of the problem seems to me substantive. Irrespective of the nature of the membrane molecular events which are responsible for moving a substance from a region of lower to a region of higher partial molar free energy, it is instructive to ask how such transport processes participate in the concerted activities which comprise a living cell. Clearly, regulation of volume is a fundamental cellular function. Errors in this function often lead to cell-swelling and lysis. This paper is an attempt to set forth contemporary views regarding the role of active transport in the regulation of cell volume. It is in the nature of a critical review and contains a description of contributions from many other laboratories besides our own.

The regulation of cell volume essentially involves the regulation of cell water content. The volume fraction of water in different living cells varies between about 0.7 and 0.9. Furthermore, water can move readily through the plasma membrane of most cells, whereas the bulk of the cell solids (measured by volume or mass) consists of molecules which are too large to pass through

3

the surface membrane. Therefore, this paper will begin with a discussion of the physical forces which determine the steady-state distribution of water between cytoplasm and environment. This discussion will summarize the large body of evidence which indicates that water is at equilibrium between these two phases. The second section of the paper will describe evidence which shows that the distribution of the alkali metal cations, Na and K, between cytoplasm and environment is not characteristic of equilibrium, but rather represents a steady state maintained away from equilibrium by an active-transport system for these ions. By virtue of its role in controlling the total Na plus K and thus the total solute content of cells, this active-transport system is a decisive determinant of cell volume. In this part of the paper, particular attention will be given to the interaction between active transport and leakage of Na and K across the plasma membrane in determining the steady-state volume of cells.

Physical Factors Affecting Steady-State Distribution of Water Between Cells and Environment

The two most important forces known to produce water movement across biological membranes are pressure differences and activity differences for water. Other forces known to occur in biological systems and to be capable of driving water movement include electrical potential differences, temperature differences, and chemical potential differences for various solutes (Teorell, 1962). However, since water movements under these driving forces have not been proven to occur in living systems, they will not be considered further here. In this paper, we are not concerned with the kinetics of water movement during transients but rather with the balance of forces which maintain the water content of a cell constant at a certain value. We now proceed to examine evidence regarding the actual balance of these forces which obtains in living cells in the steady state.

Few measurements of the pressure in cytoplasm of individual cells have been reported. Rand and Burton (1964) have recently estimated the pressure in human red blood cells by a modification of the technique of Mitchison and Swann (1954). The method involves drawing a red cell part way into a glass pipette. When the part of the red cell inside the tip approximates a hemisphere, the pressure difference between the inside and outside of the pipette (across the red cell in the tip) is recorded. From the law of La Place relating tension, pressure, and radius of spheres, and from the known radii of the pipette tip and red cell, the pressure inside the cells was computed to be 2.3 ± 0.8 mm H_2O higher than that outside. This agrees rather well with the estimate of the internal pressure of a sea urchin egg made much earlier and by a different approach by Cole (1932). Were the red cell membrane perfectly semipermeable, this pressure difference could be characteristic of osmotic equilibrium if the total solute concentration inside the cells exceeded that on the outside by only 0.2 mOs/l. The magnitude of the internal pressure was not increased when the cells were swollen in hypotonic medium, provided that the swelling did not proceed to the extent that the cells had reached their hemolytic volume. From measurements of the rigidity of the cells, Rand and Burton estimate that an internal pressure excess of less than 1 mm H_2O (difficult to detect by their technique) could be sufficient to produce the changes in curvature associated with swelling. When the cells do swell to their hemolytic volume, the internal pressure and rigidity increase abruptly. On the basis of these facts, it is reasonable to conclude that the pressure inside animal cells is only slightly higher than that outside. The situation is, of course, very different for plant cells, including most bacteria, which have tough cell walls that can and do resist large pressure differences. In such cells, volume regulation would appear to be accomplished by the processes which control the synthesis of the cell wall and, in particular, its total area. It seems unlikely that the transport of substances between the inside and outside of plant cells is of great importance in regulating their volume. For this reason, this paper will be confined to a consideration of the relation between transport processes and regulation of volume in animal cells, which have a mechanically weak plasma membrane.

Considerable controversy has arisen during the past decade regarding the activity of water in cytoplasm. The work of Opie (1949) and of Robinson (1960) suggested that the activity of water in most animal cells is substantially less than it is in the extracellular fluid. However, measurements of the freezing-point depression of cytoplasm in various cells by Conway and McCormack (1953), Appelboom et al. (1958), and Maffly and Leaf (1958) have now established beyond reasonable doubt that the activity of water is the same in both intra- and extracellular phases. Since the total milliosmolarity of mammalian cells is about 300, a difference in water activity of the magnitude suggested by the pressure estimates of Rand and Burton would be almost impossible to detect.

A few comments are necessary about the movement of water across plasma membranes when these driving forces are displaced from equilibrium. Animal cell membranes are, in general, highly permeable to water. Because of this fact and because of the smallness of the cells, gradients of water activity between cytoplasm and extracellular fluid are rapidly dissipated, in considerably less than 1 sec in most cells (with the exception of certain eggs). Thus, water traverses the plasma membrane more rapidly than do virtually all polar solutes and very much more rapidly than do ions.

We are now in a position to summarize the steady-state relationship between intracellular and extracellular water. The activity of this component appears to be the same in both phases. Furthermore, only a very small pressure difference exists between the phases. It would seem that water is at equilibrium in the system, although certain features of the equilibrium are unexpected. Cytoplasm is known to contain a large number of macromolecules which cannot pass through the plasma membrane: proteins, nucleic acids, etc. The system also contains small ions like Na, K, and Cl which are capable of traversing the membrane. In such systems, Gibbs-Donnan equilibrium is characterized by a difference in both activity of water and pressure between the two phases, these two forces exactly balancing one another. The activity of water would be expected to be lower and the pressure higher on the side containing the macromolecules. For example, if mammalian red cells were at Gibbs-Donnan equilibrium, the milliosmolarity of the cytoplasm would be expected to exceed that of the medium by 25–30 mOs and the pressure excess to be of the order of 5800 mm H_2O, far larger than current estimates of these quantities (Maffly and Leaf, 1958; Rand and Burton, 1964). Thus, animal cells are not at Gibbs-Donnan equilibrium, since both the activity of water and pressure appear to be the same in the two phases. For many years, this paradox was resolved conceptually by assuming that the plasma membrane was impermeable not only to the intracellular macromolecules, but also to the monovalent cations Na and K. If this were true, the observed findings with regard to water would conform to those expected for the Donnan equilibrium. This position was set forth clearly in the classical work of Van Slyke et al. (1925) on red blood cells. The term "double Donnan equilibrium" was used to indicate that the equilibrium between cytoplasm and environment involves the impermeability of the cell membrane to both intracellular macromolecular anions and the monovalent cations Na and K in both intra- and extracellular phases. However, in the 1930's, increasing evidence accumulated which cast doubt on the validity of this view. Jacobs and Parpart (1933), Davson and Danielli (1938), and Davson and Ponder (1940) all observed losses of K from red blood cells in vitro. They pointed out that the development of permeability to cations would inevitably lead to cell-swelling and ultimate lysis. Wilbrandt (1941) referred to this process as colloid-osmotic swelling and lysis. At that time, there was a sharp division of opinion as to whether normal cells in vivo are permeable to K and Na. Shortly before World War II, the experiments of Mullins et al. (1941) with radioactive ions demonstrated unequivocally that normal cells are indeed permeable to these ions. Furthermore, Harris (1941) and Danowski (1941) showed that human red cells in vitro are capable of reaccumulating previously lost K under appropriate conditions. Since that time, an enormous amount of evidence has accumulated which establishes that animal cells are normally permeable to both monovalent cations. As anticipated by Jacobs, Parpart, Wilbrandt, Ponder, Davson, and others in the late 1930's, these findings destroy a fundamental foundation of the double-Donnan concept of cell-volume stability and require a resynthesis of the problem of volume regulation. The next section of this paper is devoted to an explicit consideration of the role of Na and K transport in the regulation of cell volume.

The Role of Na and K Transport in the Regulation of Cell Volume

The problem of volume regulation was relatively neglected during the burst of work on active transport of alkali metals which took place during the first ten years after World War II. However, during the last decade, several investigators have considered the problem. Mudge (1951), Deyrup (1953), Wilson (1954), Whittam (1956), Leaf (1959), Robinson (1960), and others have published papers on the subject. Leaf reviewed the problem in 1959.

It is necessary now to review briefly the state of small ions in animal cells. We will confine our attention to Na, K, and Cl, with the understanding that HCO_3, the other major small monovalent anion in biological systems, behaves essentially as does Cl. All three ions traverse the plasma membrane. Small anions appear to be at or near equilibrium between cytoplasm and environmental fluid. In contrast, neither Na nor K is at equilibrium. The electrochemical potential of K is higher and that of Na lower in cytoplasm than in environmental fluid. The steady-state distribution of these monovalent cations can be usefully considered to be the resultant of leakage of the ions down their respective electrochemical gradients and active transport of Na out of and K into the cells. Since the steady-state concentration of each individual ion in the cytoplasm is determined by these processes, it is obvious that the total cation content of the cells is also dependent on them. From a qualitative point of view, it is apparent that alterations in either the leakage permeabilities for the ions or the active transport rates will affect the total cation content of the cell. In particular, if the leakage permeabilities are increased or the active transport rates decreased, the total cation content of the cell will increase. For reasons of electroneutrality, the total Cl or small anion content of the cell will increase *pari passu*. This addition of monovalent cations and anions to the cytoplasm increases the total solute concentration and thus reduces the activity of water in the cells. Since the plasma membrane is highly permeable to water, this will lead to prompt inward movement of water and a resultant increase in cell volume. There follows a description of some experimental examples of cases in which cell-swelling is observed in response, first, to an increase in the leakage permeabilities of the plasma membrane to Na and K and, second, to a reduction in the rate of active transport of these ions. Two characteristics of the colloid-osmotic swelling which occurs under these two conditions should be kept in mind. First, the cells swell by taking on fluid which contains solute in a concentration equal to the total solute concentration in the extracellular phase. Put another way, the activity of water in the accumulated fluid is equal to the activity of water in the extracellular phase. Further, the increase in solute content of the cells is due entirely to the addition of salt from the external medium. Second, addition of nonpenetrating solutes to the extracellular phase in sufficient quantity prevents cell-swelling by this mechanism.

First, we will consider cases in which colloid-osmotic swelling occurs due to increase in leakage permeabilities of the plasma membrane to Na and K. These examples will be taken from the large number of experiments made on this subject by many different workers with red blood cells. As noted above, during the 1930's, several investigators noticed that red blood cells lose K *in vitro*. It was further noted by Davson and Ponder (1940), Ponder (1948), and others that these losses of K were markedly accelerated by a great variety of lysins. They referred to this loss of K as prolytic cation loss. They suspected that the mechanism of lysis in systems showing such prolytic cation movements was colloid-osmosis. Subsequent work has amply confirmed this view. The result is not surprising, since red cells have a relatively small capacity for active transport of Na and K and depend in large part on their relative impermeability to these ions for control of their cation content. An agent which increases the permeability of the membrane to diffusion of Na and K enough to exceed the active transport capacity will inevitably lead to accumulation of cation and swelling by the colloid-osmotic mechanism.

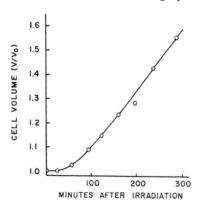

Perhaps the most completely documented case of colloid-osmotic swelling and lysis of red cells due to increased leakage of Na and K is provided by the work of Cook on ultraviolet hemolysis of human red cells (1956, 1961, 1964). He points out that UV radiation is a particularly desirable hemolytic agent because it can be added and then removed from the suspension of cells, thus eliminating the possibility of continuing action of the lytic agent on the kinetics of the swelling process. Furthermore, he also showed that the effect of UV light on red cells is independent of the dose rate and determined only by the total dose of radiation given.

Fig. 1. Increase in cell volume with time after exposure to UV radiation. For details, see text. (Kindly provided by Dr. J. S. Cook.)

Figure 1 shows the time-course of cell-swelling after exposure to a given dose of UV light. That this swelling is related to an increase in the permeability of the red cell membrane to the leakage of K is illustrated in Fig. 2. Here the logarithm of the ratio of the rate coefficient for inward movement of K after exposure to UV to the rate coefficient for inward movement of K in the control situation is plotted as a function of the logarithm of the total dose of UV light. The slope of the line is two and indicates that the rate coefficient for inward movement of K increases as the square of the total dose. Cook also measured the effect of UV light on the permeability of the red cell membrane to Na and found it to be increased in the same proportion as the permeability to K. He observed a similar relation between the rate of hemolysis and the total dose of radiation. The results are consistent with the view that UV light produces hemolysis by causing a two-event reaction in the plasma membrane which increases its permeability to the leakage of Na and K. From the observed rate coefficients for Na and K movements, Cook calculated the predicted rate of increase in total cation content of the cells. By the further assumption that the increase in cell volume occurs by accumulation of fluid with the same activity of water as that in the external fluid, Cook calculated the predicted rate of swelling for a given increase in Na and K permeability. It is important to note in passing that the calculation neglects the possible role of active transport in this process, which is justifiable here, because the rate coefficients for K and Na movement after exposure to UV far exceed those in normal cells. Furthermore, Cook carried out his experiments in the presence of 10^{-6} M/l strophanthidin, which is known to inhibit almost completely active Na and K movement in human red cells. Table 1 shows a comparison between the observed rate of swelling and that predicted from measurements of the rate coefficients for Na and K movement and the assumption of colloid-osmotic swelling. Thus, the swelling of cells after exposure to UV light conforms to the first of the two criteria for the colloid-osmotic mechanism; namely, the fluid accumulated has an activity of water equal to that observed in the external medium, and the increase in the total cell solute is entirely in the form of NaCl derived from the external medium. Cook also showed that hemolysis of human red cells after exposure to UV light is inhibited by the addition of sucrose to the external medium. Thus, UV hemolysis conforms to both criteria for the colloid-osmotic mechanism. It is produced by an effect of the incident radiation on the plasma membrane of the cell

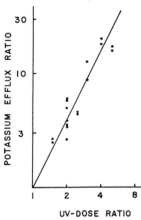

Fig. 2. Increase in K permeability with increasing dose of UV radiation. (From Cook, 1961, in *Progress in Photobiology*, ed. B. Chr. Christensen and B. Buchmann. Amsterdam: Elsevier. P. 453.)

TABLE 1

CALCULATED AND OBSERVED RATES OF SWELLING OF HUMAN
RED BLOOD CELLS AFTER EXPOSURE TO ULTRAVIOLET
LIGHT. $^{o}k_{K}$ IS OUTWARD RATE CONSTANT FOR K;
dV/dt IS RATE OF CHANGE OF VOLUME

Expt. No.	$^{o}k_{K}$	dV/dt Calc.	dV/dt Meas.
	Hr^{-1}	Liters/liter-hour	
415	1.19	0.137	0.120
424a	0.49	0.057	0.060
424b	1.32	0.155	0.156

such as to render it much more permeable to the leakage of Na and K by diffusion.

It is of interest to note in passing that even hypotonic hemolysis involves the colloid-osmotic mechanism. This is well illustrated in Fig. 3, taken from the work of Lowenstein (1960). In these experiments, washed human red cells

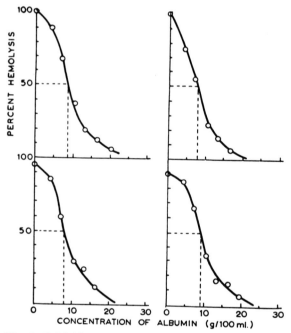

Fig. 3. Inhibition of hemolysis by albumin at constant total osmolality of the hemolysis solution. For details, see text. (From Lowenstein, 1960, *Exptl. Cell Res.* 20: 56.)

were suspended in a large volume of hypotonic medium sufficient in itself to produce hemolysis. In the case shown in the figure, the cells were suspended in solutions containing a total of 100 mOs/l. Plotted on each ordinate is the per cent hemolysis, and on each abscissa the concentration of serum albumin in the external medium. Note that as the concentration of serum albumin is increased, the observed per cent hemolysis decreases. When the concentration of serum albumin reaches a value of about 20 gm %, no appreciable hemolysis is observed. This effect cannot be due to the osmolality of the albumin itself, since the NaCl concentration was adjusted to maintain the external osmolality at 100 in all cases. This surprising result can be rationalized in terms of the colloid-osmotic mechanism. Upon suspension in the hypotonic medium, the cells swell rapidly until they reach their hemolytic volume, at which time the plasma membrane stretches and becomes much more permeable to Na and K. These ions diffuse rapidly to bring the cytoplasmic osmolality to a value equal to that in the external medium. At this point, no further driving force remains to produce inward movement of water except the presence of the intracellular macromolecules which have not yet had time to diffuse out of the cells. In the absence of external macromolecules, the intracellular hemoglobin maintains the pressure in the cells sufficiently greater than that on the outside to maintain the membrane stretched so that the hemoglobin can itself diffuse out of the cells. Addition of albumin to the external medium prevents this action of hemoglobin by rendering the concentration of nonpenetrating solutes approximately equal on both sides of the membrane. Thus it is probable that the end stages of osmotic hemolysis are colloid-osmotic in nature.

We turn now to cell-swelling due to inhibition of the rate of active transport of the alkali cations. Examples of this process have been studied extensively by Mudge (1951), Deyrup (1953), Leaf (1956), Whittam (1956), Opie (1949), and Robinson (1960). All of these investigators observed swelling of various tissues when they were incubated in buffered NaCl in the cold *in vitro*. In contrast, incubation of these tissues at 37°C under appropriate metabolic conditions prevented this swelling. Robinson initially interpreted such results to indicate the existence of an active-transport system for water. However, Mudge (1951), Deyrup (1953), Whittam (1956), and Leaf (1956), all pointed out that the results were more sensibly interpreted in terms of inhibition of active transport of Na and K in the chilled tissues. That the swelling observed in chilled tissues *in vitro* is colloid-osmotic in nature was established by Leaf (1956) and Whittam (1956), who showed that the accumulated fluid had an activity for water equal to that which obtained in the extracellular fluid and further that the increase in cell solutes was made up entirely of NaCl derived from the external solution. Furthermore, Deyrup (1953) showed that the swelling did not occur when the external medium contained sucrose instead of NaCl. Thus, the presence of a nonpenetrating external solute prevents swelling of kidney cells at low temperatures. Colloid-osmotic swelling observed in these experiments with chilled tissues is probably referable to reduced active transport rather than to increased leakage of Na and K. This follows from the fact that, although both leakage and active-transport processes are inhibited by reduction in temperature, the temperature coefficient for the active-transport process is substantially higher than that for the leakage process in those cells where these quantities have been measured. Further, the addition of substrate to such systems prevents swelling presumably by allowing active Na–K transport to proceed normally. An example of cell-swelling due to inhibition of active Na–K transport is shown in Fig. 4. This figure is taken from the work of

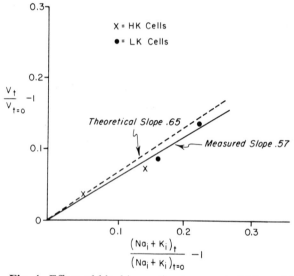

Fig. 4. Effect of blocking active transport of Na and K by strophanthidin on the volume and total cation content of sheep red blood cells. For details, see text. (From Tosteson and Hoffman, 1960, *J. Gen. Physiol.* 44: 169.)

Tosteson and Hoffman on sheep red blood cells (1960). In this experiment, both high-K (HK) and low-K (LK) sheep red cells were incubated in the presence of a concentration of strophanthidin sufficient to block the pump completely. Relative cell volume is plotted on the ordinate as a function of relative cell cation content on the abscissa. If the cells swell by colloid-osmosis under these conditions, the relation between the variables should be defined by the dotted line. When their Na–K pumps are blocked by strophanthidin, both HK and LK cells swell in a manner which agrees quite well with that predicted for colloid-osmosis. Thus, in a qualitative way, cell-swelling occurs either when leakage permeabilities to Na and K are increased or when active transport of these ions is decreased. We now proceed to a more quantitative exploration of the relations between these processes as they affect the steady-state cation content and volume of cells.

For this purpose, we consider first the steady-state theory which was formulated to treat HK and LK sheep red cells (Tosteson and Hoffman, 1960). This formulation defines the steady-state composition of cells in terms of three membrane parameters, α, β, N. α is the ratio of the rate coefficient for inward movement of Na by diffusion to the rate coefficient for inward movement of K by diffusion through the red cell membrane. β is the ratio of the active-transport influx of K to the diffusion influx for K. N is the coupling ratio of the active-transport system or pump, i.e., the number of sodium ions pumped out per potassium ion pumped into the cell. Since this ratio was found experimentally to be one in sheep red cells, it drops out of the formula that we will use in this paper. With the use of these parameters and the assumptions that the activity of water is the same inside and outside the cells, that there is no pressure difference between the phases, that Cl is at equilibrium between cytoplasm and environment, and that electroneutrality obtains within the cells, it is possible to set down a closed system of four equations which defines the steady-state composition, including the volume of the cells when they are placed in any external environment. Figure 5 shows a com-

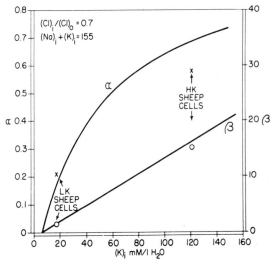

Fig. 5. K concentration and membrane transport properties in sheep red blood cells. The lines are calculated from the steady-state equations, while the points represent experimentally measured values of α and β. (From data of Tosteson and Hoffman, 1960.)

parison between the membrane parameters predicted from the known steady-state composition of HK and LK sheep red blood cells with kinetically measured values for parameters. Note that both α and β are much lower in LK than in HK red cells. Since both parameters are important in defining the steady-state cation composition of the cells, it follows that they are both involved in the regulation of cell volume. Experimental verification of the fact that β is important in volume regulation in sheep red blood cells was provided in Fig. 4. That the parameter α is also important in the volume behavior of cells is shown in Fig. 6. Here HK cells were incubated in the presence of a

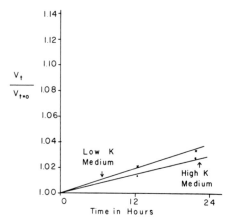

Fig. 6. Effect of cation composition of medium on rate of swelling of HK sheep red blood cells with Na-K pump blocked by strophanthidin. Cells in buffered NaCl and KCl. For details, see text. (From Tosteson and Hoffman, 1960, *J. Gen. Physiol.* 44: 169.)

pump-blocking concentration of strophanthidin in a medium containing NaCl and a medium containing KCl. Since the parameter α is about 0.6 for these cells, one would expect that the swelling rates would be approximately the same in the two media. The experiments bear out this expectation. By contrast, Fig. 7 shows a similar experiment performed with LK sheep red cells. Here the swelling rate with active transport blocked is much greater in cells incubated in KCl than it is in cells incubated in NaCl. This follows from the fact that α for LK cells is about 0.2; that is, they are substantially leakier to K than to Na. This greater leakiness to K allows them to swell more rapidly in the KCl medium.

It should be noted that the parameters α and β are unspecified functions of the external composition of the medium. This follows from the fact that both leakage and active transport of K into the cells may be expected to vary as the concentration of K in the medium is varied. Strictly speaking, the argument used is applicable only to the steady state in a given external medium and gives no information with regard to what changes in cell composition may be expected when the cells are placed into a different environment. Therefore, it cannot be applied quantitatively to experiments of the type shown in Figs. 4, 6, and 7. In order to increase the range of relevance of this mathematical formulation, we have recently modified the argument by choosing membrane parameters which are independent of the composition of the

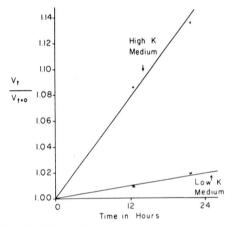

Fig. 7. Effect of cation composition of medium on rate of swelling of LK sheep red blood cells with Na-K pump blocked by strophanthidin. Cells in buffered NaCl and KCl. For details, see text. (From Tosteson and Hoffman, 1960, *J. Gen. Physiol.* 44: 169.)

medium. A given membrane is characterized by six such independent parameters. These are rate coefficients for the leakage of K, $^i k_K^l$, and Na, $^i k_{Na}^l$, "Michaelis-Menten" constants, K_m^K and K_m^{Na}, and maximum velocities, $^i M_K^{p\,max}$ and $^o M_{Na}^{p\,max}$, for the active transport of K into and Na out of the cells. The rate of active transport of both Na and K is assumed to depend on both external K and internal Na. Further, it is assumed that the rate coefficients for leakage of K and Na are invariant with the external composition. This assumption is certainly not valid for excitable cells such as muscle and nerve but appears to be true to a first approximation in red blood cells (Shaw, 1955; Tosteson, 1955). The differential equations which characterize the time dependence of the cell composition in this model are as follows:

$$\frac{dK_i}{dt} = {}^i k_K^l \left[(K)_o - \left(\frac{(Cl)_o}{(Cl)_i} \right) (K)_i \right] + \frac{{}^i M_K^{p\,max}}{(1 + K_m^K/(K)_o)(1 + K_m^{Na}/(Na)_i)} \quad (1)$$

$$\frac{dNa_i}{dt} = {}^i k_{Na}^l \left[(Na)_o - \left(\frac{(Cl)_o}{(Cl)_i} \right) (Na)_i \right] + \frac{{}^o M_{Na}^{p\,max}}{(1 + K_m^K/(K)_o)(1 + K_m^{Na}/(Na)_i)} \quad (2)$$

$$\frac{dCl_i}{dt} = \frac{dK_i}{dt} + \frac{dNa_i}{dt} \quad (3)$$

$$\frac{dV_w}{dt} = \frac{dCl_i/dt}{(Cl)_o} \quad (4)$$

where K_i, Na_i, Cl_i are the amounts and $(K)_i$, $(Na)_i$, $(Cl)_i$ are the concentrations (per liter of water) of these ions in the cells. $(K)_o$, $(Na)_o$, $(Cl)_o$ are concentrations (per liter of water) in the extracellular fluid, and V_w is the liters of water per liter of cells. These equations have been solved for various relevant boundary conditions on the IBM 7070 digital computer at Duke University (Tosteson *et al.*, in preparation). In particular, they have been solved for the cases of membrane parameters characteristic of HK and LK sheep red cells. Solutions have been obtained both for the case when ${}^o M_{Na}^{p\,max}/{}^i M_K^{p\,max}$ is 3/2 and for the case when it is 1/1 (Post and Jolly, 1957). In this paper, only the 1/1 results will be presented. Values for the membrane parameters used in solving the equations for the two types of sheep red cells are shown in Table 2. In all the solutions, it is assumed that the composition of the external medium does not vary with time.

TABLE 2

PARAMETERS USED IN SOLVING EQUATIONS DESCRIBING MODEL HK
AND LK SHEEP RED BLOOD CELLS

Cell Type	${}^i k_{Na}^l$	${}^i k_K^l$	K_m^K	K_m^{Na}	${}^o M_{Na}^{p\,max}$	${}^i M_K^{p\,max}$
	1/hr		mM/l		mM/(initial liter RBC) × (hr)	
HK	0.0053	0.0078	2.0	16.0	1.203	1.203
LK	0.0036	0.0234	2.0	16.0	0.250	0.250

Figure 8 shows the behavior of cells with membrane parameters characteristic of HK and LK sheep red cells when they are placed in a medium containing 145 mM NaCl and no KCl. Note that under conditions of zero K in the external medium, the HK cells slowly swell, lose K, and gain Na. All of these changes are due to the inhibition of active transport by removal of external K. After 400 hr, both types of cells have swollen to 1.3 times their initial volume.

Figure 9 shows the reversal of the swelling of model HK cells when KCl (5 mM/l) is restored to the medium. Note that return of cell K and Na contents toward normal begins immediately after addition of K but that cell-swelling continues for some time after restoration of the normal, plasma-like medium. After more than 1,000 hr, the cell composition has returned to normal.

Figure 10 shows the effect of increasing external K concentration on model HK cells. The effects of both 60 and 100 mM/l KCl are shown. In both cases, the concentration of NaCl is reduced to keep the sum of Na plus K constant. In 60 mM/l KCl, the cells swell to a new steady-state volume

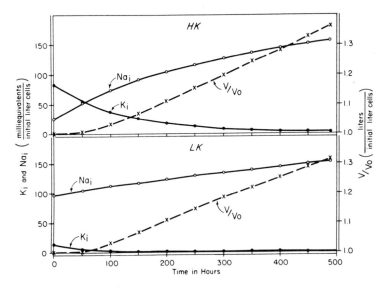

Fig. 8. Effect of absence of external K on model HK and LK sheep red blood cells. Cells suspended in 145 mM/l NaCl (no KCl). Values for parameters used in the solution of the equations are shown in Table 2. K_1 and Na_1, the cell contents (not concentrations) are plotted on the left-hand ordinate and relative cell volume (V/Vo) on the right-hand ordinate as a function of time on the abscissa. For details, see text.

about 30 % higher than the normal value observed when external K is 5 mM/l. This swelling is due to an increase in the cell K content which is referable to the increased inward leakage of K when external K concentration is increased. The new steady state develops when internal K concentration has risen sufficiently to make net outward leakage once more equal to the rate of inward active transport of K. The K concentration difference required to establish this equality when $(K)_o$ is 60 mM/l is less than that required when $(K)_o$ is 5 mM/l, because the rate of inward active transport of K is less when $(K)_o$ is 60 mM/l. This paradoxical result is due to the reduction of $(Na)_i$ when

(K)$_o$ is increased (and (Na)$_o$ decreased). For example, the steady-state value of (Na)$_i$ for model HK cells when (K)$_o$ = 60 mM/1 is only 3.6 mM/1 H$_2$O, less than one-quarter of the value of K_m^{Na} for the pump (16 mM/1 H$_2$O). When (K)$_o$ is increased to 100 mM/1, the model HK cells swell to about 1.5 times their original volume in 500 hr. This would be sufficient to produce hemolysis in these relatively small cells.

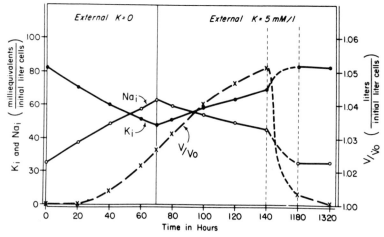

Fig. 9. Recovery of model HK sheep red blood cells from absence of external K. The cells were suspended first in 145 mM/1 NaCl (no KCl) and later in 140 mM/1 NaCl plus 5mM/1 KCl. The ordinates and abscissa are the same as in Fig. 8, but note that the scale for V/Vo has been expanded. For details, see text.

Figure 11 shows the response of model LK cells to increased external K. Note that swelling also occurs in these cells but that the time-course of the process is very different from that observed with model HK cells. In particular, model LK cells exhibit rapid initial swelling followed by recovery. In the case when (K)$_o$ is 60 mM/1, recovery proceeds to a new steady-state volume which is actually less than that observed when (K)$_o$ is 5 mM/1. This surprising result is due to two factors. First, the model LK cell is leakier to K than to Na. Therefore, elevation of external K leads to a rapid net inward leakage of K and resultant swelling. Continued active transport gradually redresses this initial effect. The steady-state volume when (K)$_o$ is 60 mM/1 is reduced below that observed when (K)$_o$ = 5.0 mM/1, because the rate of active transport is greater in the former case. This occurs because both (K)$_o$ and (Na)$_i$ are much greater than K_m^K and K_m^{Na}, respectively. Thus, steady-state (Na)$_i$ is 52 mM/1 H$_2$O in model LK cells when (K)$_o$ = 60 mM/1, a value of (Na)$_i$ much greater than that observed in the model HK cell under the same

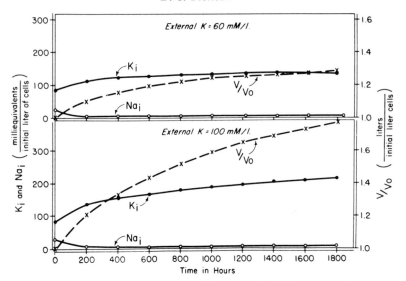

Fig. 10. Effect of increased external K on model HK sheep red blood cells. Cells suspended in 85 mM/l NaCl plus 60 mM/l KCl and in 45 mM/l NaCl plus 100 mM/l KCl. The ordinates and abscissa are as in Fig. 8, but note changes in scale. For details, see text.

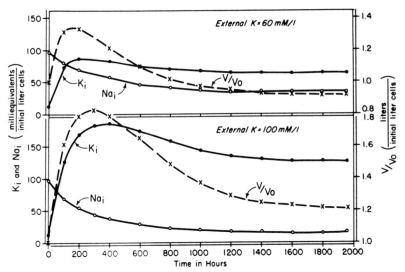

Fig. 11. Effect of increased external K on model LK sheep red blood cells. Cells suspended in 85 mM/l NaCl plus 60 mM/l KCl and 45 mM/l NaCl plus 100 mM/l KCl. The ordinates and abscissa are as in Fig. 8, but note changes in scale. For details, see text.

conditions. When model LK cells are incubated at $(K)_o$ of 100 mM/l, the initial transient swelling greatly exceeds the hemolytic volume, but the steady-state volume is only 1.2 times the normal volume, much less than the volume of HK cells after a similar period of incubation. These striking differences in the response of model HK and LK cells to increased external K may provide a new experimental basis for evaluating the transport properties of cells. The approach would obviate the use of tracers with the concomitant confusion introduced by the presence of exchange diffusion. Attempts are under way to solve the formidable experimental problem of maintaining red cells in good condition *in vitro* for hundreds of hours.

From these experimental data and theoretical formulations, it is apparent that the regulation of volume of weak-walled animal cells depends on the interrelationships between the active transport of Na and K and the leakage of these ions across the cell membrane. The time-course and steady state of cell composition and volume depend both on the ratio of the active transport to the leakage rate for the two ions and on the relative leakiness of the membrane to Na as compared with K. All of these factors must be taken into account in rationalizing the observed volume behavior of cells when suspended in different media under different metabolic conditions.

Summary

From the point of view of cell function, the role of active Na and K transport in the regulation of the total cation content and thus volume is of equal importance to its role in controlling the specific concentrations of K and Na in cytoplasm. The observations on HK and LK sheep red cells emphasize that the role of the active Na–K transport system in regulating cell volume is to some extent independent of the specific alkali cation composition of the cytoplasm. Several workers (Wilson, 1954; Leaf, 1959), including ourselves (Tosteson, 1963), have speculated previously on the implications of these reflections for cellular evolution. In so far as a living cell consists of macromolecules in close spatial relation to one another, one of the most fundamental requirements for persistence of the system is the avoidance of dispersion of macromolecules by diffusion. The formation of a surface membrane relatively impermeable to dissolved solutes was apparently a first step toward solution of this problem. However, as pointed out above, Gibbs-Donnan equilibrium conditions between intracellular and extracellular solutions do not permit volume stability in such a system. The problem could have been solved by the evolution of a membrane impermeable to Na, the major cation in the marine environment, or of a tough cell wall which could resist large pressure difference. However, the former solution would not have permitted the evolution of excitable cells as we know them today. The latter solution was actually adopted in the evolution of plants, but with the liability that motility was severely restricted. For animal cells, nature appears to have chosen the more plastic course of evolving a weak and flexible membrane which was permeable to Na and K but contained an active-transport system for these ions which rendered the structure *functionally* impermeable to the ions. This system allowed the development of concentration gradients for K and Na between cytoplasm and environment and thus the storage batteries necessary to produce current flow across the membranes of excitable cells during activity. It further provided an envelope with mechanical properties which would allow changes of cell shape in response to contraction of intracellular proteins. It would appear reasonable to conclude that volume regulation is the most fundamental and primitive cellular function of active Na and K transport. Without it, we would all be, at best, mute dryads of the trees imprisoned in cellulose walls.

REFERENCES

Appelboom, J. W. T., W. A. Brodsky, W. S. Tuttle, and I. Diamond. 1958. *J. Gen. Physiol.* 41: 1153.

Cole, K. S. 1932. *J. Cellular Comp. Physiol.* 1: 1.

Conway, E. J., and J. J. McCormack. 1953. *J. Physiol. (London)* 120: 1.

Cook, J. S. 1956. *J. Cellular Comp. Physiol.* 47: 55.

Cook, J. S. 1961. In *Progress in Photobiology, Proc. 3rd Int. Congr. Photobiol.*, ed. B. Chr. Christensen and B. Buchmann. Amsterdam: Elsevier. P. 453.

Cook, J. S. 1964. In preparation.

Danowski, T. S. 1941. *J. Biol. Chem.* 139: 693.

Davson, H., and J. F. Danielli. 1938. *Biochem. J.* 32: 991.

Davson, H., and E. Ponder. 1940. *J. Cellular Comp. Physiol.* 15: 67.

Deyrup, I. 1953. *J. Gen. Physiol.* 36: 739.

Harris, J. E. 1941. *J. Biol. Chem.* 141: 579.

Jacobs, M. H., and A. K. Parpart. 1933. *Biol. Bull.* 60: 95.

Leaf, A. 1956. *Biochem. J.* 62: 241.

Leaf, A. 1959. *Ann. N. Y. Acad. Sci.* 72: 398.

Lowenstein, L. M. 1960. *Exptl. Cell Res.* 20: 56.

Maffly, L. H., and A. Leaf. 1958. *Nature* 182: 60.

Mitchison, J. M., and M. M. Swann. 1954. *J. Exp. Biol.* 31: 443.

Mudge, G. H. 1951. *Am. J. Physiol.* 165: 113.

Mullins, L. J., W. O. Fenn, T. R. Noonan, and L. Haege. 1941. *Am. J. Physiol.* 135: 93.

Opie, E. L. 1949. *J. Exptl. Med.* 89: 112.

Ponder, E. 1948. *J. Gen. Physiol.* 32: 53.

Post, R. L., and P. C. Jolly. 1957. *Biochim. Biophys. Acta* 25: 118.

Rand, R. P., and A. C. Burton. 1964. *Biophys. J.* In press.

Robinson, J. R. 1960. *Physiol. Revs.* 40: 112.

Shaw, T. I. 1955. *J. Physiol. (London)* 129: 464.

Teorell, T. 1962. *Biophys. J.* 2: 27.

Tosteson, D. C. 1955. In *Electrolytes Biol. Systems, Symp. Marine Biol. Lab., Woods Hole, Mass., 1954*, ed. A. M. Shanes. Washington: Am. Physiol. Soc. P. 123.

Tosteson, D. C. 1963. *Federation Proc.* 22: 19.

Tosteson, D. C., and J. F. Hoffman. 1960. *J. Gen. Physiol.* 44: 169.

Van Slyke, D. D., A. B. Hastings, C. D. Murray, and J. Sendroy. 1925. *J. Biol. Chem.* 65: 701.

Whittam, R. 1956. *J. Physiol. (London)* 131: 542.

Wilbrandt, W. W. 1941. *Pfluegers Arch. Ges. Physiol.* 245: 22.

Wilson, T. H. 1954. *Science* 120: 104.

Membrane Function and Physiological Activity of Microorganisms[1]

Aser Rothstein

Department of Radiation Biology
University of Rochester School of Medicine
Rochester, New York

Of the many thousands of species of microorganisms (defined for purposes of this paper as the walled forms, bacteria, fungi, and algae), living in every conceivable environment, membrane function has been examined in only a few, and with thoroughness in only *Escherichia coli* and *Saccharomyces cerevisiae* (bakers' yeast). In view of the exceedingly small sample, the generalizations to be made in this discussion must be considered as highly speculative.

Given the diversity of species, of their environments, and of their life problems, is there a common membrane function or group of functions that meet common needs of all such organisms? The question can be answered only by first defining the "needs" of microorganisms; from their "point of view," the primary goal is the filling of every possible ecological niche, by multiplication in competition with other life forms. The membrane functions will therefore be discussed in the context of growth, ecology, and evolution.

The cell membrane is primarily a traffic-regulating and -promoting system. It restricts the loss of essential metabolites and the entry of potentially toxic

[1] This study is based on work performed under contract with the U.S. Atomic Energy Commission at The University of Rochester Atomic Energy Project, Rochester, New York.

and unwanted substances; and it promotes the uptake of metabolites, electrolytes, and other essentials of life, and the secretion of waste and surplus products. The specific natures of the various mechanisms of transport need not concern us here, but only the consequences of their operation, that is, the regulation of the composition of the cell with respect to diffusible substances. The membrane is, of course, only one of the cellular factors in the flow and balance of materials. Other factors include binding within the cell, compartmentalization in cellular structures, and metabolic conversions. Although the general pattern may be similar for the important classes of materials, the present discussion will be limited to the electrolytes. It will be further limited primarily to two organisms, E. coli and S. cerevisiae, but the membrane properties of these organisms will be discussed in the context of our knowledge of animal cells.

Electrolyte Balance, Volume Regulation, and Growth

The evolution of body fluids of animals and of the pattern of electrolyte distribution between cells and environment has been discussed in a series of provocative papers by distinguished physiologists—McCallum (1926), Fenn (1940), Conway (1957), and Steinbach (1962a, b). The problem centers around the prevalence of K over Na in cells as compared with the environment and the role of the cell membrane. The discussions, with the exception of a few pertinent comments by Conway (1957), have concerned themselves with animal cells. I wish to extend the discussion to microorganisms.

In the evolution of the cell, a membrane around the catalytic centers has the obvious advantage of preventing, by its relative impermeability, the loss, by diffusion, of intermediates and cofactors. It would, however, introduce problems relating to the access of substrates and the elimination of unwanted products. These problems, in turn, could be solved by membrane transferring systems which allowed rapid movements of specific substances down their diffusion gradients. Active transporting systems for accumulation of substrates or for secretion of undesirable materials would be a great improvement, making the cell relatively independent of diffusion gradients. Another problem of the membrane-bounded cell has been discussed in detail in the previous paper by Tosteson (1964). With a membrane of limited structural strength, the colloidal osmotic pressure of the macromolecules in the cytoplasm results in continuous swelling. This problem has been met by two properties of the membrane, a specific cation-transport system which maintains a ratio of K/Na greater in the cells than in the medium, and a permeability that is greater for K than for Na, often called the "pump and leak" system. One can speculate that volume regulation was the primary reason that the complex discriminating mechanism evolved. Other possibilities do not seem to be as compelling. It has been suggested, for example, that cells evolved in a sea that was richer in K (K/Na of 1/3 compared to 1/50 at present) and that the enzyme systems were therefore adapted to this high level of K. But why should cells, at a cost in energy, maintain a K/Na ratio of 10/1 or higher when 1/3 should be adequate? Present-day cells that live in the soil or in ponds are exposed to a K/Na ratio approximating that estimated for ancient seas, yet they concentrate K over Na by as great a factor as do animal cells. Furthermore, in the course of evolution, as the K/Na ratio of the ocean decreased, it seems likely that essential metabolic functions could have become Na- rather than K-centered. Certainly many existent cells, plant, animal, or microorganism, can tolerate high internal Na levels very well. Other specialized functions based on K/Na gradients, such as conduction in nerve and stimulation in muscle, are undoubtedly late evolutionary developments and cannot be used to explain the origin of discriminating mechanisms.

Another problem of volume regulation faced by naked cells is associated with growth. Because they are in osmotic equilibrium with their immediate environment, any change in size preceding cell division must occur as a consequence of a change in osmotic balance. Further, because the major part of the osmotic content is electrolyte, growth and electrolyte accumulation must occur simultaneously, reflecting changes in the properties of the membrane. The specific nature of the changes has not been investigated.

With the evolution of the cell wall, volume regulation was solved in a simple manner. The maximum size of a cell was determined by the space within the wall. Regulation by active mechanisms was not necessary, because diffusion gradients alone plus the colloid-osmotic pressure within the cell would insure that the osmotic pressure within the protoplast was at least as high as that outside, and that the protoplast would always fill its compartment within the wall. In actual fact, the osmotic pressure within microorganisms (and plants) is usually considerably higher than that of the environment, so that the protoplast is always pressing outward against the wall with a turgor pressure (Mitchell and Moyle, 1956; Rothstein, 1959; Conway and Armstrong, 1961). The difference in osmotic pressure may be very large. For example, *Staphylococcus aureus*, *Micrococcus lysoducticus*, and *Acetobacter chromobacter* (a marine bacterium) have internal osmotic pressures of 25–30 atm. Many other microorganisms have internal pressures of 10–20 atm. Some live in sea water (22 atm), normal ·saline (8 atm), or in water (0 atm). If the wall structure is dissolved or softened by enzymes, its protective action is destroyed and the cell will literally explode from the inrush of water, unless protected by very high concentrations of nonpenetrating solutes such as sucrose. With the wall removed, protoplasts are in osmotic equilibrium with the environment and, as with all naked cells, their size is determined by their osmotic balance.

Turgor pressure is essential for growth of walled cells. A local softening of the cell wall allows water to move into the cell driven by the turgor pressure stretching the softened part of the wall. As the wall stretches, new wall material is synthesized, and when the appropriate size is reached, the wall rehardens, and a new cell is eventually formed. The process of softening and hardening is complex. In yeast, it involves enzymatic breakdown and reformation of disulfide bridges in a protein component of the wall, as well as synthesis of glucan and mannan (Falcone and Nickerson, 1959).

Growth in size in both naked and walled cells occurs as a consequence of osmotic gradients created primarily by the accumulation of electrolytes. In naked cells, the two processes occur simultaneously, whereas in walled cells, the osmotic content is accumulated in advance, and the growth is triggered later by changes in the cell wall.

Factors Controlling Electrolyte Content

Apart from the requirement that the osmotic pressure in the cell be greater than that of the environment, regulation of osmotic content in walled cells seems to be minimal. For example, in *E. coli*, during the log phase of growth, the osmotic pressure is of the order of 15 atm, but in the stationary

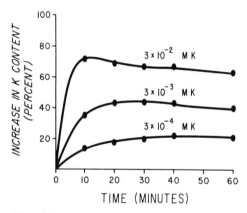

Fig. 1. Increase in the K content of yeast in the presence of different concentrations of K during respiration of glucose. (From data of Rothstein and Bruce, 1958.)

phase it falls to 8 atm, about that in the environment (Schultz and Solomon, 1961). The higher tonicity during the period of rapid growth is probably related to the need for high turgor pressure to stretch the cell wall during cell division.

In yeast, the osmotic content can vary considerably even during the stationary phase. K, which constitutes a large proportion of the cellular osmotic pressure (Conway and Armstrong, 1961), can increase remarkably in cells given substrate, as much as 80% in 10 min (Fig. 1). The controlling factor that determines the K content depends upon specific conditions. For example, in Fig. 1, the curve at 3×10^{-4} M K flattens out because the K in the medium had been depleted to the extent that influx and efflux are equal (Rothstein and Bruce, 1958). If K depletion of the medium is not allowed to

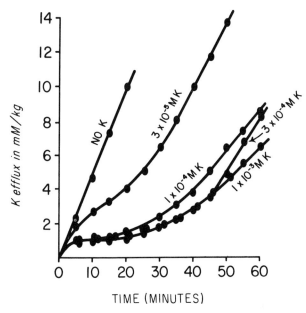

Fig. 2. Efflux of K from yeast at different concentrations of external K during respiration of glucose. (From Rothstein and Bruce, 1958, *J. Cellular Comp. Physiol.* 51: 145; Fig. 6.)

become a controlling factor, then changes in the rates of influx and of efflux are determining. Both fluxes are influenced by the external K concentration. The efflux is transiently inhibited by K, so that for a period of 30–40 min losses are minimal (Fig. 2). The rate of influx, on the other hand, increases rapidly with external K (Fig. 3) in a relationship that follows the Michaelis-Menten relationship (see next section). At lower concentrations of K, the influx is linear for at least 60 min, but at higher concentrations, it slows down and virtually stops after short periods of time. As a result, the K content at low concentrations of K is determined primarily by changes in the rate of efflux, but it is controlled at higher concentrations by changes in the rate of influx. The two situations are illustrated in Fig. 4 in terms of influx, efflux, and net accumulation at a high and at a low concentration of K. The yeast cell is geared to accumulate large amounts of K whenever the

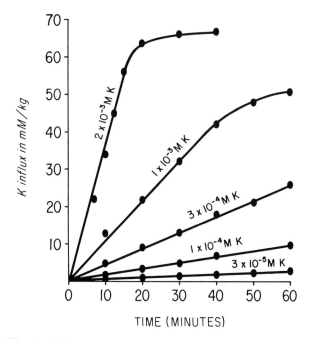

Fig. 3. Influx of K into yeast at different concentrations of K during respiration of glucose. (From data of Rothstein and Bruce, 1958.)

opportunity presents itself, with no attempt to maintain a constant cellular K. The maximum uptake seems to be limited primarily by the changes in acid-base balance that result from high K (Rothstein, 1960), to be discussed in a following section.

Na–K Discrimination

If the Na–K discriminating mechanism evolved only to permit control of cell volume in naked cells, the evolution of the wall would remove the need for this mechanism. Walled cells do not have a size problem, and they do not have to regulate their osmotic content. Indeed, microorganisms do not always discriminate between K and Na. In the experiments with *E. coli* cited earlier, the Na/K ratio during the stationary phase is essentially equal to that in the medium (Schultz and Solomon, 1961). The same is true for Na/K ratios in other bacteria. Yet these organisms require K to grow (Friedman and Fox, 1954), and during periods of growth, they demonstrate a capacity to discriminate between K and Na (Schultz and Solomon, 1961) which may be as great as or greater than that of animal cells (Fig. 5). In yeast, 98% of the K can be replaced by Na (Conway and Moore, 1954).

In animal cells, discrimination between Na and K depends on the balance between a transport system that forces exchange of Na and K and a permeability which allows a somewhat faster outward leakage of K than inward leakage of Na, the "pump and leak" system. In yeast cells, in contrast, the

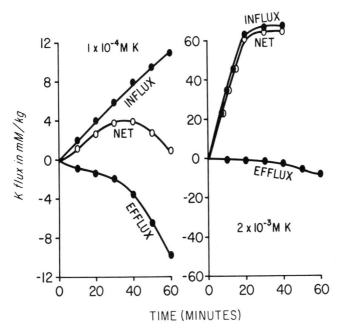

Fig. 4. Influx, efflux, and net movements of K in yeast. (From data of Rothstein and Bruce, 1958.)

permeability to cations is minimal, and the discrimination between Na and K depends almost entirely on the properties of the active-transport systems. As in animal cells, the transport seems to involve a one-for-one cation exchange, with an outwardly directed system that can favor Na over K and an inwardly directed system that prefers K to Na. Normally, however, the cells have virtually no Na (yeast cells are generally grown in media low in Na), and in this case, the outwardly directed system transports H^+ derived from substrate. With such low-Na cells, the factors that allow a high degree of discrimination in favor of K by the inwardly directed transport system can be investigated (Conway and Duggan, 1958; Armstrong and Rothstein, 1964).

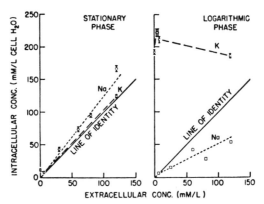

Fig. 5. Intracellular concentrations of K and Na in *E. coli* in the stationary and logarithmic phases of growth as functions of the extracellular cation concentrations. (From Schultz and Solomon, 1961, *J. Gen. Physiol.* 45: 355.)

One characteristic has already been mentioned in connection with Fig. 3. As the K concentration of the medium is raised, its transport reaches a maximal rate and is, thereafter, independent of the external concentration (Fig. 6). The curves describing the saturation can be fitted by the Michaelis-Menten

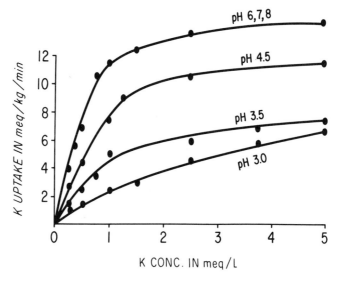

Fig. 6. Rate of K uptake by yeast as a function of K concentration at different *p*H's, during respiration of glucose. (From Armstrong and Rothstein, 1964, *J. Gen. Physiol.*, in press.)

equation, so that a straight line results when the reciprocals of K concentrations and rates are plotted against each other (Fig. 7). The other alkali metal
cations can be transported with similar kinetics, and if any two are present
at the same time, they compete with each other. The order of preference
(Armstrong and Rothstein, 1964) in agreement with previous data (Conway
and Duggan, 1958) is K > Rb > Cs > Na > Li. On the basis of affinity
alone, K is preferred to Na by a factor of 25/1.

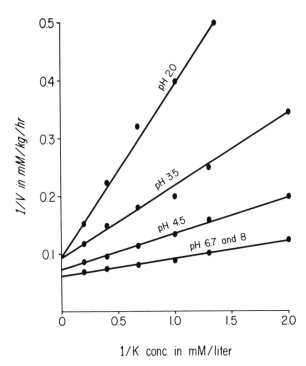

Fig. 7. Data of Fig. 6 replotted as the reciprocals of
the rates of K uptake against the reciprocals of the K
concentrations. (From Armstrong and Rothstein, 1964,
J. Gen. Physiol., in press.)

A second discriminatory factor in favor of K relates to the maximal rates
of transport of the various cations. In order to discuss this factor, however,
a phenomenon must be described which has only recently been investigated
(Armstrong and Rothstein, 1964). In mixtures of Na and K at a 25/1 concentration ratio, the rates of uptake were approximately equal when the *p*H
of the medium was above 6, but as the *p*H was reduced below this level, the
discrimination in favor of K increased markedly (Fig. 8). Below *p*H 4, the
sum of Na and K decreased considerably. If the data are replotted as the

ratio of K/Na transport, then the curve resembles the dissociation of a single proton with a pK of 4.8 (Fig. 9). Consequently, at low pH, the discrimination in favor of K was increased fivefold, from a factor of 20 to a factor of 100. A similar pattern was demonstrated with Cs and Li (Armstrong and Rothstein, 1964).

The dependence of cation discrimination on pH was analyzed by a study of the kinetics of uptake of single ions. The relationship of the rate of uptake of K to the K concentration was the same at pH 6, 7, and 8, a typical asymp-

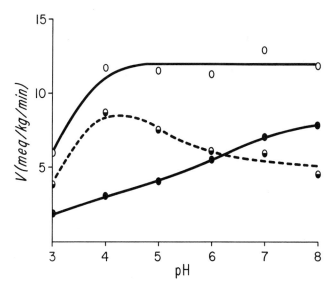

Fig. 8. Effect of pH on the rates of uptake of K and Na by yeast when both cations are present together at a ratio of 1/25 (5 mM K and 125 mM Na). (From Armstrong and Rothstein, 1964, *J. Gen. Physiol.*, in press.)

totic curve in each case (Fig. 6). Between pH 6 and 3.5, the maximal rate was reduced, but the curvature was unchanged, a pattern typical of noncompetitive inhibition. Below pH 3.5, however, the maximal rate was not altered, but the curve was shifted toward higher concentrations of K, typical of competitive inhibition. The two kinds of actions of H$^+$ on K transport are more readily apparent in the reciprocal plot of Fig. 7. Each set of data can be represented by a straight line. From the slopes and intercepts, the Michaelis constants (K_m's) and maximal rates (V_m's) can be calculated. They are plotted in Fig. 10. Between pH 8 and 5.5, H$^+$ has no effect on K transport; between

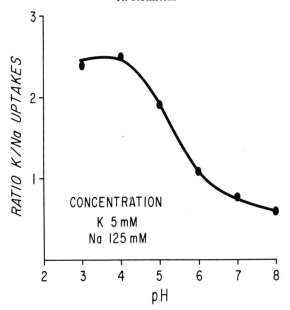

Fig. 9. Effect of *p*H on the ratio of K to Na uptakes by yeast. (Data of Fig. 8.)

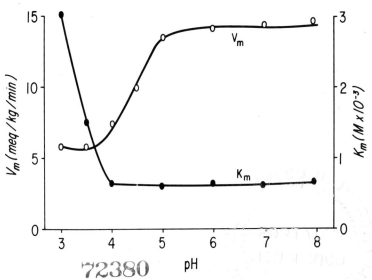

Fig. 10. Effect of *p*H on the Michaelis constant (K_m) and maximal rate (V_m) of K uptake in yeast. (From Armstrong and Rothstein, 1964, *J. Gen. Physiol.,* in press.)

pH 5.5 and 3.5, H⁺ produces a noncompetitive inhibition (no change in K_m, but a reduced V_m), by associating with a ligand having a pK of 4.5; and below

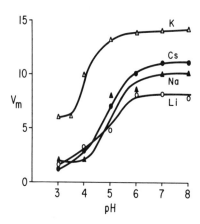

pH 3.5, H⁺ produces a competitive inhibition (constant V_m and an apparent increase in K_m), presumably by combining directly with the transport site.

The pattern seen with K was also found with the other alkali metals. In each case, the K_m for transport was apparently increased below pH 4.0, due to competition, and the V_m was markedly reduced between pH 6.0 and 4.0 (Fig. 11). The nature of the proton-dissociating site responsible for the noncompetitive effect (for convenience, called the modifier site) has not been established. It is quite distinct from the transport site, not only on the basis of differences in the nature of inhibitory effects, but also on the basis of its chemistry. It has already been pointed out that the pK for the modifier site

Fig. 11. Effect of pH on the maximal rate (V_m) of transport of the alkali metal cations by yeast. (From Armstrong and Rothstein, 1964, *J. Gen. Physiol.*, in press.)

is 4.5, whereas the pK for the transport site (based on the K_m) is 3.5, a tenfold difference. In addition, a series of studies which will not be presented here (Armstrong and Rothstein, 1964) indicates that the modifier site can bind many cations but that the array of affinities is quite different from that of the transport site (Table 1). For example, Ca has virtually no affinity for the transport site but has a high affinity for the modifier site. The modifier site influences the turnover rate of the cation-transport system, with a maximal rate if the site is occupied by K and with a reduced rate if it is occupied by H⁺ or by Ca. The modifier site is not itself a transport site. Ions combined with it and inhibiting transport of K are not themselves transported into the cell.

Further discussions concerning the details and complexities of the transport system are not necessary at the present time. The important point relating to cation discrimination is shown in Fig. 11. Because the modifying effect (reduction in V_m) of H⁺ on Na transport is greater by a factor of five than it is on K transport, the discrimination between Na and K at low pH is increased to 125/1 rather than the 25/1 predicted from the affinity constants. Furthermore, the higher level of discrimination is favored under normal circumstances by the yeast cell itself, through acidification of the medium, an acidification that results largely from the activities of the transport system

TABLE 1

AFFINITY CONSTANTS OF THE TRANSPORT SITE
AND THE MODIFIER SITE FOR CATIONS

Ion	Transport		Modifier	
	mM	Relative	mM	Relative
H^+	0.3	0.4	0.05	0.02
Li	20	30	20	7
Na	15	20	20	7
K	0.7	1	3	1
Rb	1.3	2	...	...
Cs	12	17	4	1
Mg	300	400	8	3
Ca	>1,000	>1,000	3	1

itself. The outward exchange of H^+ for K can reduce the pH of the medium to values as low as 1.7 (Conway and Duggan, 1958).

Na–K Discrimination and the Tonicity of the Environment

The evolution of the cell wall, by removing the need for osmotic regulation, allowed cells to migrate into media of low tonicity. This move, however, required changes in membrane properties which are best described by a comparison with cells that live in a normal saline environment. As already pointed out, naked cells, because they are in osmotic equilibrium, require a saline environment, and they must also continuously discriminate between Na and K in order to regulate their size. Walled cells that live in a saline environment, such as *E. coli*, have no need to discriminate between Na and K in order to regulate cell size. Indeed, in the nongrowing state, active transport is minimal, and because the membrane is relatively leaky to ions, the Na, K, and Cl composition of the cell becomes approximately the same as that of the medium, a normal and tolerable situation (Schultz and Solomon, 1961). When these cells start to grow, however, drastic changes in electrolyte distribution are initiated. The internal osmotic pressure increases by at least a factor of two, presumably to create sufficient turgor pressure to stretch the cell wall during cell division. Simultaneously, a large degree of discrimination appears between Na and K. Cellular Na is reduced to about half that of the medium and K is raised to as much as 3,000 times that of the medium by active-transport systems. The Cl is passively distributed, but because of the increased osmotic gradient, the Cl ratio inside-to-outside rises from 1.13 to

3.0, equivalent to a potential of 29 mv (Schultz *et al.*, 1962). Apparently, the mechanism by which the internal osmotic pressure is raised is obliged to discriminate between K and Na.

Walled cells such as yeast that live in a highly diluted medium cannot relax and come to equilibrium with their environment, even when they are not growing, or their cytoplasms would become diluted beyond tolerable limits. They must maintain a large osmotic gradient relative to the medium, of the order of 500 mOs. They cannot afford to be leaky toward either anions or cations. For example, if they were permeable to Cl, its distribution ratio might be as high as 100/1 or even 1,000/1, representing a very large electrical potential that would act against the cations, and against the transport system. If, on the other hand, the permeability to the cations were appreciable, the back leakage would prevent cation accumulation to the observed ratios of greater than 2,000/1. Thus, the yeast cell cannot afford a "pump and leak" system. It operates by ion-exchange pumps alone, with separate systems for cations and for anions. Because it cannot use ions that leak in as exchange partners for the ions it accumulates, it makes its own exchange partners— H^+ for K, and OH^- for H_2PO_4. Because the source of H^+ is limited only by the amounts of substrate available and because the accumulated K is balanced by metabolic anions, the only limit to K accumulation in the absence of phosphate is the rise in cellular *p*H as the concentrations of organic anions increases. When both K and H_2PO_4 are transported at the same time, the acid-base problem is solved and much larger amounts of both ions can be taken up than of either one alone (Rothstein, 1960).

The pattern of electrolyte metabolism in yeast seems to represent the manner in which the electrolyte problem has been solved in other walled cells living in a diluted medium. Thus, roots of higher plants, which are exposed to low concentrations of salts, have separate ion-exchange mechanisms for absorbing cations and anions. As in yeast, the cations are taken up in exchange for cellular H^+ and the anions for cellular OH^-, and the cation mechanism prefers K to Na (Jackson and Adams, 1963).

Genetic Control and Electrolyte Regulation

Adaptation of living organisms to electrolyte environments that differed to a large degree from the one in which they first evolved has depended on modification of the electrolyte-regulating systems of the membrane or on the development of new mechanisms. The nature of the modifications in terms of genetic control has not, however, been intensively studied. Recently, mutants defective in K-transporting systems have been described in red blood cells (Tosteson, 1963) and in *E. coli* (Lubin and Kessel, 1960; Schultz and

Solomon, 1960). In yeast, Tokuno and Sherman at Rochester (personal communication) have isolated some mutants in which K may be required to induce the appearance of the K-transport mechanism. With these mutants, the lag period preceding growth is dependent on the concentration of K, but once growth starts it proceeds at a rate approaching that of the wild type (Fig. 12).

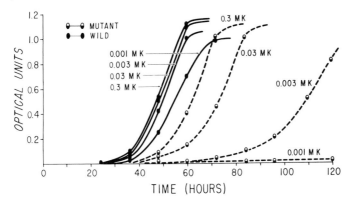

Fig. 12. Effect of K concentration on the growth of wild-type yeast and of a mutant. (Tokuno, Sherman, and Rothstein, unpublished observations.)

Discussion and Conclusions

In an evolutionary sense, the K–Na discriminating mechanism must be a very old cellular system which perhaps developed in order to counteract the swelling tendency due to the cellular colloidal osmotic pressure. In animal cells, it is still operative as a volume-regulating system in both non-growing and growing cells. It has also been adapted to special functions in certain cells of multicellular organisms, as in nerve conduction, muscle stimulation, fluid absorption, and secretion. The internal metabolic systems have also adapted themselves to optimal operation in a high-K environment.

The evolution of the cell wall removed the problem of volume regulation from the K–Na discriminating systems of the membrane. Indeed, microorganisms that live in a saline environment, when not growing, come to virtual electrolyte equilibrium. The wall did, however, introduce a problem relating to growth, the necessity of expanding the wall space. The problem was solved by a complex mechanism. The wall is softened in a controlled manner at a specific location, by specific enzymes. The osmotic pressure of the cell is raised above that of the environment, and the resulting turgor pressure forces expansion at the softened spot in the wall. In the accumulation of the required osmotic content, the cells discriminate strongly between K and Na. The mechanism is apparently the same kind of forced Na–K exchange system operative in animal cells, although H^+–K exchanges may also occur.

The cell wall made it possible for cells to move into diluted environments, without bursting, but drastic changes in membrane properties were required. In order to retain a "normal" osmotic content in the face of very large outward gradients, the membrane must be "tight," with ion permeability minimized. "Pump and leak" systems for cations, with passive anion distributions, are, therefore, inadequate. The cells possess separate active-transport systems for cations and anions, each of which operates as an exchange system. Because no ions leak into the cells, exchange partners have to come from within the cell, H^+ for cations and OH^- for anions. The balance of cation and anion accumulation, therefore, influences the acid-base balance of the cell. The cation-accumulating system prefers K over Na. In fact, if Na is "loaded" into the cell, it can be extruded instead of H^+ in exchange for K. The H^+–K exchange system, therefore, seems to be a modification of the Na–K that seems to be a universal endowment of cells.

If the K–Na discriminating system is indeed ancient in an evolutionary sense, preceding the appearance of a wall, then the walled cells have retained that system and adopted it for producing the osmotic gradients necessary for their growth and for maintaining electrolyte levels in a diluted environment. The retention of the K–Na discriminating system in walled cells may have been influenced by a dependence of the synthetic centers on high K that developed in ancestral cells. It is important to note that, in this regard, the protozoa that have also successfully invaded diluted environments also discriminate strongly between K and Na (Dunham and Child, 1961). These cells have met the osmotic problem by learning to live with a low electrolyte level in the cytoplasm, by development of a semirigid pellicle, and by development of the contractile vacuole, which is a water-excreting system (Kitching, 1954).

From limited studies on electrolyte metabolism of microorganisms, made primarily on two species, and from comparisons of this metabolism with that of animal cells, some broad generalizations concerning membrane phenomena with respect to growth, ecology, and evolution have been made. Some of the arguments are teleological. Most are based on inadequate data. Nevertheless, a pattern exists that will be seen more clearly, if only we keep looking for it. Comparative studies of membrane phenomena in a variety of life forms and studies of their genetic control can help to reveal the pattern. The membrane must be examined in the context of the whole cell, and specific cells in the context of all life forms.

REFERENCES

Armstrong, Wm. McD., and A. Rothstein. 1964. *J. Gen. Physiol.* In press.

Conway, E. J. 1957. *Physiol. Revs.* 37: 84.

Conway, E. J., and Wm. McD. Armstrong. 1961. *Biochem. J.* 81: 631.

Conway, E. J., and F. Duggan. 1958. *Biochem. J.* 69: 265.

Conway, E. J., and P. T. Moore. 1954. *Biochem. J.* 57: 523.

Dunham, P. B., and F. M. Child. 1961. *Biol Bull.* 121: 129.

Falcone, C., and W. J. Nickerson. 1959. *Proc. Intern. Congr. Biochem., 4th, Vienna, 1958.* 6: 65.

Fenn, W. O. 1940. *Physiol. Revs.* 20: 377.

Friedman, S., and C. L. Fox. 1954. *J. Bacteriol.* 68: 186.

Jackson, P. C., and H. R. Adams. 1963. *J. Gen. Physiol.* 46: 369.

Kitching, J. A. 1954. *Symp. Soc. Exptl. Biol.* 8: 63.

Lubin, M., and D. Kessel. 1960. *Biochem. Biophys. Res. Commun.* 2: 249.

McCallum, A. B. 1926. *Physiol. Revs.* 6: 316.

Mitchell, P., and J. Moyle. 1956. *Symp. Soc. Gen. Microbiol.* VI: 150.

Rothstein, A. 1959. *Bacteriol. Revs.* 23: 175.

Rothstein, A. 1960. *Ciba Found. Study Group* No. 5: 53.

Rothstein, A., and M. Bruce. 1958. *J. Cellular Comp. Physiol.* 51: 145.

Schultz, S. G., and A. K. Solomon. 1960. *Nature* 187: 802.

Schultz, S. G., and A. K. Solomon. 1961. *J. Gen. Physiol.* 45: 355.

Schultz, S. G., N. L. Wilson, and W. Epstein. 1962. *J. Gen. Physiol.* 46: 159.

Steinbach, H. B. 1962a. *Perspectives Biol. Med.* 5, No. 3: 338.

Steinbach, H. B. 1962b. In *Comp. Biochem.,* Vol. 4, pt B. New York: Academic Press, Inc. P. 677.

Tosteson, D. C. 1963. *Federation Proc.* 22: 19.

Tosteson, D. C. This volume.

Physiological Aspects
of Ion Transport
in Plant Cells and Tissues

Jack Dainty

School of Biological Sciences
University of East Anglia
Norwich, England

Our knowledge of ion transport in plant cells and tissues is quite meager, particularly when it is compared with the situation in animal cells and tissues. This is not entirely caused by the very much greater amount of manpower and money devoted to transport problems in the animal body. There are intrinsic difficulties in working with plants. The plant cell would appear to be more complicated than a typical animal cell. It has a cell wall composed principally, but not entirely, of polysaccharides of various kinds; within this cell wall and pressed up against it, perhaps even intimately penetrating it, there is usually a thin layer of protoplasm, and this in turn surrounds, in mature cells, a large central vacuole. It is usually assumed, though not wholly accepted, that the protoplast is bounded by two membranes: the outer one has come to be called the plasmalemma, and the inner, bounding the vacuole, the tonoplast. The central vacuole is an aqueous solution of salts, in higher plants often salts of organic acids such as malic acid. The protoplast contains the usual organelles—nucleus, mitochondria, endoplasmic reticulum, etc.— together with chloroplasts in green cells, and the whole cell clearly has a much more complex structure than do most animal cells and is, therefore, correspondingly difficult to work with.

41

Another way in which transport problems in plant cells differ from those in animal cells is that growth and development of the plant cell is a more usual concomitant of transport experiments. Whereas workers on, say, nerve or muscle cells or red blood cells are usually concerned with a state of flux equilibrium, those working on plants are almost always confronted with a situation in which ion influx greatly exceeds ion efflux; thus, plant physiologists speak of ion *accumulation*, salt *uptake*, and so on. Further, whereas the extracellular fluid bathing animal cells is customarily quite well defined, ionically, this is rarely the case in plants. It is true that when studying ion transport in algal cells, the bathing fluid would be water, fresh or salt, of known ionic concentrations, but it is not yet clear what is the fluid bathing the cells which make up higher plants. The epidermal cells of the root are bathed by the "soil solution," and the cells close to the xylem bundles are presumably bathed by a liquid not too different from the xylem fluid. But there are many cells and tissues in intermediate positions, for example, the cortical cells of the root, where the extracellular fluid is most ill defined and the effect of the high concentration of fixed negative charge in the cell walls on the ionic medium "seen" by the plasmalemma is quite obscure.

Finally, there is one other difficulty in working with plants; the plant body is not clearly differentiated into a number of organs and tissues which can be studied separately. One speaks of root, stem, leaf as organs, but they are not so well marked as are kidney, heart, intestine, etc., nor can one work so well with tissues such as phloem, xylem, and parenchyma as with nerve, muscle, and so on. This is a difficulty which does not appear to have been sufficiently stressed, yet I am convinced that it makes a sizable contribution to the relative backwardness of our knowledge of and insight into ion-transport problems in plant cells and tissues.

In view of the difficulties and deficiencies discussed above, this paper will be devoted largely to raising problems rather than indicating answers, or indeed giving much factual information. But first, I will give a brief account of what we know about the ionic relations of single plant cells. This has largely been derived from a study of giant algal cells in conditions of flux equilibrium, and it is obvious from what I have said above that this is an unnatural situation in which to look at the ionic relations of higher plants. Certain authors (Steward and Sutcliffe, 1959) doubt that algal studies are relevant to salt uptake by higher plants, but most plant physiologists would accept that our knowledge of the ionic relations of the giant algal cells is the firmest foundation we have on which to speculate about the ionic relations of higher plant cells.

Statement of Position with Respect to Ionic Relations of Plant Cells

The ionic relations of the giant internodal cells of *Nitellopsis obtusa*, a member of the Characeae living in brackish water, were the first to be worked out in some detail (MacRobbie and Dainty, 1958a). The ionic concentrations and fluxes and later information on electrical potentials suggested the following picture. K was in approximate electrochemical equilibrium among the external solution (sea water diluted about 13 times), the protoplasm, and the vacuole; the electrochemical potential of Na, $\bar{\mu}_{Na}$, was lower in the protoplasm and in the vacuole than in the external solution; the electrochemical potential of Cl, $\bar{\mu}_{Cl}$, was much higher in the vacuole than in the external solution; and it was inferred, largely on osmotic grounds now believed to be incorrect, that $\bar{\mu}_{Cl}$ was the same in protoplasm and in external solution. Since the cell was in a state of flux equilibrium—experimentally proved— the existence of a Na-extrusion pump and an inwardly directed Cl pump was deduced. The values of the electrochemical potentials showed that the Na pump was located at the plasmalemma and the Cl pump at the tonoplast. According to MacRobbie (private communication) and Spanswick and Williams (1964), it is more likely that the Cl pump is at the plasmalemma, the previous reasoning from osmotic equilibrium being probably erroneous. (In passing, it might be said that, though the Cl pump in green, actively photosynthesizing, cells might be at or near the plasmalemma, in cells which do not contain chloroplasts, the tonoplast is a more likely place for an anion pump.) Although in *Nitellopsis*, K was in approximate electrochemical equilibrium among the various phases, it seems likely from later work on other members of the Characeae that an inwardly directed K pump was being masked, in the usual way, by the comparatively high passive permeability to K; this pump should also be located at the plasmalemma and is probably part of a Na–K coupled pump of the type we are familiar with in animal cells like the squid giant axon (see Dainty, 1962).

Our interpretation of the kinetic data from isotope experiments was that the plasmalemma fluxes of Na and K (8 and 4 $\mu\mu$mole cm^{-2} sec^{-1}, respectively) were much higher than the tonoplast fluxes (0.4 and 0.25 $\mu\mu$mole cm^{-2} sec^{-1}, respectively) in *Nitellopsis*.

More recent investigations, particularly by Walker (1960), Hope and Walker (1961), and MacRobbie (1962), on other members of the Characeae— *Chara australis* and *Nitella translucens*—raise some doubts about the finding of MacRobbie and Dainty (1958a) that the plasmalemma is more permeable than the tonoplast, though it should be kept in mind that the medium in which *C. australis* and *N. translucens* grow and in which the experiments were performed is about 30 times more dilute than the corresponding external medium for *N. obtusa*. Essentially, the electrical findings of Walker (1960) and Hope and Walker (1961) were that most of the electrical resistance between the vacuole of *C. australis* and the external medium resides in the plasmalemma, indicating, though not proving, that the passive permeability of the plasmalemma is much lower than that of the tonoplast. Mac-Robbie (1962), on the other hand, has investigated the ion fluxes across the plasmalemma and tonoplast of *N. translucens* and has found that the Na and K fluxes across the plasmalemma are of the order of 1 $\mu\mu$mole cm^{-2} sec^{-1}, while the corresponding fluxes across the tonoplast are very much greater, indicating, in agreement with the electrical measurements discussed above, that the tonoplast is a much more permeable structure than the plasmalemma. It thus seems rather clear at the moment that there is general agreement about the existence and the sites of the ion pump (except some dubiety about the site of the Cl pump), but there is some contradiction between the relative permeabilities of the plasmalemma and tonoplast of the fresh-water species *C. australis* and *N. translucens* and the brackish-water *N. obtusa*. There is also an interesting large discrepancy between the measured electrical resistance of the membranes of these plant cells and that calculated from the ion fluxes (Hope and Walker, 1961; Williams *et al.*, 1964).

Work supporting this general picture of a Na–K pump and an inwardly directed Cl pump also comes from Blount and Levedahl (1960) on *Halicystis ovalis*, MacRobbie and Dainty (1958b) on *Rhodymenia palmata*, and Etherton and Higinbotham (1960) and Etherton (1963) on higher plant cells. However, in some species—*Valonia, Halicystis osterhoutii*—there appear to be interesting anomalies. In general, much of the work done on salt uptake by higher plant cells and tissues shows little more than ions being accumulated to a concentration higher than that in the external medium. If one can be sure that *both* ions are accumulated to a higher concentration and that both ions exist in the free state, then one can certainly deduce that at least one of the ions is actively transported into the cell. These conditions are clearly satisfied in much of the work on salt uptake by storage tissue slices (see Steward and Sutcliffe, 1959, for an account of this work). Whether the anion, usually Cl, or the cation, usually K or Na, is actively transported cannot be deduced from this work, for no electrochemical potentials have been determined. I would certainly expect the anion to be actively transported—at least into the vacuole—but the cation may well be actively transported, too, by some modification of the basic Na–K pump.

There is a great deal of work on salt uptake by storage tissue slices and excised roots which purports to prove, by arguments based on metabolic connections, competition, shape of curve of uptake *vs.* concentration, temperature coefficient, etc., that one or both ions of a salt are actively transported into the cells. The metabolic connections with salt uptake are discussed later. Here is to be mentioned the work on uptake of ions by excised roots initiated by Epstein and Hagen and carried on principally by Epstein (see Epstein, 1956). These workers and others have shown that the rate of uptake of an ion is not directly proportional to the concentration of that ion in the external solution, but rather that it shows saturation characteristics. The rate of uptake, in fact, can be described by an equation of the same form as the familiar Michaelis-Menten equation of enzyme kinetics:

$$u = \frac{U_{max}[S]}{K_m + [S]} \tag{1}$$

where u is the rate of uptake of the ion by the plant tissue, U_{max} is the maximum rate of uptake at high concentrations $[S]$ of the ion in the external solution, and K_m is a constant analogous to the Michaelis constant of enzyme kinetics. It is natural to press the analogy somewhat and say that if the kinetics of uptake fits an equation such as (1), then a carrier-mediated transport is involved (or at least binding sites of some kind are involved) and K_m can be identified with the dissociation constant of the ion-carrier complex. This picture of uptake is supported by competition experiments, when Rb and K, for instance, seem to compete for the same site and Ca, Sr, and Ba compete for another site. Again, this competition fits the appropriate Michaelis-Menten equation.

This kind of work is not free from the doubts of those who do not like to place so much reliance on kinetic data. Sutcliffe (1959) has criticized the competition experiments on the grounds that they ignore the possible effects of the other ion in the solution, e.g., Cl in an experiment using various concentrations of KCl and RbCl to study the competition between K and Rb. Briggs (1963) has made the obvious point that the true driving force on an ion is the electrochemical potential gradient and, therefore, the change in membrane potential should be taken into account, as well as the change in concentration. By manipulating the permeability parameters in a not unreasonable way, one can obtain almost any relation between uptake and concentration. Despite these criticisms, the work of Epstein and his colleagues does lend support to the idea of carrier-mediated and, therefore, active uptake of both cations and anions, though work on excised roots raises great difficulties when one is trying to discover where these carriers or binding sites are located. Recently Epstein and coworkers (1963) have found evidence for a dual mechanism of uptake of K by excised barley roots, one with a very small "Michaelis constant" operative at low external K concentrations such as might occur in the soil solution and one with a large "Michaelis constant" operative at high concentrations.

To summarize the situation in higher plant cells before discussing the metabolic aspects, there is plenty of evidence of active transport of all kinds of salts and ions into plant cells, though all of it is of a rather tenuous nature, and there seems to be a need of a proper electrochemical approach to these problems.

Ion Transport in Relation to Metabolism and Photosynthesis in Plant Cells

In the plant field, as in the animal field, there are two schools of thought on the nature of the form of the energy immediately available for doing so-called osmotic work on ions. One school, whose chief protagonists are Lundegårdh (1955) and Robertson (1960), considers that the redox energy available in the electron-transport chains is used directly by means of a mechanism like that of Conway's redox pump (Conway, 1959). Basically, ion transport is looked upon as a consequence of a primary separation of positive and negative charge during respiratory electron transfer or during the early stages of photosynthesis. The other, perhaps more numerous, school takes the apparently more conventional view that adenosine triphosphate (ATP), the usual form of available energy in the cell, whether it be produced by respiration or photosynthesis, is the immediate source of energy for driving the ion pumps.

Lundegårdh has produced much evidence in favor of his redox-pump ideas, but has been continually forced to modify his schemes. Robertson (1960) gives an excellent discussion of the relationship between ion transport and respiration from the point of view of a protagonist of the redox-pump theory, particularly with respect to the active transport of anions. He and his colleagues have done basic experiments on the uptake of salts by storage tissue discs which have provided arguments both for and against the direct utilization of redox energy. They found that when salts were added to the solution bathing suitably prepared carrot discs, the respiration of the discs increased and the salts were taken up by the tissue. The ratio of the number of equivalents of salt taken up to the moles of O_2 consumed approached, but did not exceed, four—the ratio to be expected on simple ideas of the operation of a redox pump. Robertson (1960) rather effectively criticizes those authors (Handley and Overstreet, 1955; Sutcliffe and Hackett, 1957) who claim ratios greater than four. This, then, is evidence in favor of the redox-pump idea, although, of course, an enhanced respiration rate in the presence of salt could equally well be explained by the utilization of ATP, thus decreasing the ratio of ATP to adenosine diphosphate (ADP) and stimulating respiration.

In the same series of experiments, Robertson and his colleagues showed that 2,4-dinitrophenol (DNP) at an appropriate concentration completely inhibited salt uptake while either not affecting the respiration rate or even increasing it (see Robertson, 1960). Classically, one would say DNP had stopped the production of ATP by decoupling phosphorylation from oxidation, hence proving the ATP is the immediate energy source for ion uptake. Robertson (1960) does not accept this classical point of view; he maintains that our knowledge of oxidative phosphorylation is so incomplete that the assumption is tenable that DNP blocks both phosphorylation and the primary separation of positive and negative charge leading to ion uptake.

It should be stressed that Robertson (1960) is discussing the metabolic connections of anion pumps, assuming—possibly quite correctly—that these are the principal agents in actively transporting a salt from the external solution to the vacuole of a plant cell. He considers that the cation of the salt is following quite passively, though he clearly recognizes that this is merely a simplifying assumption and that his scheme will have to be modified to take account of cation pumps like the Na–K pumps clearly demonstrated in the Characeae. He seems prepared to contemplate the direct utilization of ATP by these cation pumps.

Recently, MacRobbie (1962) has started an investigation of the metabolic connections of ion transport in the Characean species *N. translucens*. Although this is probably not directly concerned with metabolic aspects, she finds that the cardiac glycoside, ouabain, inhibits the cation active-transport processes—Na extrusion and part of the inwardly directed K movement—but not the inwardly directed, active, Cl transport. Further, the efficiency of the cation-transport processes seems to decrease with cell age, whereas the anion transport is unaffected. These facts support the presumption that the anion and cation active-transport processes are independent of each other.

MacRobbie (1962) also found that the (active) Cl influx was practically eliminated when the cells were transferred from light to dark. She also found that the K influx was reduced, but she did not measure the Na efflux. She thus concluded that the energy for both cation and anion active-transport processes is closely geared to light-dependent metabolism rather than to respiration. There is much early evidence of some connection between photosynthesis and ion transport in plants. Hoagland and Davis (1923) first clearly demonstrated a relationship between light and uptake of Cl, Br, and NO$_3$ by *Nitella clavata*. Later, Jacques and Osterhout (1934) showed that light increased the absorption of K by *Valonia macrophysa*. Scott and Hayward (1955) investigated the effect of light on Na and K movements in *Ulva lactuca* and concluded that the cellular Na and K contents are regulated by different mechanisms and that the Na-efflux pump is coupled more directly with the action of light. The action of light had been explained in many ways: by altering the permeability of the membranes perhaps due to the changes in *p*H occurring during photosynthesis, by the production of some photosynthetic intermediate which could act as a carrier, by the production of sugars which stimulated respiration, and so on. The work of Arisz (1948), Arisz and Sol (1956), and Van Lookeren Campagne (1957) on the uptake of Cl by *Vallisneria* leaves introduced a new slant to the ideas of the connection between photosynthesis and ion transport. They observed that the uptake of Cl was unaffected, and indeed enhanced, by the absence of CO_2 from the medium. Thus, carbon fixation during photosynthesis is not necessary for the operation of the Cl pump. Naturally, it became assumed that photosynthetically produced ATP was the energy supply for the Cl pump and the connection between ion uptake and photosynthesis was this photophosphorylation.

MacRobbie (private communication) now doubts that both the cation- and anion-transport processes in *N. translucens* are directly dependent on photosynthetically produced ATP. It will be recalled that both the Cl influx and part of the K influx were light-dependent. She has studied the effect of NH_4 on these fluxes, on the assumption that the NH_4 is acting solely as uncoupler of phosphorylation from electron transfer during photosynthesis (Krogmann *et al.*, 1959; Good, 1960). She found that in the presence of NH_4, the K influx decreased to the passive value, whereas the Cl influx was unaffected. This suggests that the inwardly directed K pump—and possibly the "linked" Na-extrusion pump—was driven by ATP, produced in this case by photophosphorylation, but it presumably could equally well have been produced by oxidative phosphorylation in the mitochondria, whereas the inwardly directed Cl pump was much more directly linked to electron-transfer processes, in this case in the photosynthetic apparatus.

Obviously, this interpretation of the NH_4 experiments must be tentative, for the effect of the competition between NH_4 and K for entry both by the passive and by the active channels must be studied. However, there is some supporting evidence for the view that the entry of Cl into the cytoplasm is directly linked to an electron-transfer process. Arisz (1948) interpreted his experiments on the effect of DNP and cyanide on the uptake and translocation of Cl in *Vallisneria* on the grounds that DNP did not inhibit uptake of Cl into the cytoplasm but did inhibit its subsequent transfer to the vacuole. Further, in the experiments of Robertson *et al.* (1951), which showed that DNP suppressed salt uptake by carrot discs, it could well be that only uptake into the vacuole was suppressed.

One thing should be clear from the above discussion: the evidence relating to the immediate energy supply for the cation and anion pumps in plant cells is very thin. Though there are suggestions from the work of MacRobbie, Arisz, Robertson, and Lundegård that the anion pumps may be directly linked to electron-transfer processes, there is no really conclusive evidence against ATP being the immediate energy supply for the pumps. If ATP is indeed the energy supply, then there are no intellectual difficulties in keeping the conventional picture of a pump as a carrier located in a plasma membrane, supplied by ATP by diffusion from the mitochondria and/or chloroplasts. This may or may not be a correct picture of ATP-driven pumps, but if one of the pumps—say the anion pump—is directly linked to electron-transfer processes, then we are compelled to consider more carefully their spatial location.

Robertson (1960), who considers that in nonphotosynthesizing storage cells, anion uptake is directly linked to electron transfer in the cytochrome chains in the mitochondria, envisages rapid passive salt movement across the plasmalemma with subsequent active uptake of salt into the mitochondria. The mitochondria then, as a result of random movements, make contact with the tonoplast and discharge their salt contents into the vacuole. This is a process which can be envisaged, for the mitochondria can be observed in rapid motion in the cytoplasm and could make frequent contacts with the tonoplast. It is more difficult to form a picture of what might be happening in a cell like *N. translucens*, if the anion uptake is tightly coupled to an electron-transfer process taking place in the chloroplasts. Here, the chloroplasts are fixed in a layer close to the cell wall and, presumably, the plasmalemma. Perhaps active uptake of salt by the chloroplasts leads to the production of vesicles periodically budded off the chloroplasts and these vesicles eventually discharge their contents into the vacuole. Sutcliffe (1962), who is not a supporter of the redox-pump ideas, thinks that the production of vesicles in the cytoplasm may play an important role in salt uptake.

Ion Transport in Relation to Growth and Differentiation of Plant Cells

It is obvious that as plant cells divide and grow, as the amount of protein increases and the vacuole expands, there must be a concomitant uptake of the appropriate ions both to maintain the correct *milieu* for the proper functioning of cellular processes and to maintain or even increase the hydrostatic pressure which keeps plant cells turgid. Whatever be the controlling mechanism, hormonal or otherwise, which maintains the orderly pattern of division, growth, expansion, and differentiation seen so clearly in, say, the plant root, it might be thought sufficient to say that ion accumulation, which must be active, is a necessary consequence of the expanded membrane surfaces, and the greater availability of carriers and of energy—whether redox energy or high-energy phosphates. However, since growth is so clearly going on in plant tissues and since some plant physiologists have been very impressed by apparently close association between growth and ion accumulation, it is worth discussing ion accumulation in its connections with growth in a little detail.

Steward (see Steward and Sutcliffe, 1959) has long been the chief protagonist of the view that there is an extremely close association between growth, more specifically protein synthesis, and ion accumulation. In his early work on the uptake of ions by suitably prepared discs of potato storage tissue, he observed that the uptake appeared to be predominantly in the surface cells which were showing signs of growth. He thus concluded that ion accumulation would only occur in growing cells. This conclusion had to be modified later, when it was shown that other storage tissues, in which no growth could be demonstrated, could take up large quantities of a salt such as KCl. It was then claimed that the cells of such storage tissues all showed a potentiality or capacity for continued growth and it was only such cells, possessing this potentiality, which would accumulate ions. This modified claim is perhaps not very impressive, but the close connection between growth or capacity for growth and ion accumulation has received experimental support from the work of Sutcliffe (see Sutcliffe, 1962).

Sutcliffe has shown that chloramphenicol, at the rather high concentrations of 3–6 mM, inhibits ion (NaCl) uptake by washed discs of beet-root storage tissue without affecting their rate of respiration. Chloramphenicol, at some ten times lower concentrations, is known to be an inhibitor of protein synthesis in bacteria. Assuming that chloramphenicol is acting solely as an inhibitor of protein turnover (there is no net protein synthesis in this storage tissue), Sutcliffe has proposed that ion uptake and protein turnover are closely connected in the following way. As a result of protein synthesis, freshly made proteins migrate to the membrane and there "bind" ions from the external solution. The protein-ion complex then moves away from the membrane—pinocytosis may be involved here—and the protein enters into the breakdown phase, perhaps by attachment to a ribonucleic acid (RNA) molecule. Sutcliffe envisages that at this time the bound ions are released, possibly into or with the formation of a little vesicle, which then eventually empties into the vacuole through the tonoplast.

Sutcliffe does not explicitly consider the question of the energy relations involved in this hypothesis, though he clearly implies that phosphorylations will be taking place at perhaps more than one point in the above protein-ion turnover cycle and, therefore, the energy will come from a high-energy phosphate bond in the conventional manner.

Others, Laties (1964), for example, have concerned themselves more with questions of energy supplies during the development of ion-accumulating power in plant cells. Storage tissue discs when freshly cut, for example, show little ability to accumulate ions. If washed in distilled water 24–48 hr, a large capacity for taking up ions develops and along with it a change in the metabolism to a high rate of oxidative phosphorylation, which presumably means a large supply of ATP.

It seems that different workers are, to some extent, stressing different aspects of the problems of active ion uptake and its relations to growth and metabolism and that some synthesis of views is required. Particularly important is the need to find out something about the factors which initiate and control growth and development, so that we can approach an integrated view of ion transport, growth, development, and metabolism.

REFERENCES

Arisz, W. H. 1948. *Koninkl. Ned. Akad. Wetenschap., Proc.* 51: 25.

Arisz, W. H., and H. H. Sol. 1956. *Acta Botan. Neerl.* 5: 218.

Blount, R. W., and B. H. Levedahl. 1960. *Acta Physiol. Scand.* 49: 1.

Briggs, G. E. 1963. *J. Exptl. Botany* 14: 191.

Conway, E. J. 1959. In *The Method of Isotopic Tracers Applied to the Study of Active Transport.* London: Pergamon Press. P. 1.

Dainty, J. 1962. *Ann. Rev. Plant Physiol.* 13: 379.

Epstein, E. 1956. *Ann. Rev. Plant Physiol.* 7: 1.

Epstein, E., D. W. Rains, and O. E. Elzam. 1963. *Proc. Natl. Acad. Sci. U.S.* 49: 684.

Etherton, B. 1963. *Plant Physiol.* 38: 581.

Etherton, B., and N. Higinbotham. 1960. *Science* 131: 409.

Good, N. E. 1960. *Biochim. Biophys. Acta,* 40: 502.

Handley, R., and R. Overstreet. 1955. *Plant Physiol.* 30: 418.

Hoagland, D. R., and A. R. Davis. 1923. *J. Gen. Physiol.* 6: 47.

Hope, A. B., and N. A. Walker. 1961. *Australian J. Biol. Sci.* 14: 26.

Jacques, A. G., and W. J. V. Osterhout. 1934. *J. Gen. Physiol.* 17: 727.

Krogmann, D. W., A. T. Jagendorf, and M. Avron. 1959. *Plant Physiol.* 34: 272.

Laties, G. G. 1964. In *Cellular Membranes in Development,* ed. M. Locke. New York and London: Academic Press, Inc. P. 299.

Lundergårdh, H. 1955. *Ann. Rev. Plant Physiol.* 6: 1.

MacRobbie, E. A. C. 1962. *J. Gen. Physiol.* 45: 861.

MacRobbie, E. A. C., and J. Dainty. 1958a. *J. Gen. Physiol.* 42: 335.

MacRobbie, E. A. C., and J. Dainty. 1958b. *Physiol. Plantarum* 11: 782.

Robertson, R. N. 1960. *Biol. Rev. Cambridge Phil. Soc.* 35: 231.

Robertson, R. N., M. J. Wilkins, and D. C. Weeks. 1951. *Australian J. Sci. Res. B,* 4: 248.

Scott, G. T., and H. R. Hayward. 1955. In *Electrolytes Biol. Systems, Symp. Marine Biol. Lab., Woods Hole, Mass., 1954,* ed. A. M. Shanes. Washington: Am. Physiol. Soc. P. 35.

Spanswick, R. M., and E. J. Williams. 1964. *J. Exptl. Botany* 15: 193.

Steward, F. C. and J. F. Sutcliffe. 1959. In *Plant Physiology*, Vol. 2, ed. F. C. Steward. New York and London: Academic Press, Inc. P. 253.

Sutcliffe, J. F. 1959. *Biol. Rev. Cambridge Phil. Soc.* 34: 159.

Sutcliffe, J. F. 1962. *Mineral Salts Absorption in Plants*. London: Pergamon Press.

Sutcliffe, J. F., and D. P. Hackett. 1957. *Nature* 180: 95.

Van Lookeren Campagne. 1957. *Koninkl. Ned. Akad. Wetenschap., Proc.* 60: 70.

Walker, N. A. 1960. *Australian J. Biol. Sci.* 13: 468.

Williams, E. J., R. J. Johnston, and J. Dainty. 1964. *J. Exptl. Botany* 15: 1.

Role of the Membrane
in the Regulation of
Conduction and Contraction

Membrane Properties of Striated Muscle and the Initiation of Contraction

R. H. Adrian

Physiological Laboratory
University of Cambridge
Cambridge, England

The problems of excitation-contraction coupling in striated muscle can be approached from a number of different directions, but there seems to be general agreement that the coupling involves the intracellular structures of sarcoplasmic reticulum. The last few years have seen very striking advances in the knowledge of the morphology of this system, of the relationships of its constituent parts, and of its specializations in the muscles of various animals. The sarcoplasmic reticulum appears to be made up of two components, probably of different origins. There is a transversely running tubular system which seems to be related to, and possibly even derived from, the plasma membrane. This has been called the T-system (Anderson-Cedergren, 1959; Porter, 1961). The other component seems to be analogous to the endoplasmic reticulum of other cells. It comprises the reticulum lying longitudinally between the myofibrils and also the vesicles which, in special relation to the T-system, comprise the terminal cisternae of the triads. Knowledge of the morphology of the reticulum is considerably in advance of our knowledge of its physiology, but I want to talk about some of the experimental evidence which may be relevant to the function of the reticulum in the events which link the action potential to the contraction of muscle.

55

I shall be mainly concerned with the early steps in the sequence of events, how the disturbance spreads into the muscle fiber, and how that disturbance might operate, rather than with the identity of the activator and how it operates on the contractile proteins. Most of the experiments that I shall be considering were done on frog muscle, and one would not necessarily expect the results to apply to muscles of different animals. The diversity of reticular structure may reflect a similar diversity of function, and it would be rash at this stage to extrapolate from one animal to another without confirmation from experiment.

The local-activation experiments of Huxley and Taylor (1958) and Huxley and Straub (1958) constitute the most compelling evidence that the sarcoplasmic reticulum is related to the initiation of contraction. The crucial observations are the positions of the locally excitable surface spots in striated muscles from the frog and from the lizard. The positions of these spots correspond with the positions of the triads in these two species, in the frog at the Z-line and in the lizard at the A–I junction (Huxley, 1959). Huxley and Taylor showed that small outward currents, when made to flow through these special surface spots, caused a contraction in the underlying sarcomere, which did not spread to adjacent sarcomeres. The contraction was not conducted inward in a regenerative manner, and it could be varied by altering the strength of the applied current. The behavior of the contraction appeared to fit the idea of an electrotonic or decremental inward spread. If the inward spread of excitation is electrical and depends on the properties of an inwardly directed tubular system, it is important to know the electrical properties of the tubular wall; and one can ask how a potential difference across that wall might be utilized in the initiation of contraction.

The small size of the components of the sarcoplasmic reticulum makes it difficult to measure directly the properties of their membranes. However, since any current carried by a reticular pathway connected to the surface of the fiber would be in parallel with current flowing through the true surface of the fiber, one can ask whether there are any electrical properties of muscle fibers which might be assigned to a parallel pathway.

In 1949, Katz showed that when a muscle is placed in an isotonic solution of K_2SO_4, the membrane allows large inward currents but only very small outward currents. In this solution, K is the only ion that can carry appreciable quantities of current between the inside and outside of the fiber. The fiber behaves as a valve for K, with a high resistance to outward K movement and a low resistance to inward K movement (Katz, 1949). Figure 1 shows the result of a similar experiment. The membrane current is plotted against the internal potential for a sartorius muscle fiber in an isotonic SO_4 solution with a K concentration of 100 mEq/l. For some years, it was not known whether this rectification, often referred to as anomalous rectification, was a property of muscle fibers in isotonic K_2SO_4 only, or whether it was also present at more physiological external K concentrations.

Ten years after Katz's observation, Hodgkin and Horowicz (1959) studied the effect on the membrane potential of independent alterations of the external K and Cl concentrations. They concluded that the Cl permeability was large and constant but that the K permeability could vary widely and depended upon the direction of the movement of K. At all the external K concentrations studied (2.5, 10, 50, and 100 mM), the K permeability, calculated from the membrane potential, was small for outward K movement

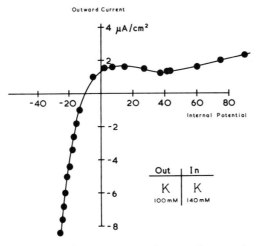

Fig. 1. Membrane current of a sartorius muscle fiber plotted against the internal potential. The fiber is in an isotonic SO_4 solution with a K concentration of 100 mEq/l. The measurements were made with the three-microelectrode technique described by Adrian and Freygang (1962).

and large for inward K movement. Hodgkin and Horowicz commented that "neither the physiological significance nor the physical nature of this rectification is understood. The matter is particularly puzzling because the rectification is in the opposite direction to that required to explain the recovery and loss of potassium during the impulse. Presumably the behaviour of the membrane at short times is different from that in the steady state. . . ."

Jenerick (1959) has shown that the membrane conductance increases when a fiber with a normal resting potential is depolarized by outward current. The increase in conductance is not seen until the fiber is depolarized by about 20 mv, but then the conductance change is similar to the delayed rectification of squid axons (Hodgkin *et al.*, 1949). Nakajima and coworkers (1962) hyperpolarized a muscle fiber in 40 mM K_2SO_4 in order to give it an internal potential of -85 mv, close to the normal resting potential. They reversed the direction of current flow to change the internal potential to 0 mv suddenly. This large depolarization caused an initial increase in conductance (delayed rectification), but this was followed by a decrease in conductance, with a half-time of about a second, to a value much less than the conductance when hyperpolarized to -85 mv. They suggest that delayed rectification is inactivated and that this inactivation "converts the delayed rectification into the anomalous rectification."

A possible interpretation of these experiments is that when a muscle fiber is depolarized from the resting potential, initially the K conductance of the membrane rises, and the subsequent fall in conductance only occurs if the depolarization is maintained by outward current. Alternatively, two K pathways could exist in parallel, one whose conductance increases on depolarization from the resting potential and is subject to inactivation by maintained depolarization, and a second capable of passing large inward K currents but only very small outward K currents. These pathways could exist side by side in the same membrane, or they could represent the behavior of two morphologically separate membranes. That two pathways exist independently is suggested by the observation of Adrian and Freygang (1962) that for the first 20 mv of depolarization from the resting potential, the K conductance actually falls. Anomalous rectification can therefore be detected both before delayed rectification occurs and after delayed rectification has been inactivated.

Other evidence in favor of two independent pathways for K movement is provided by muscles which have had 80–90% of their internal K replaced by Rb (Adrian, 1963). The replacement was achieved by soaking sartorius muscles for five days in an isotonic SO_4 solution with a Rb concentration of 100 mEq/l. At the end of this period, the average intracellular Rb concentration was 125 mEq/l fiber water; the average intracellular K concentration had dropped to only 23 mEq/l fiber water. If the ability of these muscles to allow inward and outward currents is measured in an isotonic Rb_2SO_4 solution, it is found that, unlike Katz's observation on muscles in K_2SO_4, the membrane will only allow small currents in either direction. With Rb on each side, the membrane hardly rectifies at all, and it has a high resistance at all membrane potentials. Figure 2 shows the relation between the membrane current and the internal potential for a Rb-containing muscle in Rb_2SO_4. The experiment is directly comparable to the experiment shown in Fig. 1, except that Rb replaces K on both sides of the membrane. It is obvious that the large inward currents which occur in the presence of K cannot occur in the presence of Rb. However, when these Rb-containing muscles are put into an ordinary Ringer's solution (or into a Ringer's solution in which RbCl replaces KCl), apparently normal action potentials can be recorded from the fibers. Figure 3 shows action potentials recorded from normal and Rb-containing muscles. If the large outward current responsible for the repolarization of the action potential is carried by K, it can also be carried by Rb. However, it seems that the pathway that can allow large inward K currents cannot allow inward Rb movement. These very different selectivities towards K and Rb strongly suggest that separate mechanisms are involved.

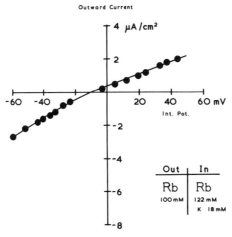

Fig. 2. Membrane current of a sartorius muscle fiber plotted against the internal potential. The fiber, which has had most of its internal K replaced by Rb, is in an isotonic SO_4 solution with an Rb concentration of 100 mEq/1. Measurements of current and voltage were by the same method as in Fig. 1, and the intracellular concentrations of cations were estimated on the whole muscle by flame photometry.

It is tempting to suggest that delayed rectification takes place in the surface membrane of the muscle fiber. The surface membrane would then be similar in its permeability properties to the membranes of axons and other excitable tissues. The mechanism responsible for anomalous rectification might then be located in the current pathway shown to be present by the local activation experiments, possibly in the wall of the T-system of the triad. The possibility that delayed rectification also takes place in the wall of the triad cannot be excluded. However, it could be argued that since events within the duration of the action potential initiate contraction, little purpose would be achieved by having two oppositely rectifying channels for K in the same membrane. The reduction of K conductance in the anomalously rectifying channel could

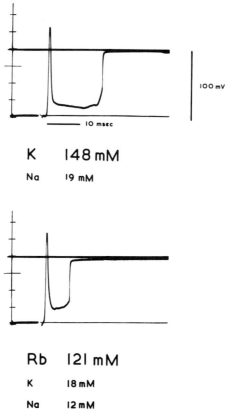

K   148 mM

Na   19 mM

Rb   121 mM

K   18 mM

Na   12 mM

Fig. 3. Action potentials from sartorius muscle fibers. The lower record is from a muscle with most of its internal K replaced by Rb. This muscle had been in an isotonic SO_4 solution for 5 days and was transferred to a Ringer's solution (NaCl, 115 mM; RbCl, 2.5 mM; $CaCl_2$, 1.8 mM; PO_4 buffer) shortly before this record was obtained. In both records, mechanical movement dislodged the microelectrode.

have little effect, if it occurred in parallel and in virtually the same place as the rise in K conductance due to delayed rectification.

What evidence is there to support the idea that anomalous rectification may be a property of a membrane of the reticulum? Hodgkin and Horowicz (1960a) have suggested that K acts on the membrane potential at a site removed from the surface of the fiber and possibly within the reticulum. They measured how rapidly K and Cl altered the membrane potential of an isolated fiber when the external concentrations were changed as quickly as possible. A sudden fall in the external K concentration affected the membrane potential more slowly than did a sudden rise in K concentration. Their results could be partially explained by supposing that K from the external solution had access to a special region of the muscle fiber with a volume between 1/500 and 1/200 of the fiber volume and that the membrane potential was affected by the K concentration within the space. The rapid and symmetrical effect of Cl on the membrane potential led them to suggest that the surface of the fiber was the site of the Cl permeability and that the K in the space could not diffuse away as rapidly as could ions at the surface of the fiber. They suggested that the space might correspond to the T-system of the triad and that its wall was permeable to K. In effect, the resting potential of muscle was supposed to result from a K potential across the wall of the T-system connected in parallel with a Cl potential across the surface of the fiber.

The structure and electrical properties of fast and slow striated muscle fibers from the frog also support the idea that anomalous rectification is the property of the T-system tubules or the triad. Peachey (1961) has reviewed the structure and function of the slow fiber system of the frog, and Peachey and Huxley (1962) have compared the structure of the sarcoplasmic reticulum in fast and in slow fibers. Slow fibers lack the T-system and triads. Burke and Ginsborg (1956) showed that the membrane conductance of slow fibers diminishes with hyperpolarization and increases with depolarization; that is, in slow fibers, only the conductance changes characteristic of delayed rectification occur. Recently, Peachey and I have confirmed the absence of anomalous rectification in slow fibers, and we have estimated the membrane capacities of slow and fast fibers from the tonus bundle of the ileofibularis. Measured with constant current pulses, the capacity of the slow fiber membrane appears to be only about 2 $\mu F/cm^2$, rather than the 5–8 $\mu F/cm^2$ characteristic of the fast fibers from the tonus bundle and of sartorius fibers. These observations suggest that both anomalous rectification and the large capacity of fast fibers may reflect the properties of the membrane of the T-system in parallel with the surface membrane of the muscle fiber (Fatt, 1961).

Many of the slow changes in potential which occur with long hyperpolarizing currents can be explained in terms of a small space in which the passage of current alters the K concentration. In the scheme put forward by Adrian and Freygang (1962), it was supposed that such a space was separated from the external solution and from the sarcoplasm by membranes, both of which were anion-impermeable.[1] The Na and K conductances of the outer

---

[1] Note added in proof. The assumption of anion impermeability was made for convenience, not from conviction. Giradier, Reuben, Brandt, and Grundfest (1963, *J. Gen. Physiol.* 47: 189) have shown recently that the walls of the sarcoplasmic reticulum in crayfish muscle cannot be impermeable to Cl.

membrane were supposed to be about equal, and the cation concentrations within the space were the same as in the external solution. The size of the space was estimated to be about 1/600 of the fiber volume. Figure 4 illustrates the proposed arrangement. K was supposed to carry all the current across the inner membrane, but Na and K were supposed to carry current across the outer membrane. For an inward current, this arrangement of permeabilities would produce a fall in the K concentration and a corresponding rise in the Na concentration. An outward current would produce the

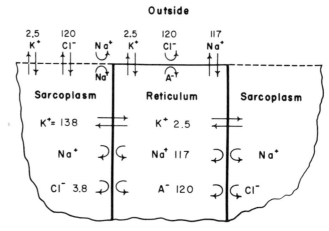

Fig. 4. Diagram to show the hypothetical relationship of the reticulum to the surface of the muscle fiber. The ionic concentrations and permeabilities were proposed to account for the changes in conductance which take place during a constant-current pulse. (From Freygang and Adrian, 1961, in *Biophysics of Physiological and Pharmacological Actions*, ed. A. M. Shanes. Washington: *Am. Assoc. Advan. Sci.*)

opposite changes in concentration. With a constant current, a new steady state would be reached when the net movement of Na across the outer membrane was zero and all the current was carried by K across both membranes. This simple scheme was able to account for a number of the observed variations of conductance with time, though it was necessary to assume that the inner membrane was the site of anomalous rectification to account for the observed variations of conductance with membrane voltage.

Thus, a number of observations seem to be well fitted by the suggestion that the T-system of the triad is a space, connected in some way to the external solution, which has in it cations at the same concentrations as in the external solution, with an inner wall which allows large inward K movements but very restricted outward K movements.

Having considered the evidence, admittedly circumstantial and indirect, which suggests that the walls of the T-system tubules are the site of the anomalous changes in K permeability, one can ask what purpose the permeability change might serve. Since activation takes place when the fiber is depolarized, the flow of current through the tubular system will be in an outward direction, that is, in the direction that diminishes the K permeability. This seems to rule out the possibility that the movement of K is involved, but if the movement of some other charged particle was produced by depolarization, the diminution of K permeability could have the effect of increasing the movement of the other ion.

Hodgkin and Horowicz (1960b) suggested that the shape of the contracture of single fibers when the external K concentration was suddenly raised could be explained on the basis of the release of an activator from a limited store of precursor and inactivation by removal of the activator after its release. To explain the appearance of a plateau and the shorter duration of contracture when higher K concentrations were used to depolarize, they supposed that above a certain concentration of activator, the contractile mechanism was saturated and that the greater the depolarization, the more rapid was the release of activator from the store of precursor. They considered the possibility that the precursor might be a Ca ion complexed with some molecule, the complex having a net negative charge and being held within the T-system tubules by the potential difference across the membrane separating the tubule from the sarcoplasm. When an action potential traverses the surface of the fiber, the potential across the wall of this tubule would be short-circuited by the low resistance of the surface membrane. Current would flow across the wall of the tubule, carried by K moving into the tubule from the sarcoplasm and by any permeant negatively charged particle moving from the tubule to the sarcoplasm. The decrease in the K permeability which is supposed to occur in the membrane of the T-system tubule with outward K movement would increase the amount of negatively charged ion which moves into the sarcoplasm. If the preceding arguments are correct, one would expect reasonably normal activation of contraction during the action potential of a Rb-containing muscle, even though it seems unlikely that the walls of the T-system tubules can carry appreciable Rb currents. Though activation of contraction has not yet been studied in detail in Rb-containing muscles, they appear to twitch in a perfectly normal manner.

Arguing teleologically, it appears that muscle has gone to some lengths to make it possible to have a steady-state K permeability which is very small for outward K movement. Such an arrangement, with the K permeability diminishing with depolarization, might easily make the resting potential unstable. The ability to pass large inward K currents when hyperpolarized (not, one imagines, a very common occurrence *in vivo*) may reflect the necessity for a high K permeability near the K equilibrium potential. The high Cl permeability of sartorius muscle may also be an adaptation for stabilizing the resting potential. Rb does not have a high permeability at the Rb equilibrium potential and cannot carry large inward currents. Muscles with their internal K replaced by Rb do not have the normal resting potential in a Cl-free medium with an external Rb or K concentration of 2.5 mEq/l. In a Ringer's fluid containing Cl, the internal potential is only large and negative so long as the internal Cl concentration is low.

There is, then, at least circumstantial evidence for the following hypothesis. The action potential at the surface of the muscle fiber short-circuits the potential difference across the wall of the T-system tubule via whatever structure makes up the sensitive spots demonstrated by Huxley and Taylor (1958). Current flows from the sarcoplasm into the T-system tubule, carried principally by a negatively charged Ca complex moving from the tubular lumen into the sarcoplasm. Once in the sarcoplasm, the complex itself might activate contraction, or it might be broken down to liberate Ca, which is known to initiate contraction. The Ca pump of the endoplasmic reticulum (Hasselbach and Makinose, 1961; Weber et al., 1963) would cause relaxation by reducing the level of Ca in the sarcoplasm. Porter (1961) suggested such a system of excitation-contraction coupling, and he pointed out that in rapidly contracting muscles, the longitudinal components of the reticulum show greater development than does the T-system. The distribution of the two components of the sarcoplasmic reticulum supports the idea that the T-system is responsible for the release of an activator and the longitudinal reticulum for its removal. The T-system is found, particularly in fast muscles, near the overlap of the A and I filaments, but the longitudinal reticulum is more evenly distributed along the length of each fibril. A wide distribution of the longitudinal reticulum would speed up the removal of Ca which will have diffused in all directions from its point of release.

The quantity of intracellular Ca and the volume of the T-system make it unlikely that all the Ca in a muscle is in the T-system. Since one must suppose that the Ca concentration in the sarcoplasm of relaxed muscle is very low indeed, it is reasonable to suggest that the longitudinal components of the reticulum contain a large proportion of the intracellular Ca. The special relation of the components of the triad might be for the transfer of Ca from the vesicles of the longitudinal reticulum to the T-system tubules in order to replenish the store of activator. Such a scheme is plainly speculative, and it is perfectly possible to suggest many other mechanisms. For instance, the T-system might be concerned only with the conduction of a potential change to the interior of the muscle, and the elements of the triad could be closely associated because the activator is released from the terminal cisternae of the triad and not from the central tubule.

Recently, Dr. Chandler and I have tried to confirm some predictions based on the ideas which have been outlined here. Our starting point was the model developed by Adrian and Freygang (1962) (see Fig. 4), and we supposed that some part of the anion present in their space was an activator anion of the kind suggested by Hodgkin and Horowicz (1960b). We further supposed that the outer wall of the space was impermeable to sucrose. Consider the consequences, in such a system, of replacing all the Na salt in the external solution by an osmotically equivalent amount of sucrose. Since the anion within the space is supposed to be unable to cross the outer membrane, the Na within the space will be replaced by K. The over-all potential difference between the sarcoplasm and the external solution will not be altered (except in so far as removing external Na causes a slight hyperpolarization), but the potential difference across the inner wall of the space will have disappeared, to be replaced by the same potential across the outer wall. If the release of activator is by the reduction of the potential across the wall of the T-system tubule, one might expect that the activator would be released when a muscle is transferred from a Ringer's solution to a solution in which the Na salt is replaced by sucrose. One would expect a sartorius muscle in the sucrose solution with a low ionic strength to have about the normal resting potential and to be unable to respond to depolarization with a contracture. One would expect it to be in the same kind of mechanically refractory state as a muscle in a solution with a high K concentration. However, this expectation is not confirmed by experiment. The contracture thresholds of sartorius muscle fibers were measured in solutions with a normal K concentration (2.5 mEq/l) made with choline chloride or choline sulfate. Choline, which was thought by Adrian and Freygang to penetrate the outer wall of their space, was used to prevent action potentials and twitches. Fibers were depolarized electrically, and the contracture threshold was measured as the depolarization just sufficient to cause visible movement of the fiber in the region of the current-passing microelectrode. When sucrose replaces either of the choline salts, the contracture threshold is not altered by more than about 10 mv. The contracture threshold is shifted towards the resting potential, but this could be due to a difference of Ca activity in the solutions. Uncertainty about the Ca activity coefficient in solutions of very different ionic strength makes it difficult to be sure that all the solutions had the same Ca activity.

Consider also what might happen to the resistance of the current pathway represented by the space in Fig. 4 when all the external Na salt is replaced by sucrose. In the Na-containing solution, the resistance will be made up of the Na and K resistances of the outer membrane in parallel, and the resistance of the outer membrane will be in series with the K resistance of the inner membrane. In the low ionic strength solution without Na, only the K resistance of the outer membrane will be in series with the K resistance of the inner membrane. Since the model predicts that the K concentration within the space will be greatly increased, one would expect that the K resistance of both membranes, and therefore the over-all resistance, would be greatly decreased. Furthermore, current flow through the two membranes and the intervening space should not alter the K concentration within the space. If one considers what would happen to a muscle in a Ringer's fluid made with Na_2SO_4 (to eliminate any current carried by Cl), the model predicts that replacing the Na_2SO_4 by sucrose would decrease the membrane resistance and abolish the slow changes of potential which occur during the passage of a maintained inward current. Neither of these predictions is verified by experiment. The slow increase in potential in the course of a constant inward current, though less marked, is still present when all the Na_2SO_4 is removed from the external solution, and the membrane resistance is increased, in some cases as much as doubled.

Using three microelectrodes inserted into a sartorius muscle fiber near the pelvic end, Chandler and I have been able to measure the relation between membrane current and electrotonic potential on a particular fiber in several solutions. In SO_4 solutions with a full complement of Na (190 mEq/l), the resistance at or near the K equilibrium potential is about 10,000 Ω cm². For large hyperpolarizing currents, the resistance, measured at the beginning of a pulse of current, may fall to a limiting value as low as 1,000 Ω cm². Figure 5 shows current-voltage relations for currents hyperpolarizing a fiber in solutions with a normal K concentration but with varying amounts of Na_2SO_4 replaced by sucrose. As the external concentration of Na_2SO_4 is reduced, the limiting slope resistance for large hyperpolarizations increases. The same increase in limiting resistance is seen whether the external K concentration is in the normal range or raised to about 10 mM (Fig. 6).

The effect of removing Na_2SO_4 from the external solution might be to remove a conductance in parallel with the K pathway or to add a resistance in series with it. Since it is unlikely that SO_4 can carry appreciable current, the first of these possibilities would require a Na current much too large to be compatible with the resting potential measured in the presence of Na. We have interpreted our findings in terms of a resistance in series with the K pathway. Over the concentration range of Na from 190 mEq/l to 10 mEq/l, the increase in the limiting resistance is very nearly directly proportional to the specific resistance of the external solution. The limiting resistance in the solution without any Na_2SO_4 is slightly lower than would be expected on the basis of direct proportionality, though it is larger than the resistance when the external Na concentration is 10 mEq/l. This behavior would be expected if the pathway for K current was via the walls of the T-system tubules and if the specific resistance of the contents of the tubules was the same as that of the external fluid. The extra resistance that is added to the membrane resistance when Na_2SO_4 is removed from the external solution is about the magnitude that would be predicted for a system of 300-Å tubules around each fibril at the Z-line.

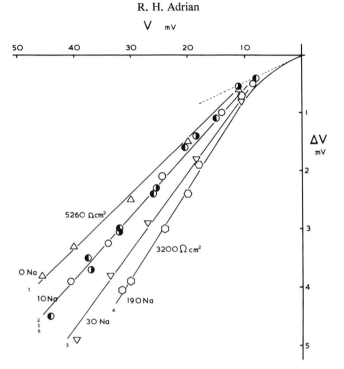

Fig. 5. Relation between the membrane current and the electrotonic potential for a sartorius muscle fiber in SO_4 solutions with physiological K concentrations. The electrotonic potential was measured at the beginning of a constant inward current. ΔV, plotted on the ordinate, is proportional to the membrane current. These measurements were made on one fiber. The microelectrodes were left in the fiber while the external solution was changed. The solutions contained different concentrations of Na_2SO_4. As far as possible, the K activity was constant, and the tonicity of each solution was maintained with sucrose. The current-voltage lines in each solution are identified by the Na concentration in mEq/1 (190 Na . . . 0 Na), and the small numbers at the end of each line indicate the sequence of solution changes. The dotted line has a slope which corresponds to a membrane resistance of 10,000 Ω cm².

The model of Adrian and Freygang (1962) was developed to mimic the changes of conductance that occur during a long pulse of inward current. That model predicts, however, that there should be no change in potential produced by a steady current in the absence of external Na. As has already been mentioned, removing Na_2SO_4 from the external solution reduces, but does not remove, the slow increase in the potential produced by a constant inward current. Changes in conductance of much the same kind as those predicted by the two-membrane model would be expected from a narrow tube open at one end to the external solution and with walls predominantly permeable to K. These conductance changes arise, if diffusion along the tube is not fast enough to replenish the K at any given point along the tube, when current is carried by K from the lumen of the tube across its wall into the sarcoplasm. In an open-mouthed tube, the contents would be expected to

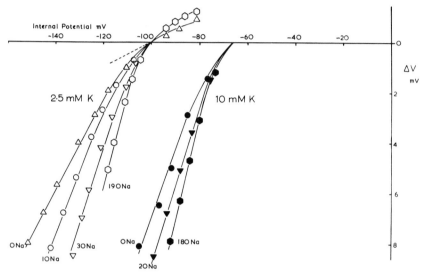

Fig. 6. Relation between the membrane current and the internal potential for two sartorius muscle fibers, one in solutions with physiological K concentrations and the other in solutions with raised K concentrations. As in Fig. 5, ΔV is proportional to the membrane current. The Na_2SO_4 concentration of the solutions was altered, and sucrose replaced Na_2SO_4 to maintain tonicity. (In this and the experiment shown in Fig. 5, small constant currents were passed to maintain the internal potential, in the absence of a pulse of current, at or near the K potential.)

have the same composition as the external fluid, and so the resistance of a tubular pathway would vary directly with the external specific resistance. Also, changes of conductance during a maintained current will occur in the presence or absence of Na_2SO_4, though they will be smaller in its absence.

The present evidence seems to favor an open-mouthed tubular space of small volume in a position which is physiologically external to the structure or structures which can pass large inward but small outward K currents. At the moment, one cannot identify this space, required by physiological experiments, with the T-system of the triad, or with any other part of the sarcoplasmic reticulum, though identification with the T-system is attractive and even probable. An open-mouthed tubular arrangement with the distribution and dimensions of the T-system of the triad, and with electrical properties suggested by the experiments, would be well suited to conduct an electrical change to the interior of the muscle fiber. However, such a system would not be well adapted to retain a mobile activator molecule within its lumen, nor does it offer any reason for the anomalous K permeability which seems to be associated with the wall of the tubule. It is conceivable that the mouth of the tube is made up of a sieve membrane capable of retaining a large molecule but which lets through most small ions and sucrose. Alternatively, the activating molecule might be released from some other structure which is influenced by current flow across the wall of the T-system. It is even possible that if this deeper structure is part of the current pathway between the inside and the outside of the fiber, it, and not the wall of the T-system, is the site of anomalous rectification.

Knowledge of the function of the endoplasmic reticulum is much more unsure than knowledge of its morphology. These speculations must seem very uncertain when compared to the elegant demonstrations of electron microscopy. Nevertheless, I hope that the lack of direct physiological evidence will not give one the impression that the sarcoplasmic reticulum is only a structure of improbable assumptions.

REFERENCES

Adrian, R. H. 1963. *J. Physiol.* (*London*) 169: 16 P.

Adrian, R. H., and W. H. Freygang. 1962. *J. Physiol.* (*London*) 163: 61.

Anderson-Cedergren, E. 1959. *J. Ultrastruc. Res.* Suppl. 7: 1.

Burke, W., and B. L. Ginsborg. 1956. *J. Physiol.* (*London*) 132: 586.

Fatt, P. 1961. *J. Physiol.* (*London*) 157: 10 P.

Freygang, W. H., and R. H. Adrian. 1961. In *Biophysics of Physiological and Pharmacological Actions*, ed. A. M. Shanes. Washington: *Am. Assoc. Advan. Sci.* P. 245.

Hasselbach, W., and M. Makinose. 1961. *Biochem. Z.* 333: 518.

Hodgkin, A. L., and P. Horowicz. 1959. *J. Physiol.* (*London*) 148: 127.

Hodgkin, A. L., and P. Horowicz. 1960a. *J. Physiol.* (*London*) 153: 370.

Hodgkin, A. L., and P. Horowicz. 1960b. *J. Physiol.* (*London*) 153: 386.

Hodgkin, A. L., A. F. Huxley, and B. Katz. 1949. *Arch. Sci. Physiol.* 3: 129.

Huxley, A. F. 1959. *Ann. N.Y. Acad. Sci.* 81: 446.

Huxley, A. F., and R. W. Straub. 1958. *J. Physiol.* (*London*) 143: 40 P.

Huxley, A. F., and R. E. Taylor. 1958. *J. Physiol. (London)* 144: 426.

Jenerick, H. P. 1959. *J. Gen. Physiol.* 42: 923.

Katz, B. 1949. *Arch. Sci. Physiol.* 3: 285.

Nakajima, S., S. Iwasaki, and K. Obata. 1962. *J. Gen. Physiol.* 46: 97.

Peachey, L. D. 1961. In *Biophysics of Physiological and Pharmacological Actions*, ed. A. M. Shanes. Washington: *Am. Assoc. Advan. Sci.* P. 391.

Peachey, L. D., and A. F. Huxley. 1962. *J. Cell Biol.* 13: 177.

Porter, K. R. 1961. *J. Biophys. Biochem. Cytol.* 10, Suppl.: 219.

Weber, A., R. Hertz, and I. Reiss. 1963. *J. Gen. Physiol.* 46: 679.

Metabolic Aspects of the Excitation-Contraction Coupling

A. Fleckenstein

Department of Physiology
Freiburg University
Freiburg, Germany

When a muscle responds to a stimulus, a chain reaction of electrical, mechanical, and chemical processes is initiated in each excited fiber. Whatever the nature of the stimulus may be, the first event consists in a change of the transmembrane electric field at the surface, whilst, as subsequent phenomena, a rapid rise of tension and many biochemical reactions preceding or following the mechanical activity are observed. The electrical responses may be local in the form of graded depolarizations, leading to contractures, or propagated in the form of action potentials followed by ordinary contractions. But in any case, an inward-going wave of activation has to be postulated which connects the primary excitation events of the membrane to the mechanical processes in the contractile elements and to the metabolic reactions occurring in the interior of the fibers. Ten years ago, in a very detailed study, Sandow (1952) called attention to the possibility that Ca may play a key role in this mysterious mechanism of excitation-contraction coupling. He proposed, as a working hypothesis, that an action potential or membrane depolarization of the muscle fiber surface promotes the entrance of Ca into the myoplasm which in turn initiates further reactions leading to the appearance of mechanical activity. Since that time, evidence has been accumulated rapidly in favor of Sandow's concept. This evidence is mainly based on the following facts.

71

1. Ca is the only physiological ion which, when injected at low concentrations into muscle fibers, causes shortening. The original results obtained by Heilbrunn and Wiercinski (1947) in this field could be further established and extended by the more recent work of Niedergerke (1955) and of Caldwell and Walster (1963).

2. Ca influx into muscle fibers is considerably augmented during activity. This was demonstrated clearly by the beautiful tracer studies of Bianchi and Shanes (1959), Shanes and Bianchi (1960), Shanes (1961), and Winegrad and Shanes (1962). Their experiments were carried out on amphibian skeletal muscle fibers of both the twitch type and the slow type and on mammalian cardiac tissue. All experimental data collected by this group show that the increased Ca influx associated with contraction and contracture is closely correlated both quantitatively and temporally with the mechanical events.

3. Variations of the extracellular Ca concentration may deeply influence the strength of shortening. The first observations indicating that the link between excitation and contraction can be broken by removal of extracellular Ca were made by Mines on heart muscle as early as 1913. De Burgh Daly and Clark (1921), Bogue and Mendez (1929), as well as Bay et al. (1933) referred to the same phenomenon. Using the frog rectus abdominis muscle, we found in 1947 that a K contracture could not be maintained in a Ca-free KCl solution, especially after addition of small amounts of Na oxalate (Fleckenstein and Hertel, 1948). Supernormal Ca concentrations, on the other hand, were able to reduce the spontaneous loss of tension which usually occurs during prolonged exposures to isotonic KCl. Further reports about this pronounced Ca sensitivity of the K contracture were published by Frank (1958, 1960) and by Shanes (1961). Denton (1948) obtained similar results on the contracture induced by acetylcholine (ACh). Even the caffeine-induced contracture which can be obtained in a Ca-free solution was proved to be Ca-dependent, since caffeine seems to release Ca from binding sites in or on the muscle fibers, thus increasing the intracellular levels of Ca (Frank, 1962; Bianchi, 1961). The requirement for Ca in the contractile response of smooth muscle to ACh, serotonin, histamine, oxytocin, and adrenaline has also been established in recent years (Robertson, 1960; Edman and Schild, 1961; Yukisada and Ebashi, 1961; Bohr and Goulet, 1961).

4. Finally, additional indirect evidence came from research work on subcellular muscle constituents. Actomyosin and myofibrils under certain conditions were found to require the addition of Ca for superprecipitation and maximal adenosine triphosphatase (ATPase) activity (see Mommaerts, 1950; Ebashi, 1961; Weber and Winicur, 1961; Weber and Herz, 1963). On the other hand, relaxation of the muscles seems to be brought about by accumulation of Ca in the vesicles of the sarcoplasmic reticulum. In

this connection, Hasselbach and Makinose (1961) have postulated the existence of a Ca pump driven by adenosine triphosphate (ATP) which initiates relaxation by the transfer of Ca into the granules which subsequently store it in an inactive form. A similar hypothesis of relaxation has been put forward by Ebashi (1961).

Keeping in mind all these significant results, even a critical reviewer must admit that our knowledge about the fundamental mechanisms of the excitation-contraction coupling has been advanced rapidly, especially during the last decade. It is the purpose of the present paper to contribute some additional new pieces of evidence and to integrate our own observations on metabolic effects of Ca into the general pattern of the excitation-contraction coupling reactions.

The Quantitative Regulation of Tension Output by the Excitation Process

In the physiological vocabulary, the action potential is commonly referred to as a "trigger" for the initiation of the mechanical events. But, as Sandow pointed out years ago, the essence of a trigger is "that the intensity of its action, provided it is at least at threshold level, bears no necessary quantitative relation to the magnitude of the change it sets off." I should like to discuss in the first portion of this paper certain observations which clearly indicate that the action potential, at least in heart muscle fibers, should not be considered as a "trigger" in this simple sense, because the quantitative regulation of the contractile elements is certainly one of the most important functions of the bioelectrical membrane processes.

Figure 1 shows simultaneous records of single-fiber action potentials and of isometric tension of an isolated strip of frog ventricle in ordinary Ringer's solution and then after addition of ACh. Here, as in all the following experiments, intracellular microelectrodes, mechanoelectronic transducer valves (RCA 5734), and double-beam oscilloscopes were used for registration. It is obvious from this picture that the contractile force of the frog myocardium is depressed to an extent similar to the shortening of the duration of the action potential by ACh, whereas the absolute height of the action potentials shows no correlation to the peak tension, since the voltage of the peak of the spike remains practically unchanged by ACh. In the experiments of Fig. 2, the integrated areas of the action potentials and of the mechanograms were registered on the screen of a second double-beam oscilloscope simultaneously with the upper original records. The curves were obtained on ACh-treated guinea pig auricles. One can easily see that the downward deflections of the two lower curves, which represent the integrated areas of both action poten-

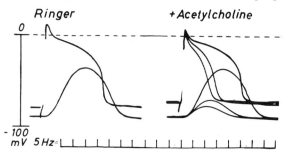

Fig. 1. Depression of the contractile force of a strip of frog ventricle by abbreviation of the action potential in an ACh-containing Ringer's solution. Here and in all following experiments, potentials were determined with microelectrodes of conventional type. Isometric tensions were always recorded with a transducer valve (RCA 5734). (Antoni and Fleckenstein, unpublished.) (In this figure and in all following figures in this paper, *Hz* indicates the frequency in cycles per second.)

tial and mechanogram, run closely parallel. The observations indicate that the total amount of tension which is produced during a heartbeat depends, under normal conditions, on the amount of membrane depolarization. This means, in the modern concept of excitation-contraction coupling, that the Ca entry or the Ca release from certain binding sites will be quantitatively regulated by the extent and by the length of time the transmembrane electric

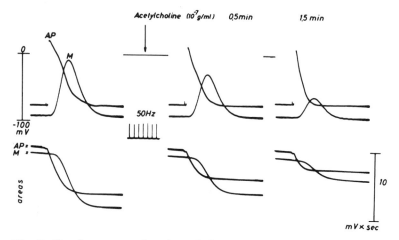

Fig. 2. Simultaneous registration of the areas of the action potentials and of the isometric tensions in an isolated guinea pig auricle treated with ACh. (Antoni and Fleckenstein, unpublished.)

field is changed during the action potential. Depolarization seems to open the door for Ca. ACh, on the other hand, can restrict the Ca entry by abbreviation of the excitation process in the myocardial fibers. But the responsiveness of the contractile system to Ca remains unchanged. This becomes evident from Fig. 3. Here, again in guinea pig auricles, the contractile force was gradually reduced by ACh in parallel to the abbreviation of the action potentials until the mechanical activity had nearly ceased. Then excess Ca was added to the ACh-containing Tyrode solution. One minute afterwards, the contractile force not only had fully recovered, but had even exceeded the

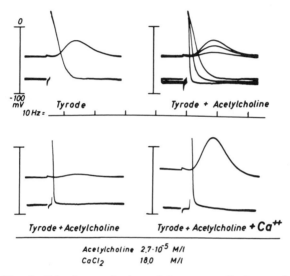

Fig. 3. Selective restitution of the contractile force of an ACh-treated guinea pig auricle by addition of excess Ca to Tyrode solution. (Antoni and Fleckenstein, unpublished.)

initial peak values by about 100%—in spite of the fact that the action potential remained short.

Figure 4 shows another interesting example in which the output of isometric tension is closely related to the duration of the action potential. It is a well-known fact that the contraction amplitude of isolated mammalian papillary muscles or auricles will increase if they are cooled. A recent analysis of this phenomenon in our laboratory has revealed a striking parallelism between the prolongation of action potential and the augmentation of the contractile force at lower temperatures (Fig. 5). As shown in this graph, the per cent increase in the duration of the action potential, measured at different heights of the spike, and the per cent augmentation of the peak tension are practically coincident over the whole range of temperature between 37°C

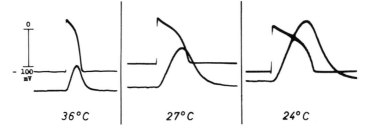

Fig. 4. Increase of duration of action potential and of isometric tension in a cooled guinea pig papillary muscle. Rate of stimulation: 3 shocks/min. (Fleckenstein and Kaufmann, unpublished.)

and 15°C. But there was a fundamental change of the situation when we increased the Ca concentration of the Tyrode solution by several times. In such a Ca-rich environment, maximal activation of the contractile machinery can be reached at 37°C, so that no further augmentation of peak tension is obtainable by cooling. The open circles in Fig. 6 represent the peak tension developed by isolated guinea pig auricles in a Tyrode solution which contained eight times the normal Ca concentration; this means 14.4 mM $CaCl_2$ instead of 1.8 mM. In these Ca-saturated auricles, the peak tension was even reduced by a lower temperature. The black dots show again the completely different influence of cooling in an ordinary Tyrode solution with only 1.8 mM Ca. One may conclude from these observations that the duration of the

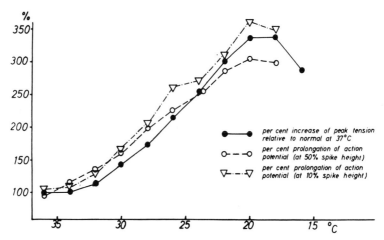

Fig. 5. Parallelism between prolongation of action potential (measured at heights of 10% and 50% of the spike) and augmentation of peak tension in cooled guinea pig auricles. Rate of stimulation: 3 shocks/min. (Fleckenstein and Kaufmann, unpublished.)

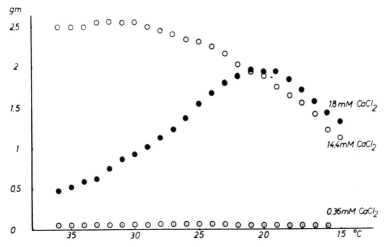

Fig. 6. Influence of temperature on isometric peak tension of isolated guinea pig auricles in Tyrode solution with different Ca concentrations. Rate of stimulation: 3 shocks/min. (Fleckenstein and Kaufmann, unpublished.)

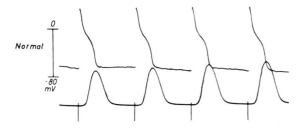

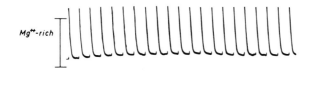

Fig. 7. Depression of the contractile force of a strip of frog ventricle by abbreviation of the action potential in Ringer's solution containing 15 mM $MgCl_2$. (Antoni and Fleckenstein, unpublished.)

action potential of an isolated mammalian papillary muscle or auricle, kept in an ordinary Tyrode solution at 37°C, is not sufficiently great to allow a Ca entry of such an extent that the absolute tension maximum will be reached. But this can be achieved, of course, by prolongation of the action potential in the cold or by increasing the extracellular Ca concentration.

As a last example of the fact that inotropic heart effects can be exerted by an influence on the duration of action potential, I should like to discuss an interesting antagonism between Mg and adrenaline which we have found in the frog myocardium. Figure 7 shows a very peculiar phenomenon which

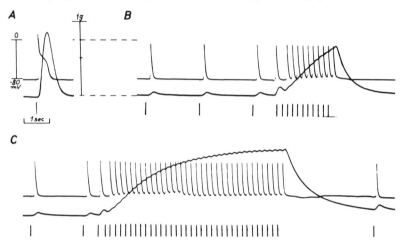

Fig. 8. Tetanus of a strip of frog ventricle after abbreviation of action potential in Ringer's solution containing 15 mM $MgCl_2$. *A*: action potential and isometric contraction in ordinary Ringer's solution; *B*: action potentials and isometric tension curves due to single shocks and to more frequent stimuli after soaking the heart strip in Ringer's solution with high Mg for 26 min; *C*: behavior of the heart strip after 35 min in Ringer's solution with high Mg. (From Antoni *et al.*, 1962, *Pfluegers Arch. Ges. Physiol.* 275: 507. Berlin-Göttingen-Heidelberg: Springer-Verlag.)

always appears if isolated strips of frog ventricle are put in a Ringer's solution with a high Mg content (7.5–15 mM $MgCl_2$). Under these conditions, the action potentials become very short, and the tension of the beats drops to such negligible values that only small mechanical oscillations are left. Nevertheless, the contractile elements can still be fully activated if the Mg-treated myocardium is tetanized by frequent electric stimuli. Now, due to the abbreviation of the action potentials, the myocardium behaves like skeletal muscle, which sums up tension to a maximal tetanic contraction (Fig. 8). Adrenaline, on the other hand, completely reverses the Mg effects

(Fig. 9). It restores the initial duration of the action potential and, by virtue of this, the normal tension. In many cases, even a supernormal recovery can be seen. In Fig. 10, a graph is shown of the effects of high Mg and of adrenaline on overshoot, resting potential, duration of action potential, and mechanical tension. It is again obvious that there is a close parallelism between the changes of duration of action potential and of peak tension both under the depressing influence of Mg and, thereafter, during the supernormal adrenaline-induced recovery. Resting potential and overshoot values, on the other hand, do not change appreciably.

The ability of adrenaline to increase the contractile force of the beating

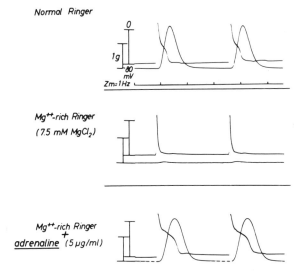

Fig. 9. Recovery of a Mg-treated strip of frog ventricle 3 min after addition of adrenaline to Ringer's solution containing high Mg. (Antoni, Engstfeld, and Fleckenstein, unpublished.)

heart by prolonging the action potential is certainly not restricted to the special case of the Mg-treated amphibian myocardium, because similar observations were made, in principle, on mammalian cardiac tissues under very different experimental conditions. So, adrenaline and ACh can be considered as true antagonists with respect to their specific influence on the duration of the cardiac action potentials. Undoubtedly, the autonomic nervous system makes use of this possibility to control the energy output of the heart muscle fibers by affecting the shape of the membrane excitation process. (Another more direct influence of adrenaline on contraction will be discussed later.) It is also interesting to note in this connection that one of the early reactions of the myocardium after a decrease of the intracellular high-energy phosphate concentrations consists of an abbreviation of the action potential. This occurs as a regular phenomenon in the state of hypoxia, as well as after treatment with cyanide, monoiodoacetate, or 2,4-dinitrophenol (DNP). The mechanism is certainly not clear, but one may perhaps

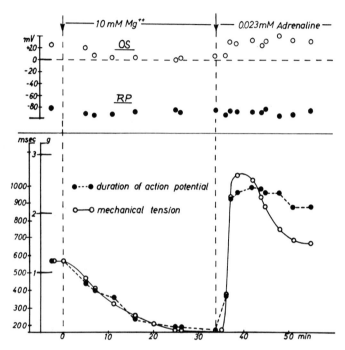

Fig. 10. Parallelism between the duration of action potential (measured at a height of 50% of the spike) and the isometric peak tension produced. Experiments on isolated strips of frog ventricle soaked in Ringer's solution containing 10 mM $MgCl_2$ before and after addition of adrenaline. *OS*: overshoot; *RP*: resting potential. (From Antoni *et al.*, 1962, *Pfluegers Arch. Ges. Physiol.* 275: 507. Berlin-Göttingen-Heidelberg: Springer-Verlag.)

speculate that such an abbreviation of action potential is an act of economy if the cardiac energy balance tends to become negative. Added adenosine triphosphate (ATP), on the other hand, can prolong the action potential of the frog myocardium previously shortened in a Ringer's solution with high Mg or high K (Kotowski *et al.*, 1959; Antoni *et al.*, 1962).

Excitation-Independent Contractility Changes, Their Relation to Ca and to the Muscle Fiber Surface

Now, I should like to discuss some excitation-independent contractility changes which clearly occur without alteration of the bioelectrical membrane processes. In fact, any agent which alters contraction independently of depolarization may influence the contractile mechanism directly or, alternatively, may affect a link in the processes between depolarization and contraction. Ca apparently acts in this way. Figure 11, which was obtained

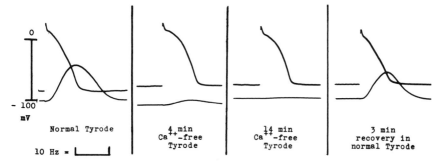

Fig. 11. Complete loss of contractility of an isolated rabbit papillary muscle in a Ca-free Tyrode solution at 37°C. Rapid recovery in ordinary Tyrode solution. Rate of stimulation: 3 shocks/min.

on an isolated rabbit papillary muscle, recalls the well-known fact that contractility ceases after removal of Ca. Subsequently, the preparation was allowed to recover in normal Tyrode. However, the action potential did not change appreciably over the whole experiment. Supernormal Ca concentrations, on the other hand, can potentiate the peak tension of papillary muscles more or less selectively by several hundred per cent (Fig. 12). More-

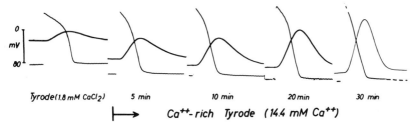

Fig. 12. Increase of isometric peak tension of a guinea pig papillary muscle after soaking in Tyrode solution containing high Ca. Rate of stimulation: 6 shocks/min. Temperature: 36°C.

over, apart from Ca, there are many other substances which also affect contractility by an excitation-independent mechanism. But, as has been discovered in recent years, they may do so by enhancing the Ca action or by interfering with it. So, even in pharmacological drug actions, the key role of Ca becomes more and more significant.

Otto Loewi was the first to attribute, as early as 1917, the inotropic heart effects of digitalis glycosides to an interaction with Ca. But more than 40 years passed before Loewi's hypothesis was further substantiated (see Thomas *et al.*, 1958; Holland and Sekul, 1959; Sekul and Holland, 1960; Lüllmann and Holland, 1962; Gersmeyer and Holland, 1963). Through this work, it was established that ouabain causes an increased rate of uptake of Ca^{45} in frog hearts and in rabbit or rat atria. The influence on Ca^{45} uptake was small but significant during the positive inotropic action of ouabain, whereas the uptake rates rose sharply with the onset of ouabain-induced contractures. Nevertheless, the tissue Ca content showed a tendency to decrease, indicating that the Ca movements were enhanced in both directions. The experimental data suggest that the inotropic effects of heart glycosides may be due to an increment in exchangeable free Ca which probably originates from an extremely labile fraction of bound tissue Ca. So the heart glycosides are presumed to "facilitate" the process of Ca entry or release by which the action potential gives rise to contraction, whereas the action potential itself does not change. In this respect, the mode of action of heart glycosides seems to be very similar to the basic effects of Br, I, and NO_3, which also, in amphibian skeletal muscle fibers, increase and prolong contraction without an influence on action potential (Kahn and Sandow, 1950, 1955; Hill and MacPherson, 1954). Moreover, these anions, in replacing Cl, can enhance the K contracture of single muscle fibers (Hodgkin and Horowicz, 1960). Bianchi and Shanes (1959) have provided data that show a correlation between augmentation of Ca influx and of the twitch by NO_3. And, in recent experiments of Ebashi *et al.* (1962), it was demonstrated that the Ca-binding capacity of the sarcoplasmic reticulum is lowered by these anions in the same order as the K contracture will be increased ($Br < NO_3 < I$). Therefore, the conclusion seems to be justified that Br, I, and NO_3 in skeletal muscle, as well as heart glycosides in cardiac muscle, enhance contraction by making more free Ca available for the activation of the contractile machinery.

There has been much speculation recently about the special topographic localization of the excitation-contraction coupling reactions. As Kahn and Sandow (1950) and Hill and MacPherson (1954) have pointed out, skeletal muscles respond so quickly to changes in the anionic composition of the medium that the reactions they produce must take place in a superficially located region of the muscle fibers. This is evident from the observations 1) that iodide, for example, after sudden immersion of a muscle in the abnormal medium, increases twitch tension at a time when there is practically none of it inside the fibers and 2) that the effect rapidly passes off as iodide is removed from the interspaces, although a large amount of it will still be inside. Hodgkin and Horowicz (1960) confirmed these conclusions by showing that in single muscle fibers, the increase in twitch amplitude occurs within a few seconds of replacing Cl by NO_3. However, since the effect of NO_3 on twitch tension was somewhat slower than the effect of Na on excitability, the slight delay observed with NO_3 seemed to be indicative of a spatial separation of the parts of the membrane connected with excitation and mechanical activation. Therefore, the suggestion has been made that the sites responsible for the action potential might be on the surface, whereas those concerned with activating the contractile system might be located in a tubular component of the sarcoplasmic reticulum which is believed to connect the fiber surface to the interior (Porter and Palade, 1957). Niedergerke (1957) and Lüttgau and Niedergerke (1958), working on the frog heart, came to more or less similar conclusions. They emphasized the fact that the superficial fraction of cellular Ca responsible for the mechanical activation competes with extracellular Na for negatively charged receptor groups. Further evidence came from experiments with caffeine. This substance can produce contractures without depolarization even in a Ca-free medium but acts, nevertheless, as Bianchi (1961) and Frank (1962) have found, through the mediation of Ca. But caffeine caused contracture only when applied externally to the muscle fiber membranes; injected caffeine was ineffective (Axelsson and Thesleff, 1958). All of these observations are consistent with the general concept that the cellular binding sites from which Ca is liberated in the excitation-contraction coupling process are probably confined more to the extracellular space than to the intracellular compartment.

I should like to contribute to this question one of our own experimental observations carried out on isolated strips of frog ventricle. The left side of Fig. 13 shows a progressive decrease of the contraction amplitude after ordinary Ringer's solution, containing 2.5 mM Ca, was exchanged for another solution with only one-fifth the normal Ca content. Finally, in part C of the picture, the peak tension persisted at a very low, but constant, new level. Then a single dose of ATP was added to the low-Ca Ringer's. Part D, on the right side, shows that, 3 min after ATP had been added, the contractile force was restored to supernormal values. Then the contraction amplitude declined again within 20 min, as shown in parts E and F of the picture.

The further analysis of this phenomenon has revealed that ATP is certainly no substitute for Ca in excitation-contraction coupling, since the inotropic ATP effects disappear in a completely Ca-free medium, but that ATP probably acts as a Ca synergist in a superficial region of the cardiac fibers. This is evident from the fact that added ATP is split to adenosine diphosphate (ADP) and adenosine monophosphate (AMP) as it contacts the fiber surface. But the fission products appeared quantitatively in the Ringer's bath, so that the total adenosine nucleotides remained constant. Thus, a significant entry of ATP into the fibers could be excluded. The observations show that even ATP can affect the excitation-contraction coupling reactions from outside. Furthermore, they indicate that metabolically active substances like ATP may perhaps participate in the Ca-dependent excitation-

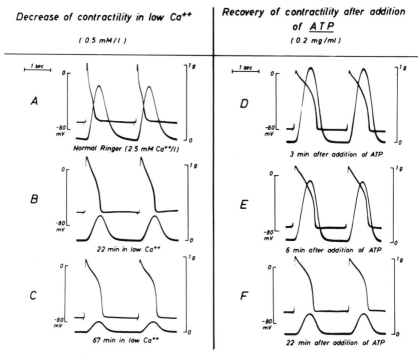

Fig. 13. Recovery of the contractile force of a Ca-deprived strip of frog ventricle after addition of ATP to the Ca-deficient medium. *A*: action potential and isometric tension in ordinary Ringer's solution containing 2.5 mM Ca; *B–C*: Decrease of contractility in Ringer's solution containing only 0.5 mM Ca; *D–F*: Recovery of contractility after addition of 0.2 mg ATP/ml. The shape of the action potential remained constant from *B* to *F*. (From Antoni *et al.*, 1960, *Pfluegers Arch. Ges. Physiol.* 272: 91. Berlin-Göttingen-Heidelberg: Springer-Verlag.)

contraction coupling reactions. Adrenaline, for instance, in our search for more effective agents, was found to be another highly potent Ca synergist which has even a wider field of action, since it enhances the contractile responses not only in frog hearts but also in the mammalian myocardium. Therefore, the inotropic heart effects of adrenaline have to be considered in most cases as consisting of two components: 1) prolongation of action potential (see foregoing section) and 2) direct inotropic actions synergistic to Ca that cannot be explained solely by an influence on excitation. Figure 14 gives an example of mixed effects of adrenaline. Here, in an isolated Rhesus monkey papillary muscle, made inexcitable by high K, the function could be restored by addition of adrenaline. But in spite of the fact that

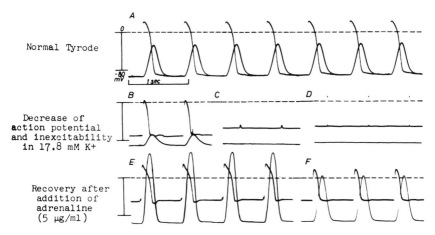

Normal Tyrode

Decrease of
action potential
and inexcitability
in 17.8 mM K+

Recovery after
addition of
adrenaline
(5 µg/ml)

Fig. 14. Restitution of excitability, impulse conduction, and contractility of an isolated Rhesus monkey papillary muscle, previously paralyzed in high K, by addition of a single dose of adrenaline. The recovery of the muscle, *E*, took place within 6 min after adrenaline had been added. In spite of the fact that the action potential was not fully restored by adrenaline, isometric peak tension exceeded the initial values observed in ordinary Tyrode solution by approximately 100%. The effect of adrenaline declines slowly. *F* represents the behavior 21 min after adrenaline had been added. (From Antoni and Engstfeld, 1961, *Verh. Deutsch. Ges. Kreislaufforsch.* 27:232. Darmstadt: Verlag Dr. D. Steinkopff.)

the action potential did not fully recover, supernormal peak tension was produced.

The Mediator Function of Ca in Connecting Membrane Depolarization and High-Energy Phosphate Breakdown

Although a Ca action on ATPase activity of subcellular muscle constituents as actomyosin or myofibrils has long been recognized, no data concerning the biochemical side of the Ca functions, obtained on living muscle, were available in the literature until recently. Therefore, we started such an investigation four years ago with an analysis of the K contracture of the isolated M. rectus abdominis of frogs. As has been already mentioned, these muscles cannot develop or sustain tension—even in an isotonic KCl solution—in the absence of extracellular Ca.

The principal result of these experiments was that the breakdown of creatine phosphate which always accompanies K contracture was also minimized after exposure of the muscle to a Ca-free medium (Fleckenstein *et al.*, 1961). The influence of variation of the extracellular Ca concentration

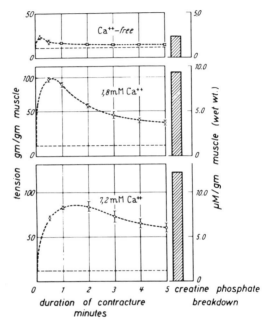

Fig. 15. K contractures of the isolated M. rectus abdominis of frogs produced by immersion in 100 mM KCl solution for 5 min. Parallel changes of tension and creatine phosphate breakdown due to variation of the extracellular Ca concentration. (From Fleckenstein *et al.*, 1961, *Pfluegers Arch. Ges. Physiol.* 273: 483. Berlin-Göttingen-Heidelberg: Springer-Verlag.)

upon tension development and creatine phosphate breakdown produced in a 100 mM KCl solution is shown in Fig. 15. As one can see, muscles which had lost most of their contractility, due to preincubation in a Ca-free Ringer's solution for 22 hr, did not split more than 2.4 μM creatine phosphate/g muscle when they were exposed to 100 mM K for 5 min. On the other hand, preincubation of the muscles in a Ca-rich Ringer's solution which contained four times the normal Ca concentration, that is, 7.2 mM instead of 1.8 mM

Ca, led to a higher or more constant tension and to an increased creatine phosphate breakdown. Thus, in a 100 mM KCl solution—after pretreatment with high Ca—an average of 12.2 μM creatine phosphate/g muscle was lost within 5 min. The results showed that during K contracture, there is a relatively close connection between the degree of mechanical tension and the amount of high-energy phosphate which is metabolized. Conversely, no direct correlation could be found between the membrane depolarization in high K and the metabolic activity, since in the absence of Ca, depolarization not only failed to produce permanent shortening, but also lost its ability to initiate a big high-energy phosphate breakdown. Therefore, it was concluded that Ca, in parallel to its established function in the process of depolarization-contraction coupling, may also be an important link between the bioelectrical phenomena at the membrane and the metabolism of the high-energy phosphates in the muscle cell.

Subsequently, our observations were extended by the study of other membrane-depolarizing substances which produce reversible or irreversible shortening (Fleckenstein and Schwoerer, 1961). From earlier investigations, it was well known that a certain decrease of creatine phosphate concentration will always occur during muscular activity (for references, see Fleckenstein, 1955). This is even true for a single twitch at 0°C, as was demonstrated recently, with improved techniques, by Mommaerts (1962), by Cain and Davies (1962), and in our own laboratory. During contractures, on the other hand, the fission of creatine phosphate is always so large that it cannot be overlooked even with less sensitive methods. Nevertheless, there are certain differences, since contractures caused by suitable concentrations of KCl, ACh, nicotine, lactic acid, or NaOH do not produce an additional loss of appreciable amounts of ATP, whereas the irreversible shortening due to caffeine, chloroform, or other muscle-destroying agents or procedures will always be accompanied by a more or less extensive ATP breakdown.

Figure 16 shows the development of tension and the simultaneous creatine phosphate breakdown during contractures of different types, both in muscles with normal Ca and in muscles pretreated with a Ca-free Ringer's solution for 12–16 hr. We see in the upper half of the picture that the maximum tension of the Ca-deprived muscles—represented by horizontally hatched columns—was usually small, whereas the contractile force of the muscles with normal Ca—represented by black columns—was always found to be considerably greater. The lower half of the graph demonstrates the simultaneous changes of the creatine phosphate content in the same muscles. It is obvious that in the muscles preincubated in a Ca-free medium, the ability to split creatine phosphate had also been considerably depressed. In contrast to this, the muscles with normal Ca will metabolize more creatine phosphate, corresponding to their more vigorous shortening. Similarly, in those contractures which are normally accompanied by an ATP breakdown,

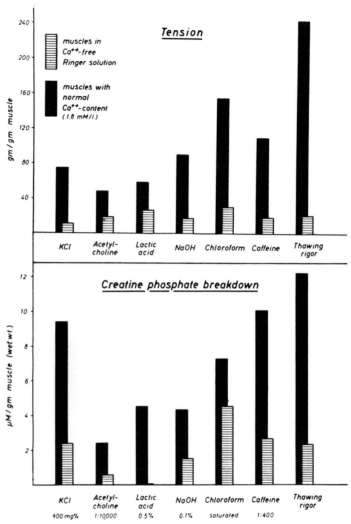

Fig. 16. Influence of Ca deprivation on tension and creatine phosphate breakdown in the isolated M. rectus abdominis of frogs during contractures of different types. Pairs of muscles were soaked for 12–16 hr in a Ca-free oxygenated Ringer's solution or in ordinary Ringer's solution containing 1.8 mM CaCl$_2$ before they were used in the contracture experiments. Long exposures in the Ca-free medium were made, since some of the contractures, as, for instance, caffeine-induced contractures, are less sensitive to Ca deprivation than is the K contracture. (Fleckenstein and Schwoerer, unpublished.)

Ca enhanced this reaction, whereas the ATP level remained high in a Ca-free medium.

It is commonly accepted that the breakdown of high-energy phosphates in the cell will give rise to intensified glycolytic and oxidative reactions.

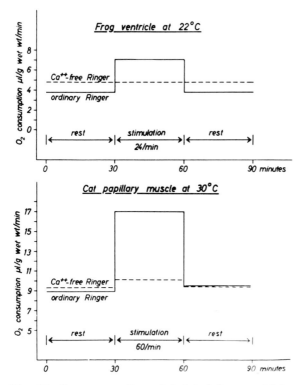

Fig. 17. O_2 consumption of isolated frog ventricles and cat papillary muscles at rest and during activity both in ordinary Ringer's solution and in a Ca-deficient medium. The rates of O_2 consumption were calculated from O_2-tension measurements in the surrounding fluid by a platinum electrode. The mechanical activity of the Ca-deprived preparations was negligible during the stimulation period. (Byon and Fleckenstein, unpublished.)

Therefore, it is not surprising that the rate of formation of lactic acid as well as the rate of O_2 consumption are also "Ca-sensitive." This applies, according to Kaye and Mommaerts (1960), even for the lactic acid production in resting frog muscle. But this Ca dependency becomes more evident, of course, in active muscle. Figure 17 illustrates the rates of O_2 consumption of isolated frog ventricles and of cat papillary muscles at rest and during stimulation, both in ordinary Ringer's solution and in a Ca-deficient medium. As can easily be seen, the O_2 consumption at rest does not differ appreciably whether or not the surrounding fluid contains Ca. But if stimulation sets in, the O_2 consumption rises sharply, but only in the presence of Ca, whereas it remains more or less at resting level in the Ca-deprived myocardium, which responds electrically but not mechanically to stimulation.

What is the meaning of these results? Obviously they provide further evidence for a mediator function of Ca in connecting membrane depolarization to the mechanical as well as biochemical reactions inside the muscle fiber. But certainly more work is needed to elucidate the special sequence of the Ca-dependent events.

TABLE 1

POSSIBLE MECHANISMS OF CA ACTION

A	B	C
Depolarization	Depolarization	Depolarization
↓	↓	↓
Inward movement of Ca	Inward movement of Ca	Inward movement of Ca
↓	↙ ↘	↓
Fission of high-energy phosphates	Fission of high-energy phosphates Contraction	Contraction
↓		↓
Contraction		Fission of high-energy phosphates

Table 1 lists the ways in which Ca might act. One attractive hypothesis (A) would be that Ca initiates the splitting of high-energy phosphates directly by activation of ATPase, thus leading to contraction according to the classical theory of Szent-Györgyi (1948). Another possibility (C) is that the breakdown of high-energy phosphates will be—at least in part—a consequence of contraction, since we found, using the new H_2O^{18} method, that the intensification of the ATP turnover continues during the recovery period after a tetanus (Fleckenstein et al., 1960). Furthermore, Hasselbach and Makinose (1961) were able to demonstrate that the Ca-binding vesicles of the sarcoplasmic reticulum, which cause relaxation after contraction, also split ATP for this purpose.

But scheme B has to be considered as well, in which the Ca-dependent activation of phosphate metabolism and of the contractile mechanism are not so rigidly linked as in scheme A or C. Scheme B would be in harmony, for instance, with the observations of Solandt (1936), Smith and Solandt (1938), Hill and Howarth (1957), and others who have found that partial depolarization of the surface of the muscle fibers by raising the K concentration in the surrounding fluid may cause an increased heat production and O_2 consumption without any detectable mechanical change. It is tempting to assume that in such cases, the first mechanical response to a gradual increase of depolarization does not appear until the rate of Ca mobilization, depending on the extent of depolarization, has surpassed the Ca-binding capacity of the sarcoplasmic vesicles. This could explain the fact that the threshold depolarization for the activation of metabolism may be lower in certain cases than that for the activation of the contractile elements.

It is, in fact, rather puzzling that each of these three schemes is supported by certain experimental observations. So the situation is still rather complex. But, in any case, Ca triggers, in some way, both muscular shortening and muscular metabolism.

REFERENCES

Antoni, H. and G. Engstfeld. 1961. *Verh. Deutsch. Ges. Kreislaufforsch.* 27: 232.

Antoni, H., G. Engstfeld, and A. Fleckenstein. 1960. *Pfluegers Arch. Ges. Physiol.* 272: 91.

Antoni, H., G. Engstfeld, and A. Fleckenstein. 1962. *Pfluegers Arch. Ges. Physiol.* 275: 507.

Axelsson, J., and S. Thesleff. 1958. *Acta Physiol. Scand.* 44: 55.

Bay, E. B., C. F. McLean, and A. B. Hastings. 1933. *Proc. Soc. Exptl. Biol. Med.* 30: 1346.

Bianchi, C. P., 1961. In *Biophysics of Physiological and Pharmacological Actions*, ed. A. M. Shanes. Washington: *Am. Assoc. Advan. Sci.* P. 281.

Bianchi, C. P., and A. M. Shanes. 1959. *J. Gen. Physiol.* 42: 803.

Bogue, J. Y., and R. Mendez. 1929. *J. Physiol.* (*London*) 67: 31 P.

Bohr, D. F., and P. L. Goulet. 1961. *Am. J. Cardiol.* 8: 549.

Cain, D. F., and R. E. Davies. 1962. *Biochem. Biophys. Res. Commun.* 8: 361.

Caldwell, P. C., and G. Walster. 1963. *J. Physiol.* (*London*) 169: 353.

De Burgh Daly, I., and A. J. Clark. 1921. *J. Physiol.* (*London*) 54: 367.

Denton, E. J. 1948. *J. Physiol.* (*London*) 107: 32 P.

Ebashi, S. 1961. *J. Biochem.* (*Tokyo*) 50: 236.

Ebashi, S., M. Otsuka, and M. Endo. 1962. *Intern. Congr. Physiol. Sci. 22nd, Leiden, 1962.* See *Excerpta Med. Intern. Congr. Series* No. 48: 899.

Edman, K. A. P., and H. O. Schild. 1961. *J. Physiol.* (*London*) 155: 10 P.

Engstfeld, G., H. Antoni, and A. Fleckenstein unter Mitarbeit von A. Nast and M. v. Hattingberg. 1961. *Pfluegers Arch. Ges. Physiol.* 273: 145.

Fleckenstein, A. 1955. *Der Kalium-Natrium-Austausch als Energieprinzip in Muskel und Nerv.* Berlin, Heidelberg: Springer-Verlag.

Fleckenstein, A., and H. Hertel. 1948. *Pfluegers Arch. Ges. Physiol.* 250: 577.

Fleckenstein, A., and W. Schwoerer. 1961. *Pfluegers Arch. Ges. Physiol.* 274: 8.

Fleckenstein, A., E. Gerlach, and J. Janke gemeinsam mit P. Marmier. 1960. *Pfluegers Arch. Ges. Physiol.* 271: 75.

Fleckenstein, A., W. Schwoerer, and J. Janke. 1961. *Pfluegers Arch. Ges. Physiol.* 273: 483.

Frank, G. B. 1958. *Nature* 182: 1800.

Frank, G. B. 1960. *J. Physiol. (London)* 151: 518.

Frank, G. B. 1962. *J. Physiol. (London)* 163: 254.

Gersmeyer, G., and W. C. Holland. 1963. *Circulation Res.* 12: 620.

Hasselbach, W., and M. Makinose. 1961. *Biochem. Z.* 333: 518.

Heilbrunn, L. V., and F. J. Wiercinski. 1947. *J. Cellular Comp. Physiol.* 29: 15.

Hill, A. V., and J. V. Howarth. 1957. *Proc. Roy. Soc. (London) Ser. B* 147: 21.

Hill, A. V., and L. MacPherson. 1954. *Proc. Roy. Soc. (London) Ser. B* 143: 81.

Hodgkin, A. L., and P. Horowicz. 1960. *J. Physiol. (London)* 153: 404.

Holland, W. C., and A. Sekul. 1959. *Am. J. Physiol.* 197: 757.

Kahn, A. J., and A. Sandow. 1950. *Science* 112: 647.

Kahn, A. J., and A. Sandow. 1955. *Ann. N.Y. Acad. Sci.* 62: 137.

Kaye, L., and W. F. H. M. Mommaerts. 1960. *J. Gen. Physiol.* 44: 405.

Kotowski, H., H. Antoni, and A. Fleckenstein. 1959. *Pfluegers Arch. Ges. Physiol.* 270: 85.

Loewi, O. 1917. *Arch. Exptl. Pathol. Pharmakol.* 82: 131.

Lüllmann, H., and W. C. Holland. 1962. *J. Pharmacol. Exptl. Therap.* 137: 186.

Lüttgau, H. C., and R. Niedergerke. 1958. *J. Physiol. (London)* 143: 486.

Mines, G. R. 1913. *J. Physiol. (London)* 46: 188.

Mommaerts, W. F. H. M. 1950. *Muscular Contraction—A Topic in Molecular Physiology.* New York: Interscience Publishers, Inc.

Mommaerts, W. F. H. M. In *Conference on the Biochemistry of Muscle Contraction, Dedham, Mass., 1962.* To be published.

Niedergerke, R. 1955. *J. Physiol. (London)* 128: 12 P.

Niedergerke, R. 1957. *J. Physiol. (London)* 138: 506.

Porter, K. R., and G. E. Palade. 1957. *J. Biophys. Biochem. Cytol.* 3: 269.

Robertson, P. A. 1960. *Nature* 186: 316.

Sandow, A. 1952. *Yale J. Biol. Med.* 25: 176.

Sekul, A. A., and W. C. Holland. 1960. *Am. J. Physiol.* 199: 457.

Shanes, A. M. 1961. *J. Cellular Comp. Physiol.* 57: 193.

Shanes, A. M., and C. P. Bianchi. 1960. *J. Gen. Physiol.* 43: 481.

Smith, C. G., and D. Y. Solandt. 1938. *J. Physiol. (London)* 93: 305

Solandt, D. Y. 1936. *J. Physiol. (London)* 86: 162.

Szent-Györgyi, A. 1948. *Chemistry of Muscular Contraction.* New York: Academic Press, Inc.

Thomas, L., W. Jolley, and R. Grechman. 1958. *Federation Proc.* 17: 162.

Weber, A., and R. Herz. 1963. *J. Biol. Chem.* 238: 599.

Weber, A., and S. Winicur. 1961. *J. Biol. Chem.* 236: 3198.

Winegrad, S., and A. M. Shanes. 1962. *J. Gen. Physiol.* 45: 371.

Yukisada, N., and F. Ebashi. 1961. *Japan. J. Pharmacol.* 11: 46.

Ion Fluxes and Excitability in Squid Giant Axon

Ichiji Tasaki and Toshifumi Takenaka

Laboratory of Neurobiology
National Institute of Mental Health
National Institutes of Health
Bethesda, Maryland

During the past decade, physiologists have carried out a variety of elaborate electric measurements on the squid giant axon with a view to elucidating the relationship between ion fluxes and nerve excitability. The methods of determining the time-courses of electric currents and potentials employed in these measurements are fairly direct and satisfactory. In interpreting the results obtained, however, there has been a great degree of arbitrariness, mainly because of the chemical complexity of the biological materials.

The recent development of the method of intracellular perfusion of the squid giant axon has made it feasible for us to analyze the electrochemical nature of nervous activity with a degree of directness which has never been achieved before. The ability of the axon membrane to develop large all-or-none action potentials can be preserved for hours under continuous intracellular perfusion with various kinds of salt solutions of known chemical composition. Under these circumstances, all the water-soluble constituents in the axoplasm are carried away by the perfusing fluid, and the axoplasm quickly reaches a state of equilibrium with respect to all the nonpermeant ion species. Movements of various permeant ions in such a stationary (i.e., time-independent) state can be followed faithfully by tagging the ion species in question with their radioactive analogs.

In this article, we wish to summarize what we have learned about the nature of the axonal membrane by the method of intracellular perfusion. So far as we are aware, this method has been successfully used by the following investigators besides ourselves: Drs. T. Narahashi and W. J. Adelman in Woods Hole, Drs. P. F. Baker, A. L. Hodgkin, and T. I. Shaw (1962a, b) in Plymouth, and Dr. A. Watanabe in Misaki. Since the publications of the results obtained by these various workers are limited at present, we are concerned in this article mainly with our own observations, published and unpublished.

Technique of Intracellular Perfusion

During the course of experiments involving massive injection of various chemicals into the squid giant axons, it became increasingly clear that a considerable portion of the axoplasm can be replaced with air, paraffin oil, or injection fluid without eliminating the ability of the axon to produce action potentials. During the time when Prof. T. Teorell from Sweden and Prof. T. Oikawa from Japan were visiting our laboratory in 1959 and 1960, attempts were made to maintain excitability of the squid giant axon under continuous perfusion with isotonic solution of KCl. We could maintain normal action potentials under continuous intracellular perfusion for a little more than half an hour and could establish some of the basic properties of perfused axons (Oikawa *et al.*, 1961).

Early in 1961, we were informed of the news that Baker and coworkers in England succeeded in a dramatic technique of altering the intracellular chemical composition of the squid giant axon. They were able to squeeze out the axoplasm from the cut end of the axon and refill the interior with artificial solutions without rendering axons inexcitable (Baker *et al.*, 1961). Although the technique employed by the British investigators is in some respect very different from ours, there seems little or no discrepancy between the results obtained by the two different techniques.

Figure 1 shows a partially cleaned squid giant axon and the arrangement of the perfusion cannulae used in most of the experiments described in this article. The inlet cannula is 150–170 μ in outside diameter and is connected to a reservoir of the perfusing fluid. The outlet cannula (300–400 μ in diameter) is first pushed into the axon through a hole at one end of the axon. As the outlet cannula is advanced along the axis of the axon, the axoplasm is gently sucked into the cannula by applying a negative pressure. Then the inlet cannula is introduced into the axon from the other cut end. After pushing the tip of the inlet cannula into the lumen of the outlet cannula and raising the reservoir of the perfusing fluid to a height of 10–50 cm above the axon, the axoplasm in the outlet cannula is removed by suction. Then the tips of the two cannulae are separated, as can be seen in the figure, and

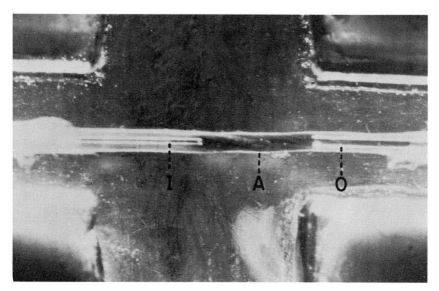

Fig. 1. Photomicrograph of an intracellularly perfused axon taken about 1 min after the start of perfusion with K-salt solution containing chlorphenol red. Note that the perfused zone is uniformly stained with the dye. I: inlet pipette; O: outlet pipette; A: axon membrane. The diameter of the axon in the middle of the perfused zone is 590 μ.

are brought to the final positions. Finally, a recording electrode (70–100 μ in diameter, not shown in the figure) is introduced into the axon through the orifice of the outlet cannula. The surrounding sea water is grounded by means of a large agar-filled electrode.

Absence of Diffusion Barrier Between Axon Membrane and Perfusing Fluid

With our technique of perfusion, there is a layer of axoplasm 50–100 μ in thickness between the axonal membrane and the perfusing fluid. We wish to show that the boundary between the axoplasm and the perfusing fluid does not constitute any significant diffusion barrier to the solutes in the perfusing fluid. The following four different pieces of evidence can be listed in support of our view.

1. When the perfusing fluid is stained heavily with a dye, such as chlorphenol red, the dye immediately starts to diffuse into the axoplasm, and, within about 1 min after the onset of perfusion, the entire space inside the axonal membrane is uniformly stained (see Fig. 1).
2. Electron-microscopic studies reveal no electron-dense layer between the axoplasm and the space occupied by the perfusing fluid.
3. When radioactive Na or K is introduced into the surrounding sea water, the perfusing fluid becomes radioactive immediately. Upon replacement of the radioactive sea water with a nonradioactive medium, there is an immediate fall in the radioactivity of the perfusing fluid. When radioisotopes of various univalent cations are introduced into the perfusing fluid, quasi-stationary fluxes of the isotopes are observed within 1–2 min.
4. Tetraethylammonium and other quaternary ammonium ions are known to prolong the action potential when applied internally by injection. When these chemicals are introduced into the perfusing fluid, the action potential starts to prolong within about 10 sec, and a final, stationary state is reached within about 1 min.

When one perfusing fluid is replaced by another, a new stationary state is reached, as a rule, within 1–2 min. There is, however, one complicating factor in the application of this general rule. If the new solution is unfavorable for the maintenance of normal excitability of the axon, a slow, secondary change in the state of the axon may appear and persist for a long time after the first, rapid change. Thus, when an axon is perfused with a fluid whose pH is very different from the most favorable value, 7.1 to 7.4, conduction block followed by irreversible loss of excitability is observed a long time after the onset of perfusion. Similarly, perfusion with a solution containing a high concentration of Ca or Mg shortens the survival time of the axon to a degree which depends on the concentration. In perfusion with solutions of various salts, Ca-salt solutions are known to be most harmful to the axons. However, even KCl solutions show depolarizing action at relatively high concentrations.

Effect of Na Added to Perfusing K-Salt Solution

The first problem we intended to solve by the use of the newly developed technique was whether or not the amplitude of the action potential varies with the internal Na concentration. We can use 400 mEq/l K in the Cl or SO_4 form as the bulk element in the perfusing fluid and add either NaCl or Na_2SO_4 to the fluid. The tonicity of the perfusing fluid can be maintained by adjusting the concentration of sucrose added. The outside fluid medium can be either natural sea water or an artificial saline solution in which excised squid axons are known to maintain their excitability.

Figure 2 shows the results we obtained by using an outside medium containing 400 mM $MgSO_4$ and 200 mM Na_2SO_4. When the perfusing fluid contains 400 mEq/1 K, and Na is absent, the resting potential observed is about 50 mv, and the amplitude of the action potential is approximately 125 mv; the overshoot of the action potential is, hence, approximately 75 mv. Addition of Na of less than 20 mEq/1 does not affect either the resting potential or the action potential. As the Na concentration is raised above

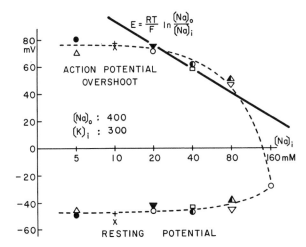

Fig. 2. Resting and action potentials determined as a function of Na concentration in the perfusing solution. The K concentration in the perfusing fluid was fixed at 300 mEq/1. The outside fluid contained 400 mM $MgSO_4$ and 200 mM Na_2SO_4. Room temperature, about 22°C.

40 mEq/1, the action potential begins to deteriorate. With 100 mEq/1 Na in the perfusing fluid, conduction block sets in within 2 min after the onset of perfusion under these experimental conditions.

The injurious effect of perfusion with the Na-rich solution is to some extent reversible. If a pure K_2SO_4 solution is readmitted in the axon at the moment when conduction is suspended, there is usually a partial or total recovery in the action potential. If, however, an interval of a few minutes elapses before removal of the Na-rich solution, an irreversible loss of excitability may result. The Na concentration at which conduction block barely sets in varies with many factors, such as the Mg or Ca concentration in the medium, the ionic strength in the perfusing fluid, and the chemical species of anions on both sides of the membrane. With axons immersed in natural sea water, conduction block takes place at concentrations lower than those in the experiment of Fig. 2. We shall discuss the problem of replacing the K in perfusing fluid with Na later.

The conclusion we wish to draw from the experiment presented in Fig. 2 is that the amount of Na normally present in freshly excised squid axons, namely, approximately 30 mEq/l, has little or no influence upon the resting and action potentials of the axon.

Effect of Diluting Perfusing Fluid with Nonelectrolyte

According to "Formulae and Methods IV," issued by the Marine Biological Laboratory in Woods Hole, a K_2SO_4 solution isotonic with sea water contains about 880 mEq/l K. Since the sum of K and Na in the axoplasm is known to be about 450 mEq/l (Steinbach and Spiegelman, 1943), it is necessary to dilute the isotonic K_2SO_4 solution with isotonic nonelectrolyte solution by a factor of about two in order to lower the K concentration to its normal level in the axon. Sucrose, lactose, glucose, and glycerol have been used for this purpose. The differences among the results obtained with different nonelectrolytes are not very significant under these circumstances. With axons immersed in natural sea water, action potentials of 120–140 mv in amplitude can be observed for more than 2 hr under continuous perfusion with a solution containing 400 mEq/l K and 40 mEq/l Na.

Figure 3 shows the effect of diluting the K-rich perfusing fluid further with isotonic sucrose solution. The ratio of the Na to the K concentration was fixed at 1/10. SO_4 and a trace of PO_4 (added for pH adjustment) are the only anions present in the perfusing fluid.

If one assumes that the squid axon membrane shows an overwhelmingly high permeability to K in the resting state, one would expect the resting membrane potential to vary with the internal K at a rate of about 60 mv for a tenfold change. The solid straight line near the lower left corner of Fig. 3 represents this Nernst relation applied to the internal and external K. The observed points (collected from 12 different axons) diverge systematically from the expected values. When the internal K concentration is lowered from 400 mEq/l to 40 mEq/l, the fall in the resting potential observed is only 5–15 mv. On further dilution of the perfusing solution, the resting potential gradually approaches zero. Dr. Narahashi in Woods Hole and Drs. Watanabe and Takenaka in Misaki examined these points in greater detail (personal communication).

The perfusing fluid used in the experiment of Fig. 3 contains Na. The membrane potential calculated from the Nernst equation applied to the Na under these conditions is shown in the figure by another straight line. If it is assumed that at the peak of the action potential the membrane becomes specifically permeable to Na (Hodgkin, 1951), the concentration dependence of the overshoot of the action potential should be expressed by this straight line. As can be seen in the figure, there is a distinct divergence of the observed values from the predicted straight line.

For investigators working in the field of nonliving ion-exchanger membranes, the complex behavior of the squid axon membrane under intracellular

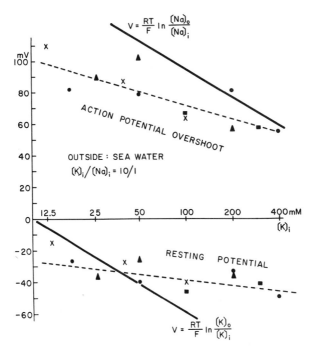

Fig. 3. Effects upon the resting and action potentials of diluting the K-rich perfusing fluid with isotonic sucrose solution. The ratio of the Na/K concentration was fixed at $1/10$. Abscissa represents the K concentration in the perfusing solution. $22°C$.

perfusion would not be surprising at all. The resting potential in the squid axon is an example of a "multi-ionic" system in their terminology (see, e.g., Helfferich, 1962, p. 384). A mixture of divalent and univalent ions always exists on the outer side of the membrane. The membrane potential observed under these conditions is, in general, a complex function of the concentrations of various components in the medium. When there is no agitation of the solutions near the two surfaces of the membrane, there is a potential difference (diffusion potential) across each of the stagnant layers of the fluid outside the membrane proper. There is a Donnan potential at each of the surfaces of the membrane. In addition, there is a diffusion potential within the membrane proper. Because the potential difference across the stagnant layer and the Donnan potential can change in magnitude when the fluid is stirred, stirring is known to produce a dramatic change in the over-all membrane potential, sometimes even a complete reversal of the over-all potential (Scatchard and Helfferich, 1956). There is little doubt that a stagnant layer potential plays an important role in the generation of bioelectric potentials.

Perfusion with Na-Rich Solutions

In the above experiments, the perfusing fluid was rich in K and poor in Na. We now wish to demonstrate that, under appropriate experimental conditions, the excitability of the axon can be maintained under continuous intracellular perfusion with Na-rich solutions.

In the experiment of Fig. 4, the Na concentration in the perfusing fluid was 100 mEq/l. The fluid was prepared by mixing isotonic sucrose solution with isotonic NaCl solution in the proper ratio. Neither the PO_4 buffer used

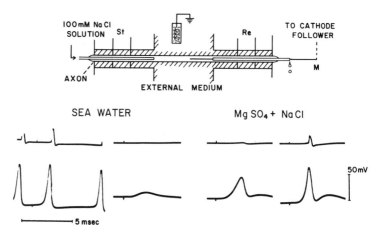

Fig. 4. Top: schematic illustration (not to scale) of the experimental arrangement employed for intracellular perfusion and the recording of potentials of excised squid giant axons. *St*: stimulating electrodes; *Re*: extracellular recording electrodes; *M*: intracellular micropipette electrode. Bottom: upper oscillograph trace shows electric responses recorded from *Re*, and lower trace shows responses obtained from *M*. External fluid medium was first (left) natural sea water and later (right) isotonic NaCl solution to which $MgSO_4$ (200 mM) had been added. Room temperature, 23°C. (From Tasaki and Shimamura, 1962, *Proc. Natl. Acad. Sci. U.S.* 48: 1571.)

nor the electrolyte in the recording electrode (NH₄Cl) contained K. At the beginning of the experiment, the fluid medium surrounding the axon was natural sea water. About 15 sec after the onset of perfusion, there was a reduction in the resting potential, accompanied by repetitive firing of action potentials. As a rule, nervous conduction was blocked within 1 min after the onset of perfusion (see the left column of Fig. 4).

At the moment when block of conduction took place, the concentration of the divalent cation (Mg in this case) was raised above the normal level in natural sea water. As can be seen in the figure, there was an immediate recovery in the resting potential and restoration of conduction across the perfused zone. Action potentials observed under these conditions show relatively large "after potentials" (after depolarization). The excitability of the axon perfused with such pure Na-salt solution could be maintained for more than half an hour.

In more recent studies along this line, Na glutamate (instead of NaCl or Na₂SO₄) and glycerol (instead of sucrose) were used. The maintenance of excitability under high internal Na concentrations became much easier with this combination.

In perfusion with K glutamate mixed with glycerol, there is of course no loss of excitability. Therefore, we are now in the position to test the effect of K–Na exchange over a wide range of concentration ratios upon the resting and action potentials. Figure 5 shows the results of measurements (on 20 axons) of the resting and action potentials as function of the internal Na concentration. The total cation concentration (Na and K) in the perfusing fluid was kept at a constant level of 400 mEq/l in this case. The external fluid medium contained 300 mEq/l Na; in addition, 45 mM MgSO₄ and 22 mM CaCl₂ were present outside.

It is seen in the figure that the resting potential of the axon is not affected to any appreciable extent by replacing various fractions of K in the perfusing fluid with Na. The broken line connecting the observed values of the resting potential is nearly parallel to the abscissa, indicating that the potential is roughly independent of the K/Na ratio in the perfusing solution. It should be stressed in this connection that this approximate independence can be observed only when the excitability is maintained in the entire range of the concentration ratio studied. A loss of excitability is, as a rule, accompanied by a decrease in the resting potential (see Fig. 2).

The amplitude of the action potential is found, on the contrary, to decrease with increasing Na concentration in the perfusing fluid. If one assumes that the peak value of the action potential is determined by the Nernst equation (ignoring the activity coefficient) applied to the concentration of Na inside and outside the perfused axon, one would expect a 60-mv change in the overshoot of action potential for a tenfold change in the internal Na concentration. The observed change shown in Fig. 2 (see

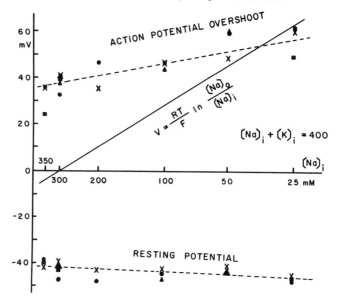

Fig. 5. Resting potential and overshoot of action potential of intracellularly perfused squid axons plotted as a function of Na concentration in the perfusing fluid, [Na]$_i$. The sum of the internal Na and K concentrations was held at a constant level of 400 mEq/l throughout. The perfusing fluid contained 470 mM glycerol besides Na- and K-salts in the glutamate form. The external medium contained 300 mM NaCl, 45 mM MgSO$_4$, and 22 mM CaCl$_2$. A 50% increase in the Mg and Ca concentrations outside did not alter the results significantly. (From Tasaki and Takenaka, 1963, *Proc. Natl. Acad. Sci. U.S.* 50: 619.)

the straight line, *action potential overshoot*) is about 20 mv for a tenfold change, namely about 1/3 of the predicted Nernst slope.

It is interesting to note that the intracellular potential rises well above that of the surrounding fluid medium at the peak of activity even when the internal Na concentration is equal to that of the external medium.

Perfusion with Other Salt Solutions

It is possible to perfuse squid axons with solutions of various salts other than Na or K salts and to maintain the excitability for some time. We have tried salts of Cs, NH$_4$, guanidine, tetramethylammonium, choline, etc. The outside medium contained Na (or Li) and Mg (or Ca). In many cases, it was necessary to adjust the concentrations of univalent and divalent cations inside and outside the axon in order to maintain excitability for more than 30 min. The configuration (the duration, in particular) of the action potential was found to be extremely sensitive to the kind of cation that is present in the perfusing fluid. The external concentrations of Na and Mg (or Ca) also influenced the duration.

When the salt concentration in the perfusing fluid is low, the effect of altering the anionic species in the perfusing fluid is, as a rule, very small. As the salt concentration is increased, different forms of salts of the same cation tend to give different results. A 200 mM Na tartrate solution, for example, shows a strong depolarizing action when used as internal perfusing fluid; but, when the concentration of Na tartrate is reduced to 40 mM by diluting with isotonic glycerol solution, the depolarizing action is greatly reduced.

Movement of Radioisotopes Across Squid Axon Membrane

We now wish to summarize the state of our knowledge concerning the fluxes of various radioactive tracers across the surface membrane of the squid giant axon. It is practically impossible to carry out any tracer measurement on axons *in vivo*. Hence, our knowledge concerning the ion fluxes is based entirely upon the results of measurements carried out on slowly deteriorating excised axons. We wish to stress at the outset the importance of realizing this situation in interpreting the results of our tracer measurements.

When an axon is in the body of a normal, live squid, there is, in all probability, little or no net flux of Na or K (nonradioactive) across its membrane. Since the permeability of the membrane to large neutral molecules is very low, it is unlikely that there are strong fluxes of these cations in some neutral form. Hence, at the time when the constancy of concentration of these cations in the axon is established, the net flux of these ions across the axonal membrane ought to be vanishingly small. There should be, however, fluxes of various metabolites across the membrane under these conditions. Because of the coupling between fluxes of metabolites and nonmetabolites, the internal concentration of the Na or K should be in general very different from the value expected from the assumption of equilibrium distribution of these ions. On the basis of the thermodynamics of irreversible processes, one can describe this situation in the following manner (see Kirkwood, 1954, equation 9): the difference between the electrochemical potential of Na or K inside the axon and that in the surrounding medium is determined by the fluxes of metabolites and their cross-coefficients.

Denoting the electrochemical potential of the ith ion species by η_i, the fluxes of various metabolites by J_m, J_n, $\cdots$, and the cross-coefficients under these circumstances by R_{im}, R_{in}, $\cdots$, we have

$$\Delta\eta_i = R_{im}J_m + R_{in}J_n + \cdots \tag{1}$$

The difference between the electrochemical potentials on the two sides $\Delta\eta_i$ can be divided into the following three terms:

$$\Delta\eta_i = RT \ln \frac{C_i'}{C_i''} + RT \ln \frac{f_i'}{f_i''} + z_i F\Delta\varphi \tag{2}$$

where C_i' and C_i'' are the concentrations on the two sides, f_i' and f_i'' the activity coefficients, z_i the valence of the ith ion species, and $\Delta\varphi$ the potential difference across the membrane. (If there is a difference in the hydrostatic pressure across the membrane, a term to account for its effect should be included.) Metabolic inhibitors, such as 2,4-dinitrophenol (DNP) or cyanide, should primarily alter the metabolite fluxes J_m, J_n, $\cdots$; but the cross-coefficients and the activity coefficients of the ions in the axoplasm may also be influenced. A strong effect of the inhibitors upon the distribution of Na across the squid axon membrane is well known (Hodgkin and Keynes, 1955). Ling (1962), as well as Troschin (1958), stresses the importance of the protein in the cell for ion accumulation; this effect is included in this treatment as a difference between the activity coefficients on the two sides of the membrane.

When such an axon is dissected out of the body, immersed in an artificial saline solution, and perfused with a K-rich fluid, an entirely different situation arises. The normal metabolites are washed away by the perfusing fluid. There is no fixed charge in the perfusing fluid. It is evident, therefore, that the normal metabolic "forces" which served to accumulate or expel various nonmetabolites are now nonexistent. Obviously, this situation tends to create a strong interdiffusion of ions inside and outside of the membrane in perfused (and to some extent in unperfused) axons. All of the measurements of tracer fluxes to be discussed below were carried out in the presence of such strong interdiffusion of ions across the axonal membrane.

Under the conditions of intracellular perfusion, it is possible to measure influxes of various tracers without accumulating the tracers in the interior of the axon. The influx determined under these conditions is simply proportional to the external concentration of the tracer. The proportionality constant is different for different tracers and can be regarded as a measure of permeability of the membrane to the tracer under study.

The permeability for influx has been determined by this method for Na[22], Na[24], K[42], Rb[86], Cs[134], Cs[137], Ca[45], Br[82], etc. in the resting (and excitable) state of perfused axons (Tasaki, 1963). For a given level of radioactivity (expressed in cpm for a given volume of fluid) in the medium, the fluxes (expressed in cpm per given collection period) of labeled Na, K, and Rb were found to be the largest among the tracers listed above; the differences among these light alkali metal ions were very small (see Fig. 6). The corresponding value for Cs was somewhat smaller. The flux of labeled Ca was about 1/2 of the value for labeled Na or K. The value for radioactive Br was 1/10 to 1/20 of that for light cations.

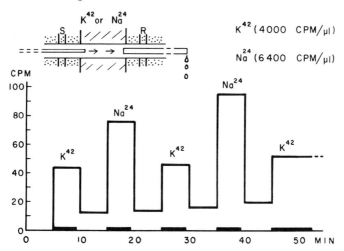

Fig. 6. Top: diagram of experimental arrangement used for intracellular perfusion. *S*: stimulating electrode; *R*: extracellular recording electrode. Bottom: comparison of fluxes of radioactive K and Na into perfused resting squid giant axon. The radioactivity in perfusing fluid collected in every 5-min period was plotted against time after start of perfusion. The bars on the base line indicate the periods during which sea water containing either K^{42} or Na^{24} was applied (From Tasaki, 1963, *J. Gen. Physiol.* 46: 763.)

Under the conditions of these measurements, the perfusing fluid contained neither Na nor Ca (nonradioactive). The existence of the influxes of labeled Na and Ca indicates that the nonradioactive (bulk) Na and Ca are constantly diffusing into the interior of the axon under these conditions. In exchange, there is an efflux of the equivalent amount of K across the membrane.

Effluxes of radioactive tracers have been studied mainly by the use of the injection technique. For a given level of radioactivity in the axoplasm, the effluxes of the tracers of light alkali metal ions were larger than those for other cations listed above. The flux of labeled Ca was large immediately after injection, but it rapidly fell to a small value, due apparently to conversion of free Ca^{45} into a bound form. The effluxes of labeled anions, such as Cl^{36}, Br^{82}, $S^{35}O_4$, $P^{32}O_4$, C^{14}-labeled D, L-glutamate, etc., were much smaller than those of cations.

The difference in behavior between cationic and anionic tracers becomes very conspicuous when one investigates the effects of repetitive stimulation of the axon upon the fluxes of tracers. The fluxes of labeled cations are markedly enhanced by repetitive stimulation, while this procedure hardly affects the fluxes of anionic tracers. The efflux of labeled Na is accelerated by a factor of five or more by stimulating the axon at 50 shocks/sec. Since this enhanced flux undoubtedly takes place during the period of enhanced membrane conductance (which lasts only about 1 msec), the increase in the flux during the action potential (average) is approximately 100-fold. At the peak of activity, then, the increase is of the order of 200-fold. Similarly, the Ca^{45} influx is enormously accelerated during activity. The effect of repetitive stimulation upon the efflux of several neutral molecules (C^{14}-labeled glycerol, urea, etc.) has been investigated; no clear effect was observed with these tracers.

Relationship Between Ion Fluxes and Excitability

So far, we have described various experimental results without discussing the relationships among different sets of experimental findings. We now wish to draw several conclusions from these experimental findings which serve to bring these findings together and to bridge the gap between ion fluxes and the process of production of action potentials.

1. *The presence or absence of interdiffusion of the internal and external cations has little or no influence upon the process of excitation.* In the preceding section we have seen that there is a strong interdiffusion of cations inside and outside the axon under continuous intracellular perfusion with K-rich solutions. Normal excitability is preserved for hours under these conditions. The amplitude and configuration of the action potential observed are not different from those of freshly excised axons or of axons remaining in the mantle of the squid. There seems no doubt that the interdiffusion is far weaker in unperfused axons.

2. *The squid axon membrane shows characteristics of a cation-exchanger in the resting as well as in the active state.* We have seen in the preceding section that the radioactive tracers of small cations (Na, K, Rb, Cs, guanidine) are more permeant than the tracers of halides and other anions. This property is typical of a cation-exchanger in which the Donnan exclusion of co-ions tends to reduce anion fluxes. In an earlier section, we have seen that the membrane potentials at rest and during activity are hardly affected by replacement of one kind of anion with another. This finding also supports the view that the squid axon membrane has negative fixed charges. Even when a certain anion shows a definite effect upon the membrane

potential, dilution of the solution with an isotonic nonelectrolyte solution tends to reduce the effect. This finding is also in agreement with the conclusion mentioned above.

3. *The resting (excitable) membrane is rich in divalent cations.* In all the experiments mentioned above, the external medium used contains either Mg or Ca, or both. The importance of divalent cations for maintenance of normal excitability is well known (see, e.g., Brink, 1954; Frankenhaeuser and Hodgkin, 1957). In a cation-exchanger immersed in a mixture of uni- and divalent cations, the divalent cations tend to be preferentially sorbed at the negative sites because of their higher valence. In fact, Dr. M. Shimamura, working in this laboratory, demonstrated by the use of autoradiography that in squid axons immersed in sea water containing Ca^{45}, the radioactivity is localized mainly in the surface layer of the axon. When the divalent cations in the membrane are displaced by univalent cations by adding either K salts or ethylene diamine tetraacetic acid (EDTA) to the medium, the axon becomes depolarized and normal excitability is lost. At least in some excitable tissues, the transition from the normal to the depolarized state is abrupt and discontinuous (Hill and Osterhout, 1938, for *Nitella;* Tasaki, 1959, for Ni-treated nodal membrane). We can regard the process of depolarization in other tissues as being essentially discontinuous and the apparent continuity as deriving from a gradual increase in the membrane area in the depolarized state.

4. *It is possible to interpret the process of action potential production in terms of an S-shaped ion-exchange isotherm.* There are many excitable tissues which do not require any univalent cation in the medium to maintain excitability (see a recent review by Spyropoulos and Tasaki, 1960). As has been stressed already, the presence of some divalent cation is essential in the outside medium. In the interior of the axon, however, there is very little free (i.e., unbound) Ca. Massive injection of EDTA (or perfusion with EDTA) has a favorable effect upon the excitability. It is well known that under various experimental conditions, excitable membranes develop action potentials of nearly rectangular configurations. Such action potentials can be interpreted as deriving from transitions between two stable states of the membrane, one a resting and the other an active state. The divalent cation concentration within the membrane should be lower in the active state than in the resting state, because the active state is usually attained by delivering an outward-directed membrane current which tends to replace the divalent cations in the membrane with the internal univalent cations.

In order to explain the time-course of short, normal action potentials, competition between different univalent cations at negative sites has to be taken into consideration (Tasaki, 1963).

Summary

The method of intracellular perfusion in the squid giant axon has made it possible for us to analyze the electrochemical nature of the excitation process with a degree of directness which has never been achieved before. The results of measurements of the membrane potentials and of fluxes of various radioisotopes indicate that the axonal membrane has the properties of a cation-exchanger in the resting as well as in the active state. The process of action potential production can be regarded as a kind of "flip-flop" phenomenon deriving from transitions between two stable states of the membrane. These two stable states are considered to arise from the difference in the fraction of the negative sites occupied by the divalent cations.

REFERENCES

Baker, P. F., A. L. Hodgkin, and T. I. Shaw. 1961. *Nature*. 190: 885.

Baker, P. F., A. L. Hodgkin, and T. I. Shaw. 1962a. *J. Physiol. (London)* 164: 330.

Baker, P. F., A. L. Hodgkin, and T. I. Shaw. 1962b. *J. Physiol. (London)* 164: 355.

Brink, F. 1954. *Pharmacol. Rev.* 4: 243.

Frankenhaeuser, B., and A. L. Hodgkin. 1957. *J. Physiol. (London)* 137: 217.

Helfferich, F. 1962. *Ion Exchange*. New York: McGraw-Hill Book Company, Inc.

Hill, S. E., and W. J. V. Osterhout. 1938. *J. Gen. Physiol.* 21: 541.

Hodgkin, A. L. 1951. *Biol. Rev. Cambridge Phil. Soc.* 26: 339.

Hodgkin, A. L., and R. D. Keynes. 1955. *J. Physiol. (London)* 128: 28.

Kirkwood, J. 1954. *Ion Transport Across Membranes*. New York: Academic Press, Inc. P. 119.

Ling. G. N. 1962. *A Physical Theory of the Living State*. New York: Blaisdell Publishing Co.

Oikawa, T., C. S. Spyropoulos, I. Tasaki, and T. Teorell. 1961. *Acta Physiol. Scand.* 52: 195.

Scatchard, G., and F. Helfferich. 1956. *Discussions Faraday Soc.* 21: 70.

Spyropoulos, C. S., and I. Tasaki. 1960. *Ann. Rev. Physiol.* 22: 407.

Steinbach, H. B., and S. Spiegelman. 1943. *J. Cellular Comp. Physiol.* 22: 187.

Tasaki, I. 1959. *J. Physiol. (London)* 148: 306.

Tasaki, I. 1963. *J. Gen. Physiol.* 46: 755.

Tasaki, I., and M. Shimamura. 1962. *Proc. Natl. Acad. Sci. U.S.* 48: 1571.

Tasaki, I., and T. Takenaka. 1963. *Proc. Natl. Acad. Sci. U.S.* 50: 619.

Troschin, A. S. 1958. *Das Problem der Zellpermeabilitat.* Jena: Fischer Verlag.

Voltage-Clamp Studies
of Molluscan Neuron
Membrane Properties

K. Frank[1] and L. Tauc

Institut Marey
Centre National de la Recherche Scientifique
Paris, France
and
Institut de Biologie Marine
Arcachon, France

Cole in 1949 and Hodgkin *et al.* in 1952 first introduced the powerful voltage-clamp technique to the study of the voltage-current relations in the membrane of the squid giant axon. This technique, with modifications, has been carefully analyzed by other workers (Tasaki and Bak, 1958a, b; Cole and Moore, 1960). Dodge and Frankenhaeuser (1958) have also used it for the study of myelinated nerve fiber membranes.

The voltage-clamp technique was applied to motor horn cells (MHCs) of the cat spinal cord by Frank *et al.* (1959), Nelson and Frank (in press), and Araki and Terzuolo (1962). These studies showed differences between the electrical properties of motoneuron soma membrane and those of the more familiar squid axon which could be due either to a difference in the nature of the membranes or to the loading effect of the motoneuron dendrites.

Studies by Freygang and Frank (1959) suggested that the motoneuron soma membrane *does not* contribute actively to the generation of spikes,

[1] During this study, Dr. Frank was a guest in Dr. Tauc's laboratory. His present address is National Institutes of Health, Bethesda, Maryland.

113

while other studies, e.g., Nelson *et al.* (1960) and Frank and Nelson (1961), supported the conclusion that the MHC soma *does* contribute actively to the generation of spikes recorded extracellularly. Measurements of Hagiwara and Saito (1957, 1959a) and Bennett *et al.* (1959) on the supramedullary ganglion of the puffer fish indicate clearly that the soma of this cell does produce a spike. Hagiwara and Saito (1959b) applied the voltage-clamp technique to the study of the membrane properties of *Onchidium verruculatum* ganglion cells and were able to show that the soma membrane of this cell has spike-generating properties similar to those observed in axons. On the other hand, Hagiwara and Bullock (1957) have shown that the soma of the large cardiac ganglion cell of the lobster *does not* have an active membrane. Tauc (1960, 1962) found that the soma of the giant nerve cell of *Aplysia* generates a typical action potential.

These variable results suggested the possibility that different parts of the membrane of a single cell might have different properties (Tauc, 1962). The present experiments were designed to test this possibility by applying voltage-clamp techniques to a molluscan cell while measuring separately the currents through a restricted patch of membrane on its soma.

The somata of these cells have no dendrites and no synapses but are sensitive to acetylcholine (ACh). Tauc and Gerschenfeld (1960) have divided these ganglion cells into two groups: "D" cells, which are depolarized and excited by direct application of ACh; and "H" cells, which are hyperpolarized and inhibited by ACh. Tauc and Gerschenfeld (1962) have shown that ACh is very probably the chemical transmitter of inhibition in "H" cells of *Aplysia*. Iontophoretic application of this drug produces the same effect (hyperpolarization) as does normal synaptic inhibition, whether applied to the proximal axon, where the synapses are located, or to the soma, which is free of synapses. They have shown that hyperpolarization of the cell membrane reverses the potential changes produced by either inhibitory synaptic input or iontophoretic application of ACh and that the reversal occurs at about the same membrane potential in both cases. Also, in both cases the membrane conductance is increased. Curare blocks both the inhibitory postsynaptic potentials (IPSPs) and the effects of iontophoretically applied ACh.

The present study was designed to determine how small spots on the somata of both "H" and "D" cells might respond to iontophoretic application of ACh. The application of ACh to such a spot is referred to in this paper as an "artificial synapse."

Methods

The abdominal or subesophageal ganglion of the molluscs *Aplysia depilans* or *Helix pomatia* was pinned to a layer of translucent solid paraffin in a special chamber (Tauc and Gerschenfeld, 1962) and immersed in an appropriate flowing physiological solution. A cut was made in the connective tissue covering the ganglion, and the yellow-pigmented cells were clearly visible by transmitted light under a binocular microscope. These ganglia contain giant cells up to 800 μ in diameter, but the cells used for the present study were 50–350 μ in diameter.

Glass capillary microelectrodes, filled with 12% K_2SO_4 or, occasionally, 2M KCl, were prepared as follows: each electrode was drawn in three stages on a de Fonbrune microforge and bent in such a way that the tips of a pair of microelectrodes could be mounted parallel while their shafts were well separated. The tips of each electrode were drawn with nearly parallel walls and with an outside diameter of 1–3 μ. Each electrode was wound with fine wire to within less than a millimeter of its tip, and, with a soldering gun as a source of heat, the wire was coated with insulating dental wax. A pair of such electrodes was mounted on the double-needle holder of a Zeiss sliding micropositioner and adjusted under a microscope to a tip separation of about 5–10 μ. The electrode pair was then fastened in this position by waxing to a cross-frame of glass rods. A glass mounting handle was attached to the frame parallel to the electrode tips. Such a pair of microelectrodes was introduced into a ganglion cell by means of a Zeiss sliding micropositioner, under a binocular microscope.

In order to measure the current through an isolated spot of soma membrane, a glass pipette electrode with fire-polished tip of about 20 μ internal diameter was filled with physiological salt solution and placed close to the surface of the cell (Fig. 1). A fourth electrode, filled with 1–2% ACh solution and measuring about 50 MΩ, was attached to the extracellular "spot" electrode and was brought close to the surface of the cell at the edge of the spot. ACh was delivered from this electrode by the application of current pulses and was kept from running out of the tip by a reverse holding potential of 0.1–0.5 v. The return path for these currents was a chlorided silver wire close to the tip of the ACh electrode. In these experiments, it was difficult to maintain a constant response to ACh applied iontophoretically, partly due to the desensitization of the membrane (Tauc and Bruner, 1963) and partly due to changes in the properties of the ACh electrode. This variability was one of the limiting factors in the present measurements.

Two reference electrodes were introduced into the bath. These were heavily chlorided spirals of silver wire at some distance from and on either side of the ganglion. One, the "working" ground, G_w, was connected to the circuit ground through a high-gain operational amplifier which served to measure the current flowing in this lead. A chlorided silver wire in the extracellular spot electrode was connected to another operational amplifier arranged to record separately the current flowing through the spot electrode.

With this arrangement, the potential of the spot electrode was maintained at the level of the left-hand reference electrode of Fig. 1, G_s.

Of the intracellular pair of electrodes, one was used to record the intracellular potential and the other to supply current from the clamping amplifier through the cell membrane to ground in such a way that the recorded intracellular potential was forced to follow precisely a command potential, V_c. The insulated shield on the current intracellular electrode was connected to

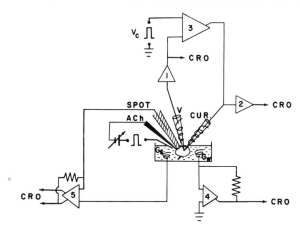

Fig. 1. Simplified illustration of experimental arrangement. V_c: command voltage; V: electrode recording intracellular potential; CUR: intracellular electrode supplying current from clamping amplifier *3;* SPOT: extracellular electrode for measuring spot current; ACh: extracellular electrode for iontophoretic application of ACh; G_w: reference electrode used as "working ground"; G_s: spot reference electrode; CRO: cathode ray oscilloscope. *1* and *2*: Bak preamplifiers; *4* and *5*: operational amplifiers for measuring total and spot clamping current. The ACh electrode is connected to a source of holding potential and a pulse generator for iontophoretic application of ACh.

circuit ground, while the shield of the voltage electrode was driven from the cathode of the voltage electrode preamplifier. Capacitive coupling between current and voltage electrodes was reduced by cross-neutralization (Tomita, 1956; Araki and Terzuolo, 1962; Nelson and Frank, in press). When all neutralization and compensation circuits were optimally adjusted, the time to clamp the membrane to a 100-mv step in command potential was less than 100 μsec. Circuit values and other details of the experimental arrangement are given in the legend of Fig. 1.

Membrane potential and spot or total clamping current were measured by means of a double-beam oscilloscope. Before clamping current was applied, the potential-compensating circuits were adjusted so that no clamping current and no spot current would flow when the cell was clamped at its resting potential. At the end of each experimental run, a check was made to see that the resting-potential clamping current was still zero; otherwise, the data were not used. Gain of the clamping amplifiers was generally increased to the point of oscillation and then reduced slightly. The frequency response of the clamping amplifiers was modified by the use of a special filter to insure that clamping of the cell membrane would be as fast as possible.

In order to introduce Cl intracellularly, the two intracellular electrodes were disconnected from the rest of the circuit and connected across a small three-volt battery. If such electrodes are filled with a concentrated KCl solution, Cl flows out one electrode into the cell while K flows out the other electrode, but there is no transmembrane current; due to the high concentration of KCl in the electrodes, a negligible part of the current is carried by any other ions.

Results

Membrane Properties. As a pair of intracellular microelectrodes is inserted into a cell, one electrode generally penetrates before the other. Further advance of the electrode pair after the first tip penetrates sometimes causes a change in the resting and spike potentials recorded by this electrode. The parallel-walled tips of pipettes formed on a de Fonbrune microforge showed an advantage over machine-drawn tips in this regard and made it easier to satisfy the requirement that both intracellular electrodes record the same resting and spike potentials prior to clamping. Such potentials were routinely recorded as in Fig. 2 before making a voltage-clamping run.

The remaining traces of Fig. 2 show the relationship between membrane current and the potential to which the membrane is clamped. The command potential, V_c, is set to the resting potential of the membrane and is suddenly changed to some new value, as shown by the upper trace in each block. Sweeps are generally separated by one or two seconds. In contrast to the method used by Hagiwara and Saito, in these experiments the membrane is clamped between sweeps and is forced back to the resting potential level after each pulse. In the left-hand column of Fig. 2, the lower trace of each block indicates the total clamping current. In the right-hand column, the lower trace indicates the clamping current flowing through the spot.

The clamping circuit supplies a large initial current transient which generally brings the membrane potential to the desired command potential in a time which is brief in comparison with the time-course of the conductance changes taking place in the membrane. After this capacitive transient is over, the current-voltage relation may be taken to represent the conductance changes occurring in the cell membrane. For hyperpolarizing and for small

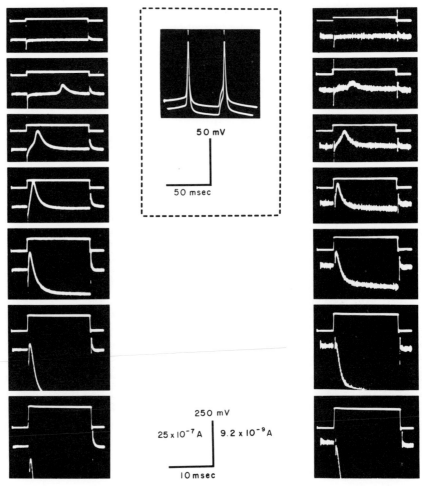

Fig. 2. Typical oscilloscope records. Inset: spike potentials from the intracellular electrodes prior to clamping. Upper trace of both columns: intracellular membrane potential during voltage clamp. Lower traces: left-hand column, total clamping current; right-hand column, clamping current flowing through spot about $300\mu^2$.

depolarizing command pulses, the steady-state clamping current is roughly proportional to the change of membrane potential (but see Addendum). As the depolarizing clamping potential is increased in successive steps, at a threshold value of about 20 mv an inward current transient appears. The peak of this transient increases to a maximum at about 50 mv depolarization and then decreases, just reaching zero at a potential around 100 mv. Following this initial inward current transient, the clamping current reverses and gradually rises to a steady outward value which is either maintained indefinitely or sags slightly. This late clamping current is a nonlinear function of the membrane potential and shows the phenomenon commonly called delayed rectification (Hodgkin *et al.*, 1949).

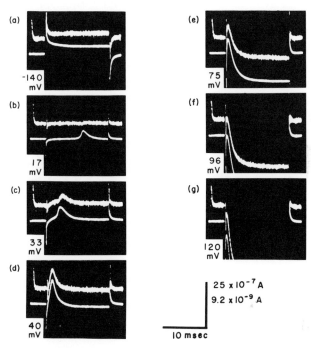

Fig. 3. Differential sensitivity of spot and total current to activity in the axon. Upper traces: spot current. Lower traces: total current. The inset in each block indicates the values of V_c for that block.

Figure 3 shows the difference between spot and total current. The upper trace in each block indicates the spot current, and the lower trace shows the total current; the blocks are arranged in the order of increasing depolarizing command potential from the upper left to lower right. Note that in the second current block, which is near threshold for activity in the axon, the upper trace shows negligible activity of the spot, while the total current indicates a late inward current transient. This current transient is supplied by the current electrode but apparently flows in the axon and not across the soma membrane. At larger depolarizing clamping potentials, the spot on the soma also becomes active.

These results may be interpreted in the following way. Clamping current which flows in the axon will not be recorded by the spot electrode. The threshold for spike activity in the axon is apparently less than that of the soma membrane (Fuortes *et al.*, 1957; Tauc, 1960). The membrane of the axon is less and less well-clamped as the distance from the clamped soma increases. Thus, at depolarizing clamp potentials which are too small to produce spike activity in the soma, lower threshold portions of the axon fire an attenuated spike, which appears under soma voltage clamp as an inward transient of clamping current. The time delay of the electrotonic spread out the axon delays this inward transient, so that near threshold the inward clamping current transient occurs up to several milliseconds after the command potential has been achieved in the soma.

Measurements from records like that of Fig. 2 are plotted in the subsequent figures. Current was measured either at the peak of the current transient (peak current) or later during the clamping pulse at the time indicated on each figure (late current). Since there is no current spike for hyperpolarizing pulses, peak and late current plots form only one curve to the left of threshold depolarization. Zero on the potential scale indicates that the membrane is clamped at its resting potential (zero clamping current). V_o is the potential of the reference electrode with respect to the intracellular electrode when the cell is at rest and is determined from potential recordings during insertion and withdrawal of the two intracellular electrodes. Similarly, V_s indicates the unclamped spike height.

There is some uncertainty in the measurement of V_o and V_s. In the case of a spontaneously firing cell, particularly at high firing rate, there is no steady potential level from which to measure resting potential or spike height. (In such cases, V_s is difficult to determine.) For a slowly firing cell, the membrane potential recovers from the postspike hyperpolarization, appears to remain constant for a time, then rather abruptly rises through a subthreshold depolarization to initiate the next spike. In such cases, potential is measured from the steady membrane level.

Figure 4 shows a plot of peak current versus membrane potential under voltage clamp for a typical active spot (dashed curve). The average resistance during hyperpolarization was about 460 ohm cm². (Near resting potential, the membrane resistance was sometimes higher. See Addendum.) Threshold depolarization is about 20 mv. At this point, an inward current spike appears which grows in amplitude with further depolarization. This reaches a maximum[1] in excess of one ma/cm² when the potential across the membrane is clamped near zero, i.e., at about 50 mv depolarization. For greater depolariz

[1] Determined by estimation of cell area from measured diameter (assuming spherical shape).

ing pulses, the amplitude of the inward current spike decreases smoothly, crossing the zero axis at a little less than 100 mv above resting potential (inside now positive).

The locus of the inward current transients as a function of voltage approximates a straight line for depolarization in excess of about 50 mv. The slope

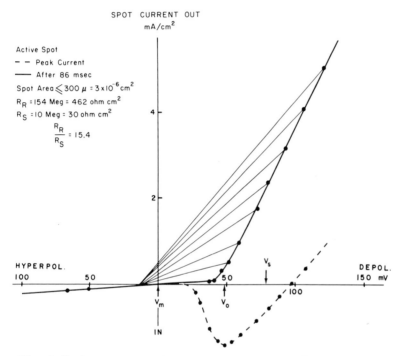

Fig. 4. Peak current and late current *vs.* membrane potential for a typical active spot under clamp. In all figures, zero membrane potential is set at resting potential, V_m; V_o is the potential of the reference electrode with respect to the intracellular electrode; and V_s is the unclamped spike height. The solid curve shows delayed rectification 86 msec after start of clamping pulse. The slopes of the fine lines show approximate conductance during late depolarization.

of this line has the dimensions of a conductance and is equivalent to a spot resistivity of about 30 ohm cm². The curves of Fig. 4 indicate a ratio of active to resting conductance of about 15 (but see Addendum). However, since each point represents the amplitude of a current spike and these spikes occur at different times, it is not proper to think of the slope of their locus as representing an actual resistance unless it has been shown that the membrane is in the same condition at each point. To determine this, it would be necessary to apply a second step in clamping command-pulse at the peak of the spike and determine the change in current accompanying such a step; such measurements have not been made in the present study.

The membrane potential at which the current spike just reaches zero clamping current may be interpreted as the electromotive force or equilibrium potential for the processes controlling membrane permeability at the time of the current spike. The intra- and extracellular ion types and concentrations are not known for these molluscan cells; hence, it is not possible to attribute the active membrane conductance to any particular ion. However, the fact that this equilibrium potential is considerably more positive than the height of the unclamped spike, V_s, indicates that some parts of the cell membrane are less active than others.

If the late clamping current, after it has become steady, is plotted against the clamping potential, a curve such as the solid curve of Fig. 4 is obtained. The conductance of the membrane measured at this time shows an increase at about 40 mv depolarization. This nonlinear behavior is also observed in the membrane of the giant squid axon and has been called delayed rectification by Hodgkin et al. (1949). Again, the locus of these points for different depolarizing pulses does not represent a true membrane resistance, since each point is obtained with the membrane in a different condition. If it is assumed that the membrane does not change its conductance abruptly in time, an approximation to the true membrane conductance during late depolarization can be obtained by observing the clamping current immediately following return of the command potential to zero. It is observed that the clamping current does not return to zero immediately, but jumps to a small outward value and then returns slowly to zero. The fine lines of Fig. 4 are the two-point plots obtained from such measurements. Capacitive clamping-current transients confuse such measurements; however, to a first approximation, it is seen that the fine lines intersect at a point approximately 10–15 mv more hyperpolarized than the resting potential. This suggests that the equilibrium potential responsible for delayed rectification may be approximately 60–65 mv inside negative. This might be simply the equilibrium potential for K, or it might be an equivalent value for a combination of ions.

The peak current curve of Fig. 4 was not a universal finding. Many spots were much less active, as illustrated in Fig. 5, but every spot always showed strong delayed rectification. By a less active spot is meant one showing smaller maximum inward current transients. It should be pointed out that deterioration of the cell also led to a decrease in the amplitude of the inward current transient, which would be interpreted as a less active membrane. However, many cells showed a much greater relative activity of the total membrane than of the particular spot under measurement, as evidenced by a comparison of total and spot currents at the peak of the inward transient. On the other hand, some spots were more active than the average of the whole soma, as indicated by the observation that the unclamped spike amplitude was less than the equilibrium potential for the spot current spike transient.

Effect of ACh. As mentioned previously, Tauc and Gerschenfeld (1960) have divided molluscan ganglion cells into two classes with respect to their responses to direct application of ACh to the soma membrane: "D" cells, which are depolarized and excited, and "H" cells, which are hyperpolarized and inhibited. It has also been shown (Tauc and Gerschenfeld, 1962) that ACh decreases the resistance of these cell membranes and shortens their membrane time constants accordingly.

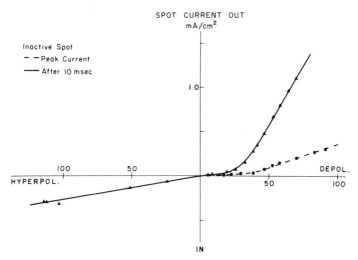

Fig. 5. Peak and late current *vs.* membrane potential for an inactive spot. Despite the absence of inward current spikes, there is a strong late current showing delayed rectification.

The voltage-clamp technique lends itself to the study of such phenomena by eliminating capacitive currents and by holding the membrane potential constant long enough to permit measurement of the time-course of conductance changes induced by the drug. Figure 6 shows the effect of ACh on the spot membrane of an "H" cell. The dashed line shows the late current before ACh, and the solid line that during ACh. ACh was applied iontophoretically just before each clamping test, and the late current was measured 200 msec after the beginning of the clamping pulse. For large hyperpolarizing potentials, the steady inward clamping current was increased several-fold, while for depolarizing pulses, the outward current was also increased. This extra clamping current required in the presence of ACh is plotted in Fig. 7 by subtracting the ordinates of the dashed curve from those of the solid curve of Fig. 6. This curve crosses the potential axis (i.e., ACh produces no change in membrane current) at a value, E_{ACh}, about 15 mv more negative inside than

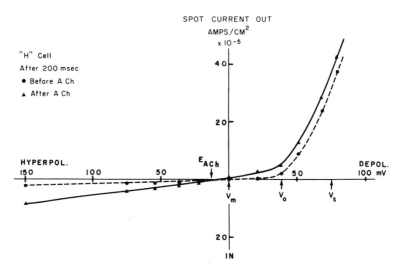

Fig. 6. Effect of ACh on the spot membrane of an "H" cell. Dashed curve: late current before ACh. Solid curve: during ACh. E_{ACh}: membrane potential at which ACh produces no change in clamping current.

the resting potential. Thus the effect of ACh on the membrane of such a spot when unclamped is to reduce its excitability. This is due partly to the increase in membrane potential and partly to the decrease in membrane resistance. It was noted that variations in the amount of ACh applied produced marked

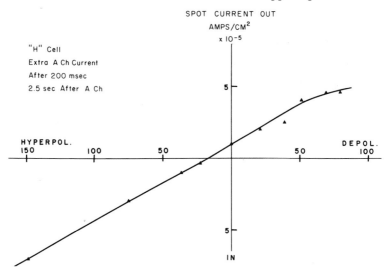

Fig. 7. "H" cell. Extra clamping current required in the presence of ACh, obtained by subtracting the dashed curve from the solid curve in Fig. 6.

changes in the amplitude of the extra ACh current, but affected very little the value of E_{ACh}.

The relation between extra clamping current and clamping potential is approximately linear up to the membrane potential at which delayed rectification begins. Above this potential, the extra current slopes off as though the process of delayed rectification had already provided for part of the permeability increase which would have been produced by the ACh. (In this particular cell, Fig. 7, the flattening is less marked than in any other so

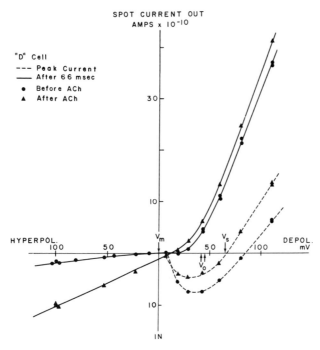

Fig. 8. Effect of ACh on peak and late spot current for a "D" cell. Double arrow at V_0 indicates small loss in resting potential during entire experiment.

measured, which may be the result of unintentional variations in the amount of ACh delivered or desensitization of the membrane to ACh.)

If clamping current is measured at the peak of the current transient (instead of late in the clamping pulse), a similar increase in membrane conductance is observed following the application of ACh. Figure 8 is a plot of the effect of ACh on both peak current and late current for a "D" cell. The filled circles show peak and late currents before ACh, and the triangles indicate the corresponding measurements after ACh. The dashed lines indicate peak current, and the solid lines late current. Both dashed and solid curves intersect at a depolarizing potential of about 10 mv.

Figure 9 shows the extra ACh current through such a "D" cell spot, derived from Fig. 8 in the same manner as was Fig. 7 from Fig. 6. Here the triangles and circles indicate the increase in peak current, while the plain triangles show the extra ACh current measured 66 msec after the beginning of each clamping pulse.

No membrane spots tested in molluscan neurons by this method have indicated equilibrium potentials (E_{ACh}) higher than 15 mv depolarizing. Figure 9 indicates that the flattening process observed at depolarizing potentials is less marked or absent in the case of the extra peak current than for the extra late current.

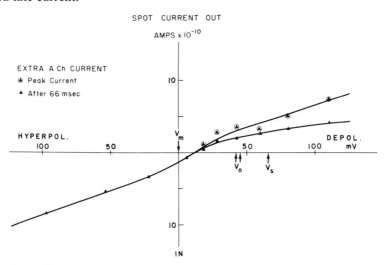

Fig. 9. Extra peak and late clamping current required in the presence of ACh, obtained by subtracting the circle curves from the triangle curves of Fig. 8.

Effect of Cl. It has been shown by Fatt and Katz (1953) for the crab muscle, by Coombs *et al.* (1955b) for the motoneuron, and by Tauc (1958) for the *Aplysia* that IPSPs have an equilibrium potential near and on the hyperpolarizing side of the resting potential. As shown by Coombs *et al.* (1955b), the introduction of Cl into the cat motoneuron through the intracellular micropipette tends to move this equilibrium potential for IPSPs to a less hyperpolarizing level. If enough Cl is introduced, the IPSP may become depolarizing with respect to the resting potential, and stimulation of an inhibitory pathway will produce a depolarizing synaptic potential. A similar effect was observed in the present experiment for both "H" and "D" cells.

As indicated under METHODS, when the intracellular electrodes are filled with concentrated KCl and are connected together by a battery, most of the current is carried by Cl flowing out one electrode and K flowing out the other. There is no transmembrane current during this process. The K introduced into the cell does not appear to affect its electrical properties (Coombs *et al.*, 1955a), but the Cl has a marked effect on E_{ACh} in both "H" and "D" cells. In both cases, E_{ACh} is moved in a depolarizing direction. If enough Cl is introduced, the hyperpolarizing effect of ACh on the unclamped "H" cell is reversed and becomes a depolarizing excitatory effect, while the depolarizing effect of ACh on a "D" cell is made more pronounced. This is

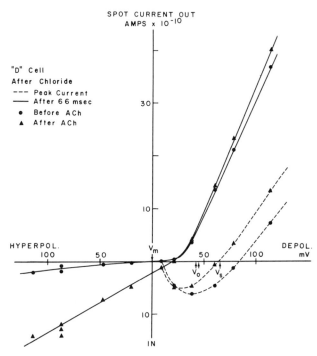

Fig. 10. Data similar to those of Fig. 8, but after injection of Cl.

illustrated in Figs. 10 and 11, which are plots similar to Figs. 8 and 9, but after several minutes of Cl injection. It may be seen that the E_{ACh} for this "D" cell has been increased from about 12 mv depolarizing to more than 20 mv depolarizing by the introduction of Cl.

Figures 12, 13, and 14 show the same results on another "D" cell, for which complete measurements were not available. Again, E_{ACh} was increased by the introduction of Cl from about 12 mv to about 23 mv depolarizing. Figure 14 shows the extra clamping current required in the presence of ACh and is the best example obtained of the difference in linearity of peak and late extra current.

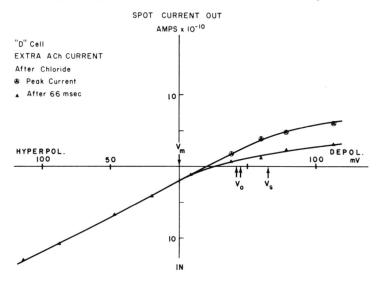

Fig. 11. Data similar to those of Fig. 9, but after injection of Cl.

No evidence was seen to suggest that the Cl introduced was pumped out again, in contrast to the observations of Coombs *et al.* (1955b) on MHCs. While more careful experiments need to be done, E_{ACh} did not return to pre-chloride values even after periods up to 1 hr following Cl injection.

It may be noted in Figs. 8, 10, and 13 that the application of ACh mark-

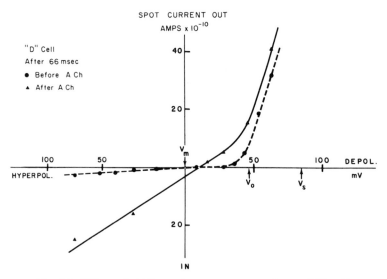

Fig. 12. Effect of ACh on late spot current for a "D" cell.

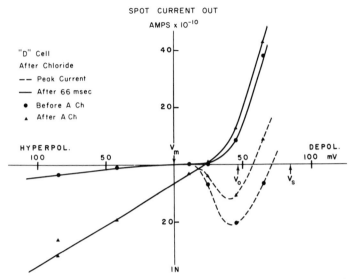

Fig. 13. Effect of ACh on the peak and late currents for the "D" cell of Fig. 12. Taken after Cl.

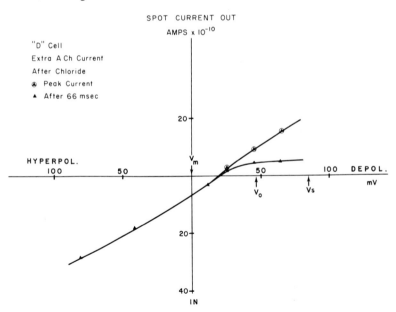

Fig. 14. Plot of the extra clamping current (both peak and late) required in the presence of ACh, obtained by subtracting the circle curves from the triangle curves of Fig. 13.

edly reduced the equilibrium potential during the current spike. By contrast, the introduction of Cl, which altered the equilibrium potential for ACh, produced practically no change in the equilibrium potential of the spike-generating mechanism.

Discussion

Voltage Clamp of Nonuniform Membrane. The technique of the voltage clamp was developed for studying the properties of a membrane which was assumed to be uniform at least in a macroscopic sense. However, the appearance of "notches" and "oscillations" in the clamping current (Tasaki and Bak, 1958a, b; Tasaki and Spyropoulos, 1958; Taylor *et al.*, 1960) has raised the possibility either that squid axon membrane and perhaps frog node may have nonuniform properties or that the techniques used may fail to clamp the membrane uniformly. It has been clearly demonstrated (Taylor *et al.*, 1960) that unless the current electrode used for clamping the squid giant axon has a sufficiently low resistance, local differences in membrane potential are possible, and the total clamping current is difficult to interpret.

It may be assumed that the membrane can be spatially voltage-clamped so long as an electrode of sufficiently low resistance is placed close enough to the membrane. While this condition is apparently difficult to realize in the giant axon of the squid, a nearly spherical cell such as the molluscan ganglion cell may be a more favorable preparation. Uniformity of membrane current over the clamped region is not a requirement of the system. Uniformity of membrane voltage depends upon cytoplasmic resistance and the electrical properties of the membrane under clamp. An experimental determination of the success of spatial clamping would be desirable, but is not practicable at present. In the absence of such direct evidence, we may assume a spatial clamp while remembering that the appearance of "notching" or "oscillations" would immediately cast doubt on our assumption.

Another indication that the soma membrane was effectively voltage-clamped was the observation that the inward current transient could always be smoothly graded. That is, if the sum of the cytoplasmic and extracellular resistance were large enough in comparison with the active membrane resistance, the effectiveness of the clamping circuit would be reduced and would ultimately permit the appearance of the inward current transient in an all-or-nothing manner. "Extended clamping" has been used by Hodgkin *et al.* (1952) and Nelson and Frank (1964) to reduce the effect of this series resistance, but would not be appropriate in a preparation where different parts of the membrane may have different properties.

In the present study, widely differing inward current transients were recorded from different spots on different cells of the same type. (It was not practical to measure more than one spot on a single cell.) It appears probable from a comparison of spot and total currents that such differing inward current transients occurred simultaneously in a single cell. It was, however, uniformly observed that all spots showed marked delayed rectification whether there was a strong or weak early inward current transient. Also, membrane spots which showed a deterioration of inward current transient with time usually continued to show strong delayed rectification.

It was usually observed that the unclamped spike peak was less positive than the clamped potential at which the spot current just reached zero. This is in agreement with the observation that there are usually regions of the soma membrane which are less active than others and which reduce the spike amplitude below the equilibrium potential of its generating mechanism.

Action of ACh. Fatt and Katz (1951) suggested that the action of ACh at the neuromuscular junction might be explained by an increase in permeability of the end-plate membrane to certain ions present in the intra- and extracellular fluids. The equivalent circuit of this model is a variable resistance and a source of electromotive force in series, across the cell membrane. Coombs *et al.* (1955b, c) have suggested that such a model also fits the synaptic generation of excitatory postsynaptic potentials (EPSPs) and IPSPs in motoneurons. The equivalent circuit of this model itself suggests that the ionic pathways responsible for the transmitter-induced increase in permeability are separate and in parallel with the pathways controlling other membrane functions. Grundfest (1957) has opposed the idea that spike potentials and graded synaptic potentials can occur in the same membrane. The present experiments show, however, that changes of conductance can be elicited in a spot of membrane 20 μ in diameter by electric currents, resulting in a normal spike, and by an applied chemical, resulting in a graded potential resembling a postsynaptic potential.

In addition, we have an opportunity to test the question: Are the current pathways opened up by ACh the same as those responsible for conductance increases associated with generation of the spike, or are these pathways parallel channels through the soma membrane?

If the membrane is adequately voltage-clamped, current through one channel should be independent of that in another parallel channel. On the other hand, if the two processes open up the same current channel, the clamping current would be expected to be less than the sum of the clamping currents for each process acting alone. This would be a kind of clamping-current occlusion.

Evidence of such occlusion is seen in the records of Figs. 7, 9, 11, and 14. A linear relationship between extra ACh-induced clamping current and membrane potential would be predicted by the model of Fatt and Katz (1951). The flattening of the extra ACh current curves during delayed rectification suggests that the same ionic pathways are opened up by both processes. On the other hand, there is certainly much less flattening of the extra ACh current curves measured during the inward current transients. While other explanations are possible, the easiest interpretation is that the pathways responsible for the inward current transient are not the same as those produced by ACh. This leaves open the possibility that both pathways may carry the same ion species.

Dr. M. V. Bennett (personal communication) has suggested an alternate explanation for the occlusion between ACh and delayed rectification currents: that the outward current tends to sweep away the positively charged ACh ions and so reduces the ACh-induced conductance change. However, if this effect is sufficient to account for the occlusion, the extra ACh current would be expected to increase nonlinearly with increasing hyperpolarization, and this was not observed.

The equilibrium potential of the ACh-induced conductance change, E_{ACh}, has been determined previously for "H" cells (Tauc and Gerschenfeld, 1960, 1962) by passing constant hyperpolarizing currents across the cell membrane. This method is less convenient for "D" cells, for these cells fire repetitively before the level of E_{ACh} is reached. Under voltage-clamp conditions, however, the extra ACh current can be measured either at the peak of the inward current transient or later, after delayed rectification is established. It is evident from these experiments that E_{ACh} for "D" cells is only about 15 mv less negative inside than resting potential, and that the ACh-induced current increases linearly as the membrane is hyperpolarized from this potential.

Tauc and Gerschenfeld (1962) have shown that ACh depolarizes the unclamped "D" cell to a level near the E_{ACh} seen in the present experiments and that the spikes are then markedly reduced in amplitude. It can be seen from the curves of Figs. 8, 10, and 13 that ACh also markedly reduces the clamping potential at which the spike current just reaches zero. These facts confirm the marked increase in conductance observed following ACh application and show that it is comparable with that of the spike-generating mechanism.

Effect of Intracellular Cl. Introduction of Cl intracellularly moves E_{ACh} in a depolarizing direction for both "H" and "D" cells without affecting resting potential or the equilibrium potential for the spike-generating mechanism. This may be interpreted as indicating that the membrane is impermeable to Cl both at rest and during the spike but becomes permeable to Cl when ACh is applied. This interpretation is in agreement with the observations of Coombs et al. (1955b) and Ito et al. (1962) on the effect of Cl on the IPSP of the MHC and of Kerkut and Thomas (1963) on snail ganglion cells. These workers have shown that permeability is increased for a number of small anions as well as for Cl, which suggests pores may be formed in the membrane by the action of the transmitter, rather than some more complex mechanism for charge transfer.

An "H" cell behaves very much like a "D" cell after introduction of Cl. It is tempting to suggest that a "D" cell may differ from an "H" cell only by the presence of some small anion intracellularly. However, this hypothesis is rather unlikely, since Tauc and Gerschenfeld (1962) have shown that hexamethonium applied by perfusion will block the action of ACh on "D" cells but not on "H" cells.

The results of these experiments differ from those obtained from both the MHC EPSP and the muscle end-plate potential. In the case of MHCs, the EPSP amplitude varies very little with membrane potential changes on the hyperpolarizing side of threshold (Coombs et al., 1955c). This difference would be expected if the MHC excitatory synapses were out on the dendrites and were separated from the soma by a large series resistance. In the case of the end-plate potential, E_{ACh} is approximately 10 mv negative inside instead of 25 or 30 mv as seen in the mollusc. This difference may reflect the different ionic environment in the two tissues. Thus, while there are some differences between the "artificial synapse" formed by the iontophoretic application of ACh to a spot on the soma membrane of a mollusc and naturally occurring synapses on other membranes, nevertheless, the subsynaptic membrane of the latter cannot be voltage-clamped. The "artificial synapse" which can be studied using this technique presents an interesting model for possible synaptic mechanisms.

Summary

1. Snail and *Aplysia* ganglion cells were studied by a special voltage-clamp technique which permitted examination of electrical properties of a patch of soma membrane about 20 μ in diameter.
2. These patches had properties like other excitable membranes (e.g., squid axon) but showed great variation in the inward current transient associated with spike generation.
3. Regardless of a strong or weak inward current transient under clamp, all patches showed a large, late outward current usually called delayed rectification.
4. ACh applied iontophoretically to a patch clamped at its resting potential produced a many-fold conductance change and an inward or outward current depending on whether the cell was an "H" or a "D" cell, respectively. E_{ACh} was up to 15 mv hyperpolarizing for "H" cells or depolarizing for "D" cells.
5. Occlusion of ACh-induced current and delayed rectification current suggests that the same ionic pathway is opened up by both processes. By contrast, inward spike current and ACh-induced current show little or no occlusion, suggesting that different pathways are established by the two processes, even though they may carry the same ion species.

6. Injection of Cl moves E_{ACh} in the depolarizing direction for either "H" or "D" cells without altering resting potential.

7. Finally, it is evident that a patch of membrane as small as 20 μ is capable of showing both electrical and chemical excitability.

Addendum

Kandel and Tauc (in press) have recently found that in certain ganglion cells of both snail and *Aplysia* there is an increase in conductance during hyperpolarization which they refer to as anomalous rectification in analogy with a similar phenomenon observed in muscle (Freygang and Adrian, 1961). In the present experiments, under voltage clamp this effect is masked and was overlooked probably because, in order to record the very large currents which occurred during depolarization, the sensitivity of the current trace was reduced to a low value. The curve of Fig. 8 in this paper indicates an increase in conductance with hyperpolarization.

REFERENCES

Araki, T., and C. A. Terzuolo. 1962. *J. Neurophysiol.* 25: 772.

Bennett, M. V. L., S. M. Crain, and H. Grundfest. 1959. *J. Gen. Physiol.* 43: 189.

Cole, K. S. 1949. *Arch. Sci. Physiol.* III: 253.

Cole, K. S., and J. W. Moore. 1960. *J. Gen. Physiol.* 44: 123.

Coombs, J. S., J. C. Eccles, and P. Fatt. 1955a. *J. Physiol. (London)* 130: 291.

Coombs, J. S., J. C. Eccles, and P. Fatt. 1955b. *J. Physiol. (London)* 130: 326.

Coombs, J. S., J. C. Eccles, and P. Fatt. 1955c. *J. Physiol. (London)* 130: 374.

Dodge, F. A., and B. Frankenhaeuser. 1958. *J. Physiol. (London)* 143: 76.

Fatt, P., and B. Katz. 1951. *J. Physiol. (London)* 115: 320.

Fatt, P., and B. Katz. 1953. *J. Physiol. (London)* 121: 374.

Frank, K., and P. G. Nelson. 1961. *Abstr. Intern. Biophysics Congr., Stockholm.*

Frank, K., M. G. F. Fuortes, and P. G. Nelson. 1959. *Science* 130: 38.

Freygang, W. H., Jr., and R. H. Adrian. 1961. In *Biophysics of Physiological and Pharmacological Actions*, ed. A. M. Shanes. Washington: *Am. Assoc. Advan. Sci.* P. 245.

Freygang, W. H., Jr., and K. Frank. 1959. *J. Gen. Physiol.* 42: 749.

Fuortes, M. G. F., K. Frank, and M. C. Becker. 1957. *J. Gen. Physiol.* 40: 735.

Grundfest, H., 1957. *Physiol. Revs.* 37: 337.

Hagiwara, S., and T. H. Bullock. 1957. *J. Cellular Comp. Physiol.* 50: 25.

Hagiwara, S., and N. Saito. 1957. *Proc. Japan Acad.* 33: 682.

Hagiwara, S., and N. Saito. 1959a. *J. Neurophysiol.* 22: 204.

Hagiwara, S., and N. Saito. 1959b. *J. Physiol. (London)* 148: 161.

Hodgkin, A. L., A. F. Huxley, and B. Katz. 1949. *Arch. Sci. Physiol.* 3: 129.

Hodgkin, A. L., A. F. Huxley, and B. Katz. 1952. *J. Physiol. (London)* 116: 424.

Ito, M., P. G. Kostyuk, and T. Oshima. 1962. *J. Physiol. (London)* 164: 150.

Kandel, E. R., and L. Tauc. *Nature.* In press.

Kerkut, G. A., and R. C. Thomas. 1963. *J. Physiol. (London)* 168: 23 P.

Nelson, P. G., and K. Frank. 1964. *Actualités Neurophysiol.* 5: 15.

Nelson, P. G., K. Frank, and W. Rall. 1960. *Federation Proc.* 19, No. 1, Pt. 1: 303.

Tasaki, I., and A. F. Bak. 1958a. *J. Neurophysiol.* 21: 124.

Tasaki, I., and A. F. Bak. 1958b. *Am. J. Physiol.* 193: 301.

Tasaki, I., and C. S. Spyropoulos. 1958. *Am. J. Physiol.* 193: 309.

Tauc, L. 1958. *Arch. Ital. Biol.* 96: 78.

Tauc, L. 1960. *J. Physiol. (London)* 152: 36 P.

Tauc, L. 1962. *J. Gen. Physiol.* 45: 1099.

Tauc. L., and J. Bruner. 1963. *Nature* 198: 33.

Tauc, L., and H. M. Gerschenfeld. 1960. *Compt. Rend.* 251: 3076.

Tauc, L., and H. M. Gerschenfeld. 1962. *J. Neurophysiol.* 25: 236.

Taylor, R. E., J. W. Moore, and K. S. Cole. 1960. *Biophys. J.* 1: 161.

Tomita, T. 1956. *Japan. J. Physiol.* 6: 327.

Role of the Membrane
in the Regulation of
Metabolic Processes

The Interdependence of
Metabolism and Active Transport

R. Whittam

Department of Biochemistry
University of Oxford
Oxford, England

Much attention in biochemistry has been devoted to the energetics of metabolism, and the main emphasis has been placed on the liberation of energy rather than on its utilization. The principal metabolic pathways have been worked out, and those reactions of intermediary metabolism in which energy is liberated have been identified. Some of the energy liberated during catabolism is dissipated as heat, and some is made available for work of various kinds by the synthesis of the high-energy phosphate bonds of adenosine triphosphate (ATP). The glycolytic synthesis of ATP is well understood but is not so quantitatively important to cells generally as the phosphorylation of adenosine diphosphate (ADP) to ATP, which is coupled to electron transport and O_2 consumption. The mechanism of oxidative phosphorylation is perhaps the outstanding problem in the field of intermediary metabolism, on a par with the molecular biological problem of energy utilization for cellular osmotic work.

Yet from the point of view of cellular energetics, there is vast knowledge of energy liberation during metabolism compared with the paucity of information on the mechanism of utilization of ATP by physiological processes. In considering energy turnover, such questions as the following arise. Are energy production and utilization interdependent? Does the hydrolysis of ATP involved in energy utilization exert a feedback effect as a pacemaker of

O_2 consumption? How general is the role of ATP as an energy transmitter to make the energy of the chemical bonds in foodstuffs available for cellular work? How much energy produced during intermediary metabolism is devoted to a particular energy-requiring process? An approach to the cell as an integrated unit is required, since one process cannot be considered in isolation as far as energy metabolism is concerned. The nature of the coupling between energy production and utilization is not just a problem in biochemistry, for cell structures of various kinds are intimately involved, and knowledge of their physical and chemical properties is still rather limited. It is clear that oxidative phosphorylation, as the main energy-generating mechanism in cells, requires an organized structure in mitochondria. Moreover, there is a connection between the structure and metabolic states of mitochondria from many tissues, suggesting a dependence of one upon the other (Packer, 1960). Both structural and metabolic states can be controlled by the level of intramitochondrial ADP, and the swelling and shrinking of the particles are closely related to the functional components of oxidative phosphorylation (Chance and Packer, 1958; Lehninger, 1962). Just as energy production is associated with mitochondrial structure, so processes utilizing energy no less appear to be associated with reactions at the surface interfaces of cell structures. The biosynthesis of proteins requires the endoplasmic reticulum, the contraction of striated muscle depends upon the Z-line of the sarcomere and the orientation of the rods of actin and myosin in the I and A bands, photosynthesis depends upon chlorophyll being in the lamellar structure of chloroplasts, and, not least, the active transport of cations is catalyzed by the highly organized cell membrane.

In each instance, an insoluble component of the cell is involved, and the reactions must occur in a heterogeneous system of cytoplasm plus insoluble structure. Energy transformation therefore involves structure. How can a reaction at one structure, the cell membrane, exert an effect on reactions in another structure, the mitochondrion? The aim of this paper is to examine the respiratory consequences to the cell of the role of the cell membrane as an energy transducer in the utilization of ATP for active transport. Only some 200 years ago was the cellular theory of tissues accepted in biology, and active transport is but one of the multifarious activities of membranes which can be considered from the view of the cell as an integrated unit.

In all the biological systems which have been studied, certain movements of ions across cell membranes occur which cannot be explained by the operation of physical forces. These forces are: 1) thermal agitation, which would cause the disappearance of the differences in chemical activity or potential which are actually found; 2) forces due to electrical potential differences which would create concentration but not electrochemical potential gradients; and 3) forces due to the flow of water through aqueous channels in the membrane (see Ussing, 1960). It is the movement of ions contrary to these physical forces that is called active transport, and metabolic energy and chemical reactions clearly must be required for the osmotic work of creating and maintaining ionic concentrations displaced from thermodynamic equilibrium. The generation of ionic concentration gradients by active transport implies the conversion of metabolic energy to a form other than heat. On the other hand, when an existing gradient is being maintained in a steady state, it follows that no net energy conversion occurs. Instead, the active transport is counterbalanced by passive ionic changes, so that the over-all effect is a conversion of chemical energy into heat. Nevertheless, in both instances, the same reactions will be responsible for the unidirectional active ion movements.

In discussing the nature of the coupling between metabolism and active transport, it seems best to consider first the evidence that ATP is indeed needed for active transport. Next, we shall discuss the features of the enzymatic hydrolysis of ATP, and, finally, the role of active transport as a pacemaker or regulator of O_2 consumption.

The Dependence of Active Cation Transport on ATP

The view that ATP is required for the active transport of ions has gained credence by analogy with its role in other systems requiring energy and from a theoretical consideration of its high-energy character. Actual experimental attempts to demonstrate a requirement for ATP date from as recently as the mid-1950's. The early widespread finding that 2,4-dinitrophenol (DNP) caused a failure of active transport could be taken as implicating ATP, but is not very convincing in view of the uncertainty as to the reaction inhibited by DNP. More cogent circumstantial evidence directing attention to ATP has come from the persistence of active transport in certain tissues when they are made anaerobic (see Whittam, 1961a). This conclusion stems from the fact that the only chemical reactions common to aerobic respiration and anaerobic glycolysis are the oxidation and reduction of diphosphopyridine nucleotide (DPN) and the synthesis of ATP from ADP. The involvement of DPN has been excluded in human red cells, in which active K transport can occur without the turnover of DPN due to the combined operation of the enzymes lactic dehydrogenase and triose phosphate dehydrogenase (Whittam, 1958). If this finding also applies to other tissues, it follows that the occurrence of active transport under anaerobic as well as aerobic conditions must depend on a supply of ATP. It is true, of course, that most tissues certainly require O_2, and this fact led to the oxidation-reduction hypothesis of active transport which is an alternative to what may be termed the ATP hypothesis (see Conway, 1957). Electron transport to molecular oxygen via the cytochrome system was an essential feature of the original redox theory, but this view cannot be correct for tissues in which active transport can occur anaerobically. It could, of course, be held that there are two distinct mechanisms —one for aerobic and one for anaerobic conditions. Whilst it is reasonable to suppose that there may be different transport systems in different cell types, such as mammalian red cells and liver cells, for example, it hardly seems likely that the same cell would transport ions differently in different metabolic conditions. It is simpler to posit a single active-transport mechanism that utilizes ATP which may be derived from either aerobic or anaerobic metabolism. The higher rates of transport found in O_2 than in N_2 are no doubt due to the greater supply of ATP available, arising from the higher efficiency of respiration over glycolysis as a generator of ATP during metabolism. Active transport under both aerobic and anaerobic conditions has been found in duck red cells (Tosteson and Robertson, 1956), seminal vesicle mucosa (Breuer and Whittam, 1957; Whittam and Breuer, 1959), frog skin (Leaf and Renshaw, 1957), and mouse ascites tumor cells (Maizels et al., 1958). Other tissues which possess the ability to transport Na and K actively under anaerobic conditions are slices of kidney cortex and liver from newborn immature animals (Whittam, 1960, 1961b; van Rossum, 1961). (This finding has some physiological bearing in connection with the survival of young animals in anoxia [Dawes et al., 1963].)

Direct evidence that ATP facilitates K uptake is provided by the work of Gardos (1954) with human red cell ghosts. ATP was introduced into the ghosts by lyzing the cells in a dilute ATP solution, and the resulting ghosts were shown to accumulate K. Later work of Hoffman (1960) has demonstrated the active extrusion of Na by ghosts containing ATP. Inosine triphosphate (ITP) did not replace ATP, in spite of its similar high-energy character. A further indication of a causal linkage between active K influx and ATP is the finding with glucose-free, intact red cells, producing not lactic acid but pyruvic acid, that the rates of fall in K influx and ATP concentration were very similar (Whittam, 1958). Another finding implicating ATP as the energy source for cation transport is the stimulation of the efflux of Na from poisoned squid giant axons when ATP or one of its precursors is injected (Caldwell et al., 1960). The injection of ATP supported only an increase in the exchange diffusion of Na and not of the Na efflux which is coupled to K influx. On the other hand, arginine phosphate and phosphoenolpyruvate, which give rise to ATP by phosphokinase reactions, caused a rise in Na efflux which was greater when K was present in the external solution. A possible explanation for the different effects of ATP and of phosphagens is that the latter compounds produce a high local concentration of ATP where it is required, whereas injected ATP would be evenly distributed within the axoplasm. Taken together, the above evidence with various tissues strongly suggests that active cation transport is dependent on metabolism because of the supply of ATP then available and that when ATP is not being produced metabolically, active transport can still be supported by ATP introduced artificially, by injection in nerve axons or osmotically in red cell ghosts.

The Mechanism of ATP Hydrolysis. What are the enzymatic features of the ATP hydrolysis associated with Na and K transport? The membrane component responsible for active cation transport can clearly be regarded as an adenosine triphosphatase (ATPase), and the question arises of what factors control the enzymatic activity. Skou (1957) first showed that the ATPase activity of a microsomal fraction of crab nerve, presumed to contain the membranes, was stimulated by the combined presence of Na and K. The enzymatic activity, like that of phosphatases generally, required Mg, and Skou suggested that the enzyme (or enzymes) involved may be responsible for Na and K transport. A similar stimulation of ATP hydrolysis by alkali metals has since been shown in many disrupted cells and tissues, and, furthermore, this part of the total ATPase activity is inhibited by ouabain and other glycosides which inhibit transport. An inhibition of ATP hydrolysis associated with the inhibition of K uptake in intact red cells by digoxin was shown by Dunham (1957) and by Whittam (1958). Such preparations as fragmented red cell membranes (Post *et al.*, 1960; Dunham and Glynn, 1961), the sheath of squid giant nerve axons (Bonting and Caravaggio, 1962), a microsomal fraction of brain (Deul and McIlwain, 1961; Schwarz *et al.*, 1962; Aldridge, 1962), and a nuclear fraction of kidney (Whittam and Wheeler, 1961; Wheeler and Whittam, 1962) and of liver (Emmelot and Bos, 1962) have been investigated in considerable detail and show broadly similar properties. A microsomal fraction of kidney cortex also possesses ouabain-sensitive ATPase activity (Skou, 1962; Landon and Norris, 1963). As shown by their presence in homogenates of some 30 tissues of the cat (Bonting *et al.*, 1961), the distribution is widespread of such ATPases that are activated by Na plus K and sensitive to ouabain.

The results with red cell membranes have shown probably most clearly and in a quantitative way the relevance of this enzymatic activity to cation transport. From the work of Post *et al.* (1960) and Dunham and Glynn (1961), it is evident that there is an intimate connection between the ATPase and the transport mechanisms. Thus,

1. both systems are located in the membrane;
2. both systems use ATP;
3. for both processes, Na and K are required together, and the concentrations of these ions required for half-maximal act vation are the same;
4. the concentrations of ouabain required for half-maximal inhibition of the two are similar; and
5. the inhibition of ATPase activity by low concentrations of glycoside is overcome by a high K concentration, just as inhibition of K influx is similarly prevented.

Other points common to ATP hydrolysis and the transport system concern the effects of NH_4 and of alkali metals other than Na and K (Post *et al.*, 1960; Whittam, 1962c).

The question of the site of activation of Na and K cannot be tackled directly with fragmented membranes, although the finding (Dunham and Glynn, 1961) of an antagonism between ouabain and K suggests that the competition is located at a site on the external surface of the membranes. The cell membrane is clearly asymmetrical in its selection of ions for transport, showing preference for K on the outside and for Na on the inside. Does the stimulation of the ATPase by Na and K also show the same spatial asymmetry? A clear answer is provided by work with red cell ghosts prepared from cells which were hemolyzed in a dilute solution of ATP and $MgCl_2$ to which NaCl or KCl was then added to restore iso-osmolality. Provided the membranes are allowed to become reconstituted after hemolysis, the Na and K concentrations in ghosts and medium can be varied independently (Hoffman *et al.*, 1960). Both Glynn (1962a) and Whittam (1962a) showed that the hydrolysis of ATP within the ghosts is stimulated by K in the medium and by Na inside the ghosts. Replacement of Na in the medium with choline did not cause a fall in ATPase activity, whereas omission of external K caused a fall approaching that produced by ouabain. Conversely, provided external K was present, an increase in internal Na concentration elicited a rise in ATPase activity. The stimulation of the ATPase thus depends on Na being on the inside and K on the outside of the red cell, and these are the locations of the ions from which they are transported. Similar results with glucose-free, intact cells in which the hydrolysis of endogenous ATP is measured support this conclusion (Laris and Letchworth, 1962; Ager and Whittam, unpublished data). The spatial asymmetry of the transport system is thus another feature shared by the membrane ATPase.

None of the work on ATPase has shown whether it is a single enzyme or a combination of a phosphokinase and a phosphatase. Such a combination of enzymes would account for ATPase activity, and suggested combinations include, first, diglyceride kinase and phosphatidic acid phosphatase, both of which are present in red cell membranes (Hokin and Hokin, 1961) and, secondly, a phosphokinase acting on protein to form phosphoprotein which is then hydrolyzed to protein and phosphate by a phosphatase (Heald, 1962; Judah *et al.*, 1962). It is highly significant that phosphoprotein becomes labeled from P^{32}-labeled ATP in a way dependent on the Na and K concentrations and on ouabain. Incorporation of P^{32} is enhanced by Na and counteracted by K, and again there is an antagonism between K and ouabain (Charnock and Post, 1963). The action of ouabain appears to be not on the formation of the phosphorylated complex, which requires Na, but on the K-dependent phosphorolysis reaction which leads to the liberation of orthophosphate.

For the purposes of the following discussion, the detailed nature of the enzymatic transport reaction is irrelevant, and it suffices that the following two points are well established. 1) Active transport derives energy from metabolism in the form of ATP. 2) The hydrolysis of ATP by membranes is stimulated by internal Na acting in concert with external K, and the activation is overcome by those glycosides which inhibit active transport in intact cells and tissues.

Having outlined the salient features of active transport as a utilizer of ATP, we can now turn to its role as a regulator of cellular respiration.

The Dependence of the Respiration of Isolated Tissues on Active Cation Transport

The role of ATP as at least one of the links between metabolism and active transport raises the possibility of an interdependent coupling between the two processes, especially with regard to respiration. Mitochondria are the major sites of ATP synthesis, and there must be a movement of ATP from them to the cell membrane, where it is utilized, and, conversely, a movement of ADP from the cell membrane to mitochondria. The turnover of ATP can occur *in situ* only if there is this kind of migration. The rate of respiration in mitochondria is governed by the concentration of ADP, a substance acting as phosphate acceptor in oxidative phosphorylation (see Chance and Williams, 1956), and the rate of formation of ADP is partly regulated by the rate of the active transport of cations. The ATPase of the membrane is, therefore, one of the factors regulating the relative concentrations of ATP and ADP in the cell. It is interesting that electric excitation of brain causes an increase in the ratio of ADP/ATP (Shapot, 1957) compatible with the concomitant increase in O_2 uptake (see McIlwain, 1961). The expectation is that a high ATPase activity will cause a raised ADP concentration and hence a high rate of respiration. Conversely, if part of the normally active ATPase of the cell is inactive, either because of inhibition by glycosides or because of nonoperation of active transport by deprivation of cations, the turnover of ATP will be lowered, and a fall in the rate of respiration is to be expected.

In order for mitochondria to respond to changes in ADP concentration or to changes in extramitochondrial ATPase activity, they have to be carefully prepared. In suitable preparations, the mitochondria are referred to as tightly coupled. It seems very likely on *a priori* grounds that mitochondria in intact cells are in this condition, for, otherwise, cells would not be able to adjust their rate of respiration to changes in demands for energy. Moreover, loosely coupled mitochondria with a low P/O ratio (phosphorylation quotient) would be inefficient as ATP producers. A test of such a situation is to see if inhibition of the active-transport mechanism, acting as an ATPase, causes a lowering of the rate of respiration resulting from the decreased fission of ATP.

The view that cells adjust their respiratory rate to energy demands is an old notion in physiology (see Barcroft, 1934). The respiration of secretory epithelia of various kinds, for instance, is raised by hormonal stimulation, and the general concept is that cells have a basal rate associated with resting conditions and a variable rate set by the demands for energy during activity. The variability of respiration of secretory epithelia is readily understandable, because net work is done in transferring material across a layer of cells. An example of this situation is the effect of neurohypophyseal hormone on the Q_{O_2} (μl O_2/mg dry wt/hr) of toad bladder in Ringer's solution. During the second hour after adding the hormone, the Q_{O_2} had increased from 1.06 to 1.76 (Leaf and Dempsey, 1960). The hormone stimulates active Na transfer across the bladder, as shown by measurement of the current in a short-circuited system, and it is highly significant that the respiratory response is almost abolished in Na-free Ringer's made with Mg or choline in place of Na. The comparable increase in Q_{O_2} after adding the hormone was then only from 0.98 to 1.13 with Mg-Ringer's and from 0.90 to 1.07 with choline-Ringer's. The increased Q_{O_2} induced by neurohypophyseal hormone is evidently entirely secondary to its action in increasing active Na transport.

Another action of the neurohypophyseal hormone is to increase the permeability of toad bladder to water and urea, and this increase occurs in the absence of Na as well as in normal Ringer's solution, in keeping with the passive nature of the passage of urea and water through the membrane. Leaf (1960) concluded that the hormone increases the passive permeability to urea, water, and Na and that the increased Q_{O_2} is elicited only when an increased active Na transport ensues to counteract the increased rate of entry into the cells. Zerahn (1956) and Leaf and Renshaw (1957) have similarly found an increase in the O_2 consumption of frog skin after the addition of Na to a Na-free medium bathing the skin. It is evident that the onset of Na transport in frog skin and toad bladder is accompanied by an increased rate of O_2 consumption which is a response to the increased energy requirement for active transport.

Instead of comparing the flow of Na across an epithelium with the tissue respiration, another approach to the problem of energy-coupling is to investigate the relationship between active K transport and O_2 consumption in tissue slices. The active transport is here between the inside and outside of cells, and secretion across an epithelium is not involved. Slices of brain and kidney cortex are particularly suitable for this purpose, because their rates of respiration are readily measurable in Warburg manometers, and their K exchange rates are sufficiently high that net changes in ionic content can be detected in a time scale of minutes. The Na and K present in the tissue *in vivo* can be maintained *in vitro* without the need for hormones to initiate active ion movements. The energy-coupling is therefore between the normal transport mechanism for the maintenance of the tissue Na and K concentrations and the O_2 consumption. In earlier studies with tissue slices, inhibition of active K uptake was invariably achieved by cutting off the energy supply by metabolic inhibition. The inhibition was not, therefore, direct, and no experimental test could be made of how much of the respiratory energy was being used for active cation transport. Indirect methods of calculation for making this assessment were distinctly dubious (Whittam and Davies, 1954b), and what was wanted was a direct method of stopping transport by specific means which do not affect mitochondrial respiration. A fall in O_2 consumption can then be legitimately ascribed to the abolition of the energy requirement for active transport. This possibility has been tested with slices of brain cortex and kidney cortex in which active cation transport is abolished by ouabain or the deprivation of Na (Whittam, 1961c, 1962b; Whittam and Willis, 1963).

Brain Cortex. The uptake and retention of K in respiring slices of rabbit brain cortex is inhibited by low concentrations of ouabain, half-maximal inhibition being produced by a concentration of about 0.4 μM. Ouabain exerted its effect when the slices were incubated in Ringer's solution containing glucose and when glutamate was also added. The K concentration (in mEq/kg dry wt) in control slices was 361 ± 29, and after incubation with 2.5 μM ouabain it fell (by 70%) to about 120. Pappius *et al.* (1958) had earlier shown that the maintenance of a high K content of brain slices depended on the presence of Na, and similarly the resting potentials recorded in brain slices by Hillman and McIlwain (1961) had a maximum value in Na-Ringer's but disappeared in Na-free Ringer's. It is therefore not unexpected that on stopping K uptake by the depletion of tissue Na and the replacement of Na of the medium with choline, the tissue K concentration falls to the same level as that found with ouabain inhibition in normal Na-Ringer's. Moreover, the addition of ouabain in Na-free medium had no effect on the tissue K concentration. In order to find out if this stoppage of active transport by ouabain and the removal of Na was accompanied by a fall in O_2 consumption, the Q_{O_2} was measured. The Q_{O_2} in a Ca-free, otherwise normal, Ringer's solution fell from 16.7 ± 0.7 to 8.0 ± 0.7 in the presence of 5 μM ouabain; in a Na-free medium, the Q_{O_2} was 9.4 ± 0.4 and was not further reduced by ouabain. The addition of ouabain to normal Ringer's solution and the replacement of Na in the medium with choline thus cause comparable falls in both tissue K concentration and rate of respiration, suggesting that reactions activated by Na and inhibited by ouabain control part of the cell's respiration.

The respiration of brain homogenates, therefore, was measured to see if the effects of Na and ouabain were still present after disruption of the cells. The results show that in a Na-rich medium the Q_{O_2} was 2.33–2.70 and was depressed about 40% to 1.40–1.69 in the presence of ouabain. Omission of

Na from the homogenate also caused the same 40% fall, and, as with slices, no further fall was caused by ouabain. There was some spread of results, but the value of the ratio, fall in Q_{O_2} with omission of Na from medium to fall in Q_{O_2} with ouabain in Na-rich medium, is close to unity. The values of 1.07 ± 0.14, 1.21 ± 0.27, and 1.02 ± 0.16 for homogenates made in KCl, choline chloride, and sucrose, respectively, show that the falls in Q_{O_2} caused by ouabain and by the deprivation of Na are of the same magnitude.

The above observations emphasize the importance of Na both for the maintenance of the respiration and for the K uptake of brain slices. Hertz and Schou (1962) have, moreover, found that Na in the medium is needed if brain slices are to make a respiratory response to K. Furthermore, in the absence of K, the Q_{O_2} was the same in both Na and choline (Na-free) media. No evidence was obtained that other ions could replace Na. Na appears to be unique in its ability to support the action of other alkali metals which stimulate respiration, such as K and Rb. It is an old observation of Dickens and Greville (1935) that the respiratory stimulation of brain slices by K has an obligatory requirement for Na in the medium, and an explanation is now possible in terms of the requirement for both Na and K of a membrane ATPase involved in active cation transfer which controls a part of the tissue respiration. These results with brain cortex slices and homogenates can, thus, be readily interpreted, if it is supposed that a fall in Q_{O_2} from an optimum level is due to a common cause. The omission of Na or K from the medium and the addition of ouabain cause a failure of active transport which is accompanied by a lowered activity of the membrane (transport) ATPase. It is, therefore, evident that the falls in the Q_{O_2} of slices result from the cessation of active Na and K transport. The similar falls in the Q_{O_2} of homogenates show that the mechanism which was sensitive to Na, K, and ouabain in slices remained sensitive after the cells were broken up. The obvious explanation is that the active transport system in the homogenate continues to act as an ATPase and thereby stimulates respiration by its generation of ADP.

Kidney Cortex. The effects of ouabain and Na on slices of rabbit kidney cortex are very similar to those on brain slices, but have been investigated somewhat more quantitatively by Whittam and Willis (1963) to establish the nature of the correlation between active K transport and respiration. The maintenance of the high K concentration in control slices incubated in normal Ringer's was inhibited by ouabain, and the Q_{O_2} fell, so that with maximum ouabain inhibition at 625 μM it was about 60% of the control. A partial inhibition of Q_{O_2} was produced by those lower concentrations which also had inhibitory effects on K uptake, so that the relative effects were precisely the same. No concentration of ouabain caused an effect on O_2 consumption without the same proportional effect on K uptake.

Incubation of slices in media in which Na was completely replaced with choline caused a failure of K uptake and a fall in Q_{O_2} which was not further affected by ouabain. The K concentration and Q_{O_2} were then essentially the same as those produced by full ouabain inhibition in normal Ringer's solution. As with brain slices, the failure of ouabain to inhibit the O_2 consumption in the absence of Na suggests that its effect in normal medium is mediated through an inhibition of active transport.

Frog Skeletal Muscle. Recent work with sartorius muscles also throws light on the nature of the energetic coupling. These muscles are able to extrude Na both aerobically and anaerobically, provided the energy barrier which has to be surmounted is not too great. Thus, no net efflux occurs when the external Na concentration is above a critical level (Conway, 1960). It is possible to initiate net Na extrusion simply by changing the external Na concentration, at a constant external K concentration (Conway et al., 1961). This finding has afforded a means of measuring the O_2 consumption associated with Na extrusion. Conway and Mullaney (1961) immersed muscles overnight to load them with Na, and then reimmersed them and measured the O_2 uptake at room temperature in saline media of composition either favorable or unfavorable for Na extrusion. The difference in composition of the media at room temperature was only 16 mM Na. The mean O_2 uptake of muscles not extruding Na was 10.5 ± 0.8, whereas a Na extrusion of 22.1 mEq/kg was associated with a mean uptake of 16.3 ± 1.0. The ratio of the Na excreted to O_2 uptake is therefore $22.1/(16.3 - 10.5) = 3.8$, which does not significantly differ from 4.0 (Conway et al., 1961). These results show that when Na transport is permitted, by lowering the energy barrier below the critical level, it is accompanied by an increased O_2 consumption. An important aspect of this discovery is that the increase in O_2 uptake occurred without a change in external K concentration, but merely by a reduction of the external Na concentration.

Stoichiometry of Ion Movements and O_2 Uptake

As Davies (1954) emphasized, a comparison of the number of ions transported per mole of O_2 is important because it may provide a clue to the mechanism of the linkage between energy liberation and utilization. In 1954, it was not possible to compare Na and K movements with the associated O_2 uptake; they could only be compared with the total O_2 uptake. The more recent results described above allow such a comparison to be made. The values in Table 1 are collected for a variety of conditions and tissues, and, without going into details, it can be seen that the K/O_2 ratio of about four for kidney slices is similar to the ratio for brain slices and to the Na/O_2 ratio for frog sciatic nerve and sartorius muscle. In contrast, the Na/O_2 ratio for transport across frog skin and toad bladder and for renal Na reabsorption *in situ* is considerably higher, being in the region of 20. Transcellular unidirectional ion movements across epithelia differ from multidirectional movements into and out of cells, but a ready explanation of the differences is not immediately obvious. It suffices to say that a ratio of more than four is inconsistent with the simple redox theory, whilst all the values are consistent with the ATP theory.

TABLE 1

UTILIZATION OF ENERGY FOR ACTIVE TRANSPORT OF NA AND K

| Organism | Tissue | Cation (equiv:mole O_2) | | Source |
		$K:O_2$	$Na:O_2$	
Dog	Kidney (*in situ*)	—	24	Kiil *et al.*, 1961.
Toad	Skin	—	22	Zerahn, 1961.
	Bladder	—	16.5	Leaf *et al.*, 1959.
Frog	Skin	—	16–20	Zerahn, 1956, 1961.
	Muscle	—	4	Conway and Mullaney, 1961; Conway *et al.*, 1961.
	Nerve	4–5	4–5	Connelly, 1959.
Rabbit	Brain cortex (slices)	6	—	Krebs *et al.*, 1951; Whittam, unpublished data.
	Kidney cortex (slices)	3–5	—	Whittam and Willis, 1963.
Guinea pig	Kidney cortex (slices)	5	—	Whittam and Davies, 1954a; Whittam, unpublished data.
	Seminal vesicle (slices)	2	—	Breuer and Whittam, 1957; Whittam and Breuer, 1959.
	Brain cortex (slices)	7.5	—	Cummins and McIlwain, 1961.

Rates of Na and K movements were determined by a variety of methods in different tissues. In all cases, the fraction of suprabasal O_2 consumption *associated with* the ion movement was used to calculate the cation:O_2 ratio.

General Comments

It was remarked by Quastel (1961) that "metabolic energy, possibly in the form of ATP, is required for active transport to take place. It is conceivable that the reverse process, i.e., the stimulation of respiratory activity by ionic movements at the nerve cell membrane, may occur by the initiation of a series of reactions, possibly involving the accumulation of ADP or phosphate ions which are now well known to play key roles in the regulation of respiratory and glycolytic processes." This admirably succinct statement aptly predicts what the results described above are held to demonstrate, i.e., a pacemaker effect of active transport on respiration. A qualification which must be made is that the hydrolysis of ATP by the membrane ATPase represents the over-all fission of ATP to ADP; but this does not exclude the possibility that a reaction coupled to ATP, such as an oxidation-reduction reaction, might be still more closely linked with transport. This possibility is rendered tenable by van Rossum's (1962) finding of 50% inhibition of cation transport in liver slices by oligomycin. It is suggested that an energy-rich intermediate of oxidative phosphorylation other than ATP can provide the energy for active cation transport and that in certain circumstances it may be synthesized from ATP by a reversal of the reactions of oxidative phosphorylation. The work of Chance (1961) especially directs attention to an energy-dependent reduction of DPN which may be concerned in active transport, as first suggested on theoretical grounds by Davies and Krebs (1952). It is, therefore, significant that oligomycin, an inhibitor of oxidative phosphorylation by an effect on an oxidation-reduction reaction, should be reported as inhibiting not only cation transport in liver, but also the (Na + K)-activated ATPase in human red blood cells (Glynn, 1962b; Van Groningen and Slater, 1963). The involvement of an oxidation-reduction reaction is in keeping with Kernan's (1962) finding that the energy for active transport in frog sartorius muscle comes from the activity of the enzyme, lactic dehydrogenase, which has DPN as a cofactor. The evidence for the pacemaker hypothesis of active cation transport on respiration is equally valid, however, whether a relatively simple ATP hydrolysis or whether an oxido-reduction reaction is implicated. Whatever the mechanism may be, there can be little doubt that active cation transport plays a vital role in the regulation of cellular respiration and that ATP is the main vehicle for the transformation of energy.

REFERENCES

Aldridge, W. N. 1962. *Biochem. J.* 83: 527.

Barcroft, H. 1934. *Features in the Architecture of Physiological Function.* London: Cambridge University Press. P. 286.

Bonting, S. L., and L. L. Caravaggio. 1962. *Nature* 194: 1180.

Bonting, S. L., K. A. Simon, and N. M. Hawkins. 1961. *Arch. Biochem. Biophys.* 95: 416.

Breuer, H., and R. Whittam. 1957. *J. Physiol. (London)* 135: 213.

Caldwell, P. C., A. L. Hodgkin, R. D. Keynes, and T. I. Shaw. 1960. *J. Physiol. (London)* 152: 561.

Chance, B. 1961. *J. Biol. Chem.* 236: 1569.

Chance, B., and L. Packer. 1958. *Biochem. J.* 68: 295.

Chance, B., and G. R. Williams. 1956. *Advan. Enzymol.* 17: 65.

Charnock, J. S., and R. L. Post. 1963. *Nature* 199: 910.

Connelly, C. M. 1959. In *Biophysical Science—A Study Program*, ed. J. L. Oncley. New York: John Wiley & Sons, Inc. P. 475.

Conway, E. J. 1957. *Physiol. Revs.* 37: 84.

Conway, E. J. 1960. *Nature* 187: 394.

Conway, E. J., and M. Mullaney. 1961. In *Membrane Transport and Metabolism*, ed. A. Kleinzeller and A. Kotyk. New York: Academic Press, Inc. P. 117.

Conway, E. J., R. P. Kernan, and J. A. Zadunaisky. 1961. *J. Physiol. (London)* 155: 263.

Cummins, J. T., and H. McIlwain. 1961. *Biochem. J.* 79: 330.

Davies, R. E. 1954. *Symp. Soc. Exptl. Biol.* 8: 453.

Davies, R. E., and H. A. Krebs. 1952. *Biochem. Soc. Symp. (Cambridge, Engl.)* 8: 77.

Dawes, G. S., J. C. Mott, H. J. Shelley, and A. Stafford. 1963. *J. Physiol. (London)* 168: 43.

Deul, D. H., and H. McIlwain. 1961. *J. Neurochem.* 8: 246.

Dickens, F., and G. D. Greville. 1935. *Biochem. J.* 29: 1468.

Dunham, E. T. 1957. *Federation Proc.* 16: 33.

Dunham, E. T., and I. M. Glynn. 1961. *J. Physiol. (London)* 156: 274.

Emmelot, P., and C. J. Bos. 1962. *Biochim. Biophys. Acta* 58: 375.

Gardos, G. 1954. *Acta Physiol. Acad. Sci. Hung.* 6: 191.

Glynn, I. M. 1962a. *J. Physiol. (London)* 160: 18 P.

Glynn, I. M. 1962b. *Biochem. J.* 84: 75 P.

Heald, P. J. 1962. *Nature* 193: 451.

Hertz, L., and M. Schou. 1962. *Biochem. J.* 85: 93.

Hillman, H. H., and H. McIlwain. 1961. *J. Physiol. (London)* 157: 263.

Hoffman, J. F. 1960. *Federation Proc.* 19: 127.

Hoffman, J. F., D. C. Tosteson, and R. Whittam. 1960. *Nature* 185: 186.

Hokin, L. E., and M. R. Hokin. 1961. *Nature* 149: 563.

Judah, J. D., K. Ahmed, and A. F. M. McLean. 1962. *Biochim. Biophys. Acta* 65: 472.

Kernan, R. P. 1962. *J. Physiol. (London)* 162: 129.

Kiil, F., K. Auckland, and H. Refsum. 1961. *Am. J. Physiol.* 201: 511.

Krebs, H. A., L. V. Eggleston, and C. Terner. 1951. *Biochem. J.* 48: 530.

Landon, E. J., and J. L. Norris. 1963. *Biochim. Biophys. Acta* 71: 266.

Laris, P. C., and P. E. Letchworth. 1962. *J. Cellular Comp. Physiol.* 60: 219.

Leaf, A. 1960. *J. Gen. Physiol.* 43, Suppl.: 175.

Leaf, A., and E. Dempsey. 1960. *J. Biol. Chem.* 235: 2160.

Leaf, A., and A. Renshaw. 1957. *Biochem. J.* 65: 82.

Leaf, A., L. B. Page, and J. Anderson. 1959. *J. Biol. Chem.* 234: 1625.

Lehninger, A. L. 1962. *Physiol. Revs.* 42: 467.

Maizels, M., M. Remington, and R. Truscoe. 1958. *J. Physiol. (London)* 140: 80.

McIlwain, H. 1961. *Ann. Rept. Progr. Chem. (Chem. Soc. London)* 57: 367.

Packer, L. 1960. *J. Biol. Chem.* 235: 242.

Pappius, H. M., M. Rosenfeld, D. M. Johnson, and K. A. C. Elliott. 1958. *Can. J. Biochem. Physiol.* 36: 217.

Post, R. L., C. R. Merritt, C. R. Kinsolving, and C. D. Albright. 1960. *J. Biol. Chem.* 235: 1796.

Quastel, J. D. 1961. In *Membrane Transport and Metabolism*, ed. A. Kleinzeller and A. Kotyk. New York: Academic Press, Inc. P. 519.

Schwarz, A., H. S. Bachelard, and H. McIlwain. 1962. *Biochem. J.* 84: 626.

Shapot, V. S. 1957. In *Metabolism of the Nervous System*, ed. D. Richter. New York: Pergamon Press. P. 275.

Skou, J. C. 1957. *Biochim. Biophys. Acta* 23: 394.

Skou, J. C. 1962. *Biochim. Biophys. Acta* 58: 314.

Tosteson, D. C., and J. S. Robertson. 1956. *J. Cellular Comp. Physiol.* 47: 147.

Ussing, H. H. 1960. *J. Gen. Physiol.* 43, Suppl.: 135.

Van Groningen, H. E. M., and E. C. Slater. 1963. *Biochim. Biophys. Acta* 73: 527.

van Rossum, G. D. V. 1961. *Biochim. Biophys. Acta* 54: 403.

van Rossum, G. D. V. 1962. *Biochem. J.* 84: 35 P.

Wheeler, K. P., and R. Whittam. 1962. *Biochem. J.* 85: 495.

Whittam, R. 1958. *J. Physiol. (London)* 140: 479.

Whittam, R. 1960. *J. Physiol. (London)* 153: 358.

Whittam, R. 1961a. *Ann. Rept. Progr. Chem.* (*Chem. Soc. London*) 57: 379.

Whittam, R. 1961b. *Biochim. Biophys. Acta* 54: 574.

Whittam, R. 1961c. *Nature* 191: 603.

Whittam, R. 1962a. *Biochem. J.* 84: 110.

Whittam, R. 1962b. *Biochem. J.* 82: 205.

Whittam, R. 1962c. *Nature* 196: 134.

Whittam, R., and H. Breuer. 1959. *Biochem. J.* 72: 638.

Whittam, R., and R. E. Davies. 1954a. *Biochem. J.* 56: 445.

Whittam, R., and R. E. Davies. 1954b. *Nature* 173: 494.

Whittam, R., and K. P. Wheeler. 1961. *Biochim. Biophys. Acta* 51: 622.

Whittam, R., and J. S. Willis. 1963. *J. Physiol.* (*London*) 168: 158.

Zerahn, K. 1956. *Acta Physiol. Scand.* 36: 300.

Zerahn, K. 1961. In *Membrane Transport and Metabolism*, ed. A. Kleinzeller and A. Kotyk. New York: Academic Press, Inc. P. 237.

The Place of Permeases
in Cellular Organization

Adam Kepes

Institut Pasteur
Paris, France

Permeases have been described by Cohen and Monod (1957) as functionally specialized permeation systems with a high degree of stereospecificity toward the transported substrate. The main role in the system is attributed to a specific protein with catalytic activity.

Subsequently, a large number of permeases have been identified in *Escherichia coli* and in other organisms. Even more have been postulated on more or less indirect evidence, and this multiplication has provoked some justified criticisms. Although very few systems have been recognized where the uptake of a hydrophilic molecule into a cell is performed by a mechanism clearly distinct from the permease mechanism, it has to be kept in mind that uptake can be due also to 1) a mechanism of free diffusion; 2) a carrier mechanism of low stereospecificity which could possibly perform either a passive facilitated diffusion or an active transport if an energy-driven, enzyme-catalyzed mechanism realizes a gradient of free carrier across the membrane; 3) a mechanism which includes chemical change in the substrate prior to transport due to surface or exoenzymes; and 4) a mechanism where transport and chemical change in the substrate are performed simultaneously by an oriented group-transfer enzyme.

The progress made in discovering more permeases has not been paralleled by progress in answering questions about the molecular mechanism underlying transport and questions about how permeases contribute to cellular regulations and how they are regulated in turn.

The present paper intends to summarize our knowledge on this last question.

First, a short summary of the kinetics of β-galactoside permease serves as introduction to the study of the coupling of transport with the energy-generating mechanisms of the cell. Then, the regulatory role and the selective advantage provided by constitutive or inducible synthesis of permeases will be discussed. Next, evidence of more than one permease for the uptake of certain amino acids will be reviewed. Finally, a system suggesting feedback inhibition on a permease will be described.

Description of a Permease

β-Galactoside permease is the transport system for β-galactosides in *E. coli*. Its physiological role can be assessed by the following observations.

1. The presence of permease is indispensable together with β-galactosidase in order to permit the growth of bacteria on lactose as sole source of carbon. Strains equipped with β-galactosidase but devoid of permease represent an important class of *Lac⁻* mutants called cryptic toward lactose.
2. The rate of hydrolysis of ortho-nitro-phenylgalactoside (ONPG), the chromogenic substrate of β-galactosidase in intact cells, is determined by the permease. Permeaseless strains hydrolyze some 50 times slower than do permease-positives. The rate of hydrolysis with both strains becomes maximal only after toluene treatment, which destroys the permeation barrier in the cell membrane.
3. Permease-positive cells accumulate nonmetabolizable β-galactosides, namely, thiogalactosides, until the intracellular concentration exceeds the concentration in the medium several hundred times. Lactose and ONPG can be accumulated only by β-galactosidase-negative cells. Calculations show that the uptake is rate-limiting in lactose utilization.
4. In inducible strains, the effect of small concentrations of inducer is multiplied by its accumulation; therefore, permease-positive cells can be induced by much lower concentrations of thiogalactosides than can permease-negatives.

The kinetics of galactoside permease in accumulating radioactive thiogalactosides have been described by Kepes (1960). The rate of the uptake against a concentration gradient can be described by the Henri-Michaelis equation, and the exit process, thermodynamically passive, follows first-order kinetics. These two processes are independent and cancel each other in the steady state of accumulation. The maximal level of accumulation varies from one substrate to the other, and, using the same substrate, it varies with the temperature, since the temperature dependencies of the two processes are unequal. The independence of the two processes is further substantiated by the fact that the rate of uptake is equal to the rate of exchange in preloaded cells, i.e., is independent of intracellular concentration which governs exit.

Galactoside permease resides on the cell membrane, since it is sensitive only to extracellular substrate concentration and since it is not linked to the cell wall. Lysozyme spheroplasts with most of the cell wall material digested away still are able to concentrate thiogalactosides. Spheroplasts provide also the most direct proof that accumulation via permease really represents active transport against a gradient of activity. The accumulated substrate contributes fully to the intracellular osmotic pressure, as detected by the increased rate of osmotic lysis of spheroplasts when a thiogalactoside is added to the medium. No such increase is observed if the spheroplasts derive from a permeaseless strain (Sistrom, 1958).

Coupling of Transport and Energy Metabolism

Since active transport means thermodynamic work of concentration, the process must be coupled with metabolic reactions yielding at least the equivalent amount of energy. If there is a simple chemical coupling, the splitting of a high-energy bond linked to transport must continue even after a steady pool has been reached, since the rate of uptake remains unchanged. Whether some of the high-energy bonds can be reconstructed by harnessing the energy dissipated by the passive exit is rather doubtful.

The process of concentration is completely inhibited by 2×10^{-2} M Na azide or by 10^{-3} M 2,4-dinitrophenol (DNP). If these reagents are added to preloaded cells, the galactoside leaks out with a slightly increased exit constant (Koch, in press). Thus, the leakage cannot provide a significant part of the energy necessary for the uptake.

The same conclusion can be reached by the measurement of the O_2 consumption associated with the active transport. With growing cells, the increase in O_2 consumption associated with the permease activity is too small to be measured accurately. The measurements have been made with the dropping mercury electrode in a suspension previously starved of its carbon and energy source. In these conditions, the endogenous respiration increases by a factor of two or three upon addition of a nonmetabolizable thiogalactoside, as shown in Fig. 1 (Kepes, 1957). Independent measurements show that the accumulation mechanism still works in these conditions to about 50% of its maximal rate. It seems that this process uses the remaining reserves of energy by priority. The concentration of thiogalactoside which gives half-maximal increase in O_2 uptake is roughly the same as the concentration which gives half-maximal accumulation. One atom of oxygen is taken up for approximately three molecules of thio-methylgalactoside (TMG) transported, and the increased O_2 uptake continues long after the steady-state pool has been built up. Thirty to forty minutes elapse before the O_2 uptake drops back to its control value, while two to three minutes are enough to build up the TMG concentration. This means that the exchange in the steady state of accumulation costs roughly the same amount of energy expenditure as the initial accumulation against a gradient of concentration.

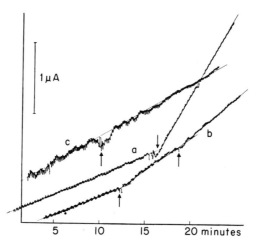

Fig. 1. O_2 consumption by a suspension of *E. coli* grown on mineral medium supplemented with maltose and starved for 45 min, measured by the dropping mercury electrode. Addition of TPG (*a*) and of TMG (*b*) causes an increase of O_2 uptake by galactoside permease-positive strain ML308. No change in the rate of O_2 uptake in permease-negative strain ML3 (*c*). (See Kepes, 1957.)

To ascertain that internal reserves provide the oxidizable substrate and not some unknown impurity added with the nonmetabolizable thiogalactoside, the experiment has been performed with bacteria completely labeled with C^{14} by growth on C^{14} fructose and subsequently washed and starved. Upon addition of a nonradioactive thiogalactoside, the radioactive CO_2 release increases in the same proportion as the O_2 uptake, thus showing that formerly incorporated cell material is oxidized in conjunction with permease activity (Fig. 2).

The immediate onset of O_2 consumption, its continuation through the steady state of accumulation, and its proportionality to rate of transport, all indicate that transport and energy consumption are very closely linked together. The signal of the addition of the substrate turns on the system as a whole. In the conditions of our experiment, there does not seem to be any sizable pool of the energy-rich compound, the direct donor for the active transport. A similar close connection is indicated by the priority relationship of transport for energy consumption. Such a priority appears as a selective advantage for the microorganism, since the transport is the rate-limiting step in lactose utilization. Lactose can theoretically provide 76 adenosine triphosphate (ATP) molecules when completely oxidized; thus it is worthwhile to set aside one molecule of ATP to pump lactose into the cell.

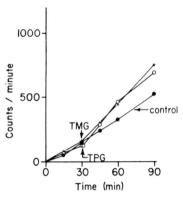

Fig. 2. Release of $C^{14}O_2$ by a starved suspension of *E. coli* grown on mineral medium with C^{14} fructose as carbon source and washed free from radioactive substrate. Additions: TMG, + — + TPG, O—O. Control: ●—●. (See Kepes, 1960.)

It is remarkable to note that in a bacterial cell both the permease and the respiratory chain reside in the protoplasmic membrane; there are no mitochondria in bacteria. This could, by itself, partly account for the close connection between transport and oxidative phosphorylation. But such a tight coupling is rather uncommon in the bacterial system, and, in fact, no other example of respiratory control has been reported in bacteria. Respiratory control (Hardy and Wellman, 1952) in phosphorylating systems is due to the absence of P acceptor, adenosine diphosphate (ADP), or sometimes to the absence of inorganic PO_4 which causes accumulation of an unknown intermediate of phosphorylation which exerts an inhibitory effect upon the respiratory chain itself. Usually, the addition of an uncoupling agent like DNP releases the inhibition by causing the energy-rich intermediate to break down as well as by supplementing the missing ADP. In bacteria, ADP does not penetrate through the membrane barrier and, unlike mitochondria, bacteria do not exhibit increased O_2 consumption upon addition of DNP or azide. Thus, it is very difficult to realize a situation where the action of permease parallels the action of ADP in releasing respiratory control. One possible way to look into this problem was to inquire whether a crossover point (Chance and Williams, 1956) can be detected in the respiratory chain. The method is based on the principle that if one step in the electron-transport chain, namely, one coupled with phosphorylation, is inhibited, the electron carriers on the hydrogen side become more reduced and those on the oxygen side more oxidized compared to their states during the normal flow of electrons. Upon release of the inhibition, some carriers become more oxidized, the others more reduced, the crossover point being the site of the inhibited step. In contrast, if respiration is limited by the hydrogen-donating substrate, all carriers are more oxidized than they are during optimal respiration, and if substrate is added back, all become more reduced. The opposite is true if O_2 is the limiting factor.

The respiratory chain in *E. coli* is not fully elucidated. Spectroscopically, the major component is a *b*-type cytochrome which, with reference to better known systems, can be supposed to be on the hydrogen side of two out of three possible phosphorylating steps. For the observation on crossover, attention had to be directed to the soret band, to which cytochrome *b* makes a predominant contribution, since the changes observed on the other, better characterized, absorption bands were too small to be measured.

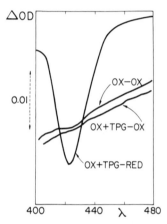

The experiment was done with the split-beam recording spectrophotometer of Yang and Legallais (1954). The test organism was *E. coli* ML 308, constitutive for galactoside permease. The carbon source for growth and during the experiment was K succinate, a strictly aerobic substrate. It has been observed that respiration on succinate can be increased by addition of a permease substrate at temperatures below 25°C. The permease substrate used was thio-phenylgalactoside (TPG), which causes the highest increase in O_2 uptake (Fig. 1). The results of the experiment are represented in Fig. 3. In spite of the skewed base line ($OX—OX$), this increased degree of oxidation of the soret band upon addition of TPG can be discerned. In this experiment, the oxidation goes from 78 % to 83 %. This increased oxidation is not observed with a permeaseless strain.

Fig. 3. Difference spectrum of an aerated suspension of *E. coli* in mineral medium supplemented with succinate. $OX - OX$: base line: $OX + TPG - OX$: decrease in absorbancy at 420 mμ upon addition of TPG; $OX + TPG - RED$: total of oxidized cytochromes in the experimental sample. Total cytochrome was measured as the RED $-$ OX difference spectrum in the same suspension starved from a carbon source.

In spite of our little knowledge about the exact sequence of the respiratory chain in *E. coli* and of our rather unspecific definition of the component which became more oxidized and in spite of the small extent of this effect, there is little doubt that a crossover actually took place, since succinate and O_2 were both saturating during the whole experiment. The main crossover point must lie somewhere between cytochrome *b* and O_2.

Under the same experimental conditions, a 15–25% decrease of the pool of ATP can be observed with a concomitant increase of the pool of ADP (Kepes, unpublished). The new steady-state level of the ATP pool is reached in less than 1 min after the addition of the thiogalactoside.

These observations do not solve the problem of the direct energy donor for transport via permease. It is clear that the transport is performed at the expense of ATP energy, but the direct donor might be as well ATP itself rather than another molecule which derives its energy from ATP or even a molecule which is the precursor of ATP on the pathway of oxidative phosphorylation. On a purely speculative basis, the last choice would explain the sort of priority given to permease in energy utilization and the respiratory control which could not be released in bacteria by means other than permease activity. The high-energy precursors of ATP are probably never released from the structural unit in which they are generated, namely from the cytochrome chain localized in the protoplasmic membrane. If they can release their energy for the use of permease without passing through the ATP stage, this would be consistent with all the known facts.

Inducible or Constitutive Synthesis of Permeases

The energy spent on transport is ultimately lost as heat during the leakage of the accumulated pool. As different sugar permeases function independently from each other, each one being able to supply its substrate at a rate sufficient to support growth if it were alone, such an arrangement would cause waste of energy. This explains the selective advantage of having inducible sugar permeases instead of constitutive ones. To allow one duplication of the cells per hour, a main carbon source has to be taken up at a rate of about 3% of the dry weight of the cells per minute, since only one-third of its carbon is incorporated into stable cell constituents, the remainder being partly oxidized to CO_2 and partly excreted as waste products.

As the number of potential carbon sources includes hexoses, pentoses, disaccharides, organic acids, and unexpected compounds such as camphor derivatives, the permanent synthesis and incidental functioning of a great number of permeases of high rate of flow could not be afforded by a bacterium.

Except for glucose permease, all sugar permeases are inducible in *E. coli*. This holds for galactoside permease, glucuronide permease (Stoeber, 1957), maltose permease (Wiesmeyer and Cohn, 1960), and also for galactose permease. This last one, first described by Horecker *et al.* (1960) in a galactokinaseless mutant, was found to be synthesized constitutively. Jordan *et al.* (1962) observed that such mutants synthesize the two other galactose-metabolizing enzymes, uridine diphosphate galactose transferase and epimerase, at nearly the fully induced level. This is attributed to the synthesis by these cells of some internal inducer, since they are able to convert glucose derivatives into galactose derivatives. The internal induction is not observed with epimerase-negative strains. In a mutant unable to synthesize all three galactose enzymes, the galactose permease has been found to be inducible (Buttin and Kepes, unpublished).

In contrast to permeases for sugars and other growth substrates, amino acid permeases are constitutively present in bacteria. So long as an amino acid is used only for incorporation into protein (an average amino acid representing roughly 1/20 of the protein carbon, or 1/40 of the total carbon of the cell), the yield of incorporation can be 100%. The maximum rate of flow in terms of carbon atoms is some 120 times lower than that of a primary carbon source. Moreover, since the number of natural amino acids is definitely limited to 20, and since they are transported by some 12 different permeases, if we assume an efficiency of the same order of magnitude as that of the sugar permeases, the synthesis of the whole amino acid permease equipment is less expensive than the synthesis of one single sugar permease. When the growth medium contains a particular amino acid, the biosynthetic enzymes involved in its synthesis cease to be produced, due to repressive regulation. To trigger this regulatory mechanism with a low concentration of exogenous amino acid, its permease must be present.

These considerations explain the selective advantage for bacteria to have inducible sugar permeases, but constitutive amino acid permeases.

Multiplicity of Transport Systems

The picture in which amino acids are required only for incorporation into protein is oversimplified. Amino acids can also be converted to each other, and some of them can also serve as carbon or nitrogen sources.

How the system for uptake can be adapted to such cases is not yet entirely clear. The basis for our ignorance stems directly from the technical difficulties which attend the measurement of the uptake of those amino acids which are readily metabolized as well as incorporated into protein. That part of the isotopically labeled pool which remains as unchanged amino acid should be established in each case by chromatographic techniques; but these are tedious, so it is difficult to collect a large amount of kinetic data. Measurement of the size of the amino acid pool by chasing it out with an excess of unlabeled compound was expected to give an answer. But in the case of alanine uptake in *E. coli*, it has been found that many of the derivatives of the labeled alanine and only a small part if any of the native alanine were displaced in such experiments. In most cases, only initial velocities of uptake, restricted to the first minute, have an unequivocal meaning.

Nevertheless, recent results tend to indicate that the uptake of metabolizable amino acids and possibly of some of the nonmetabolizable ones is performed by more than one system.

The first case of a dual system was suggested by the results of Britten and McClure (1962) on the accumulation of proline by *E. coli*. The curve of concentration dependence of proline accumulation exhibits two regions, one of high affinity and low capacity and another of lower affinity and high capacity.

A similar duality, detected so far only kinetically, has been observed in the uptake of isoleucine, threonine, serine, and alanine by *E. coli*, but the difference in the role and specificity of the high and low affinity portions is not yet clear (J. P. Veillat and M. Vallee, unpublished results).

The study of histidine uptake by *Salmonella typhimurium* (Ames, in press) led to more significant results. When the accumulation of this amino acid is observed under conditions of carbon starvation, the concentration dependence of the initial velocity of uptake, as represented in Lineweaver-Burk plots, results in a broken line. One uptake process has a K_m of 1.7×10^{-7} M and the second a K_m of 1.1×10^{-4} M. The maximal rate of uptake of this second process exceeds that of the first by a factor of about five. All of the other amino acids have been tried as competitors, and none of them affects histidine uptake in the range of the low concentrations; but, in contrast, the mechanism with low affinity and high flow rate is completely inhibited by relatively low concentrations of tryptophane, phenylalanine, or tyrosine. This part represents an aromatic group-specific permease which can be identified genetically.

Mutants resistant to azaserine have been selected, and among them one proved to be devoid of the aromatic permease responsible also for the uptake of azaserine. This mutant still possesses all the permeases specific for individual amino acids.

During histidine uptake by growing cells, a very small pool is built up within the first minute, and then the histidine appears entirely in a form precipitable by trichloroacetic acid (TCA). The incorporation rate is very similar to the accumulation rate in the carbon-starved cells. But, in these conditions, the portion of the uptake mechanism with high flow rate and low affinity cannot be detected, since the protein-synthesizing capacity is saturated before the histidine concentration reaches the corresponding range. The limiting concentration of histidine determined in this way corresponds to a two-third saturation of the specific histidine permease.

It has to be stressed that *S. typhimurium* also possesses specific permeases for tryptophane, phenylalanine, and tyrosine, so that incorporation of these amino acids into protein is not solely dependent upon the aromatic group-specific permease.

It happens that the strain of *Salmonella* used in these studies does not metabolize histidine otherwise than to incorporate it into protein. It does not metabolize aromatic amino acids which are substrates of the aromatic permease. Nevertheless, it is known that other strains of *Salmonella* can degrade histidine; *E. coli* uses the aromatic amino acids in transamination, and it degrades tryptophane by an inducible tryptophanase. Thus, if the aromatic permease has no physiological significance in the particular strain, it is certainly used by other members of the genus for supplying metabolizable amino acids at a high rate.

If this mechanism is the solution generally adopted by microorganisms, it can be expected for teleological reasons that permeases with high flow rates should be inducible. This might be the case for the inducible tryptophane permease described by Boezi and DeMoss (1961) in a tryptophanaseless mutant of *E. coli*. Wild-type *E. coli* has been found to possess a constitutive permease for tryptophane (Veillat, unpublished observations) which could be the specific tryptophane permease designed to satisfy the needs for incorporation, the inducible permease being necessary only for metabolism.

It can be expected that further dual uptake systems will be discovered in the near future. Then, a more complete picture can be outlined, describing how bacteria are equipped to deal with metabolic needs at the permease level, similar to the way dual enzymes (which differ only with respect to their regulation, repression, or feedback inhibition) deal with the same problem at the biosynthetic level.

Feedback Inhibition

Feedback inhibition is a fairly widespread phenomenon in bacteria. Usually, the end product of a biosynthetic or metabolic chain exerts an inhibitory effect on the first enzyme of the series. As the final product has usually a steric configuration quite different from the substrate of the inhibited enzyme, the effect is said to be an allosteric one. Allosteric inhibitions can exhibit competitive or noncompetitive patterns.

As permeases are usually the very first enzymes in a metabolic pathway, the question can be asked whether they can exhibit allosteric effects.

Of course, many of these effects could go unnoticed, since permease cannot be tested *in vitro*. *In vivo*, in cases where some metabolic product induces a change in an uptake mechanism, the actual intracellular effector could be difficult to identify and its concentration would be difficult to control.

Several permeases have been reported to be partly inhibited by glucose. Uptake of galactosides is unaffected, but their exit rate is stimulated by glucose, and this causes a decrease in the pool size. Histidine permease is strongly inhibited by glucose. Proline pool size is reduced 35% because of decreases in the rate of uptake. In all these cases, the question remains open whether glucose acts by competition for the permease, by competition for a carrier involved in entry or in exit, by competition for the energy donor involved in permease function, or because one of its metabolic products is an allosteric inhibitor.

Recently, Englesberg (1961) described a glucose permease in *S. typhimurium* and studied its kinetics with the nonmetabolizable analog, α-methylglucoside (α-MG). This permease is in many respects similar to other permeases. For instance, it is very similar to the galactoside permease in its substrate specificity, the maximal concentration ratio which can be achieved, the rapid attainment of a steady state and the complete reversibility of the accumulation, and the Michaelis-type concentration dependence. But this permease exhibits a striking feature. Upon addition of an uncoupling agent like Na azide or DNP, the pool of α-MG increases instead of decreasing.

Later, Hoffee and Englesberg (1962) described an impressive body of evidence showing that the increased pool size was provoked by a decrease in ATP production. In bacteria starved in carbon and energy source, large pools of α-MG were observed, and the addition of the carbon source used for the growth caused a decrease in pool size. Only a compound metabolized rapidly could cause this change, irrespective of its structural analogy with glucose. In the presence of a carbon source, anaerobiosis caused the pool size to increase, and O_2 caused it to decrease again (Fig. 4).

With carefully selected concentrations of the metabolic inhibitors, the pool size was increased seven- to ninefold. Carbon starvation or anaerobiosis seemed to increase the pool size to about the same limit. The opposite effect would be expected, for osmotic work must be performed at the expense of metabolic energy.

It was shown, indeed, by Hoffee and Englesberg (1962) that higher concentrations of azide or DNP ultimately inhibited the uptake and also that carbon starvation combined with anaerobiosis decreased the pool size instead of increasing it further. Therefore, it was clear that the uptake of α-MG against a gradient of concentration depends on some metabolic energy; but the question could be asked whether this energy was furnished by a compound other than ATP or as ATP, but at concentrations well below those obtained during optimal growth.

A pool accumulated via the permease can be increased in two ways. One is by the increase of the rate of uptake, the second is by decreasing the rate of exit.

Hoffee *et al.* (1964) showed a decrease in the rate of exit when uncoupling poisons, carbon starvation, or anaerobiosis cause an increase of the α-MG pool.

Nevertheless, a careful examination of their data shows that this can explain only part of the observed facts.

Particularly interesting here is the concentration dependence of the α-MG pool with and without a carbon source (Fig. 5). At a saturating concentration of α-MG, the pool is increased by 50%, due to starvation. In contrast, the half-saturating concentration of α-MG in the presence of an energy source is some five times higher than in its absence. Thus the relation of pool size *vs.* concentration of α-MG in bacteria with the energy source present behaves,

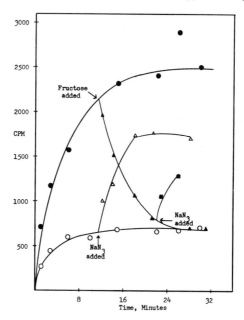

Fig. 4. Accumulation of α-MG by *S. typhimurium* in the presence and absence of an oxidizable substrate. ●—● indicates accumulation without a carbon and energy source. At the first arrow (11 min), fructose (final concentration, 0.1%) was added to a portion of the reaction mixture, ▲—▲; at the second arrow (22 min), azide was added to the portion of cells containing fructose, ■—■. The control mixture, ○—○, had fructose (final concentration, 0.1%) present at zero time. At the arrow (11 min), azide was added, △—△. 25°C. (From Hoffee and Englesberg, 1962, *Proc. Natl. Acad. Sci.* 48: 1759.)

compared to starved organisms, as if inhibited 33% by a noncompetitive agent; together with a competitive inhibitor to such an extent that the apparent K_m increases fivefold. So in the region above the K_m of the starved but below that of the fed bacteria, a concentration of α-MG can be found where the pool sizes differ by a factor of 7.5. This concentration lies between

2×10^{-5} M and 4×10^{-5} M. Most of the experiments of increased pool size, namely, those of Fig. 4, have been done at concentrations of 4×10^{-5} M α-MG.

Similar results have been reported by Kessler and Rickenberg (1963) on the α-MG permease of *E. coli*. The presence of an energy source, glycerol or fructose, causes a competitive type of inhibition on α-MG accumulation. The apparent K_m is increased by a factor of two, as compared to the starved state. They could not observe an effect of uncoupling poisons similar to those shown by Englesberg in *S. typhimurium*.

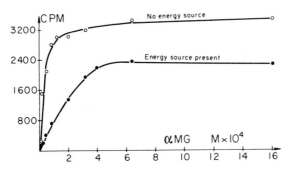

Fig. 5. Effect of increasing external concentration of α-MG on the accumulation of α-MG in *S. typhimurium* $(C^- dg^s)$. (From Hoffee *et al.*, 1964, *Biochim. Biophys. Acta* 79: 343.)

Combining all these observations, it can be definitely stated that optimal ATP production by *S. typhimurium* and *E. coli competitively inhibits α-MG uptake*, besides causing an accelerated exit. More specifically, *an intracellularly generated high-energy compound decreases the apparent affinity of glucose permease for extracellular substrate*. It is very unlikely that the intracellular agent is endogenous glucose or some analog of it. To produce the observed effect, the glucose pool should be much greater than ever observed with any sugar. Furthermore, there is no reason to suppose that intracellular substrate can compete with extracellular substrate. This is definitely not so in the well-studied cases of galactoside permease, proline permease, and valine-leucine-isoleucine permease of *E. coli*. No kinetic peculiarities in α-MG permease give a hint that it would be different in this respect from other permeases. But even if a glucose pool were built up, and even if it could compete with external α-MG, the pattern of inhibition would be expected to be different.

It is much simpler and ultimately much more reasonable to suppose that ATP or some close derivative of it in the pathway of energy transfer is the actual intracellular agent which causes the competitive inhibition. Of course, in this hypothesis, the competitive inhibitor would not bind to the active site of permease, which is oriented outward, but, more likely, to a different site on the inner face of the membrane.

As ATP can be considered to be one of the most important end products of glucose metabolism, the hypothesis of inhibition by the end product is in line with many recent findings in metabolic regulation. Moreover, ATP has no steric analogy with glucose, and in this hypothesis, it must act on a site of the permease protein opposite to the substrate-binding site; therefore, this system would be an excellent illustration of allosteric inhibition, where the effect is mediated across the protein molecule.

It must be realized that the hypothesis is not readily amenable to direct experimental proof, until the permease mechanism in general yields its secret. But it must be admitted that this hypothetical mechanism would provide an obvious and large selective advantage to the microorganism which had acquired it. There is no need to stress that in case of starvation or in case of anaerobiosis, the microorganism profits greatly from its ability to use very dilute glucose with high efficiency, whereas in optimal conditions, it benefits by not accumulating more glucose than it needs.

In spite of the considerable gaps in our knowledge on the physiological integration of permeases, the demonstrated facts and those not quite demonstrated which are reviewed in the above pages show sufficiently that permeases participate in metabolic regulations and are regulated much the same way as are other enzymes. One possibility is special for permeases and some other enzymes fixed on a structural unit, the membrane, which allows them to interact by virtue of their vicinity. In other words, their microscopical—as opposed to molecular—structure is the reason for their functional integration. Besides this, permeases are susceptible to repressive regulation, duality of permeases is probably a factor of better adaptability of the organism to highly variable environmental conditions, and permeases can probably be regulated by allosteric effectors to provide fine and immediate adjustment.

REFERENCES

Ames, G. FerroLuzzi. *Arch. Biochem. Biophys.* In press.

Boezi, J. A., and R. D. DeMoss. 1961. *Biochim. Biophys. Acta* 49: 476.

Britten, R. J., and F. T. McClure. 1962. *Bacteriol. Rev.* 26: 292.

Chance, B., and G. R. Williams. 1956. *Advan. Enzymol.* 17: 65.

Cohen, G. N., and J. Monod. 1957. *Bacteriol. Rev.* 21: 169.

Englesberg, E. 1961. *Cold Spring Harbor Symp. Quant. Biol.* 26: 261.

Hoffee, P., and E. Englesberg. 1962. *Proc. Natl. Acad. Sci. U.S.* 48: 1759.

Hoffee, P., E. Englesberg, and F. Lamy. 1964. *Biochim. Biophys. Acta* 79: 343.

Horecker, B. L., J. Thomas, and J. Monod. 1960. *J. Biol. Chem.* 235: 1580.

Jordan, E., M. B. Yarmolinsky, and H. M. Kalckar. 1962. *Proc. Natl. Acad. Sci. U.S.* 48: 32.

Kepes, A. 1957. *Compt. Rend.* 244: 1550.

Kepes, A. 1960. *Biochim. Biophys. Acta* 40: 70.

Kessler, D. P., and H. V. Rickenberg. 1963. *Biochem. Biophys. Res. Commun.* 10: 482.

Koch, A. L. *Biochim. Biophys. Acta.* In press.

Lardy, H., and H. Wellman. 1952. *J. Biol. Chem.* 195: 215.

Sistrom, W. R. 1958. *Biochim. Biophys. Acta* 29: 579.

Stoeber, F. 1957. *Compt. Rend.* 244: 1091.

Wiesmeyer, H., and M. Cohn. 1960. *Biochim. Biophys. Acta* 39: 440.

Yang, C. C., and V. Legallais. 1954. *Rev. Sci. Instr.* 25: 801.

The Role of an Alpha-Methylglucoside Permease in the Inducted Synthesis of Isomaltase in Yeast[1]

H. O. Halvorson, H. Okada,[2] and J. Gorman[3]

Department of Bacteriology
University of Wisconsin
Madison, Wisconsin

It is now clear that microorganisms contain a number of stereospecific permeation systems (or permeases) for the uptake of organic nutrients. Although these systems have not been isolated and characterized, the available evidence suggests that they involve specific proteins. The permeation systems provide regulatory mechanisms for the utilization of substrates and for growth, enzyme induction, repression, and feedback inhibition of enzyme activity. For example, in *Escherichia coli*, a β-galactoside permease is the rate-limiting step in lactose utilization (Cohen and Monod, 1957). The induced synthesis of the lactose-hydrolyzing enzyme, β-galactosidase, parallels the induction of the permease. In low concentrations of inducer, the rate of β-galactosidase induction is dependent upon the inducer concentrated by the

[1] This work was aided in part by research grants from the National Institutes of Health (E-1459 and 2G-686) and by a grant from The Red Star Yeast Company.

[2] Present address, Department of Fermentation Technology, Faculty of Engineering, Osaka University, Osaka, Japan.

[3] Present address, Lab. Physiol. Genetique, Gif sur Yvette, France.

inducible permease. The net result is an autocatalytic type of kinetics and an all-or-none response to induction by individual cells in a population (Novick and Weiner, 1957). At high concentrations of inducer, entry of inducer by free diffusion is sufficient to provide immediate and maximal induction of β-galactosidase.

Autocatalytic kinetics of induction have commonly been observed in yeast. It was therefore of interest to examine the possibility that these were reflections of an inducible permeation system rather than of the regulatory system for enzyme synthesis. Yeasts have one advantage for this study in that the membrane exerts a rigid control over permeability of sugars. There is no free diffusion of sugars; the impermeability of cell membrane to nonfermentable sugars is one of the characteristics of the yeast cell (Cirillo, 1961). One would therefore expect that if permeases controlled the rate of enzyme induction, such a relationship should be rigorously demonstrable in yeast.

In selecting a suitable test system in yeast, it is essential that the function of the permeation system be distinguished from the enzymes involved in substrate metabolism within the cell. This criterion can be achieved if the substrate of the permeation system is found unchanged inside the cell. Although a number of permeation systems have been suggested in yeast (Cirillo, 1961), in only one case has it been possible to study the phenomenon under strict conditions of gratuity. In the present paper, an examination will be made of the permeation system for α-ethyl-thioglucoside (α-TEG), a gratuitous inducer of isomaltase. The natural substrates for both the permeation system and isomaltase are isomaltose and α-methylglucoside (α-MG).

Genetic Control of Facilitated Diffusion

Hawthorne (1958) reported that the fermentation of α-MG by *Saccharomyces cerevisiae* is controlled by the complementary gene pairs MG_1MG_2, MG_2MG_3, or MG_4MA_1. *MG* and *MA* are genes for α-MG and maltose fermentation, respectively. This finding was confirmed by Terui *et al.* (1959), who found the complementary gene pairs XY_1 and XY_2 for α-MG fermentation in another strain of *S. cerevisiae*. The genes Y_1 and Y_2 were found to control the production of isomaltase, and the X gene was postulated to control α-MG uptake.

The uptake of S^{35} α-TEG by glucose-grown cells, dominant and recessive for the MG_2 gene, is shown in Fig. 1. In the MG_2 strain (5002-5C), two α-TEG pools are observed. One is filled at 0°C and is completely lost on washing, whereas the second occurs at 30°C and is retained upon removal of α-TEG. The first α-TEG pool is the only one observed in the mg_2 recessive strain (5001-2B).

The uptake of α-TEG at 30°C into the two pools of glucose-grown cells

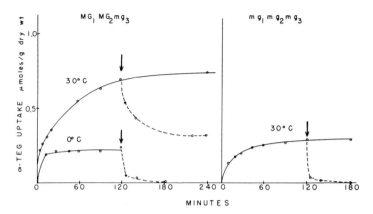

Fig. 1. Time-course of S^{35} α-TEG uptake. Glucose-grown cells of 5002-5C ($MG_1MG_2mg_3$) and 5001-2B ($mg_1mg_2mg_3$) were suspended in acetate medium containing 10^{-3}M S^{35} α-TEG and incubated at either 30°C or 0°C. At 120 min, each culture was divided, and one portion was filtered, washed, and resuspended in α-TEG-free acetate medium.

of various genotypes is summarized in Table 1. The maximum level of α-TEG taken up by MG_2 dominant strains was 0.6–0.9 μmole/g dry yeast, of which 0.3–0.4 μmole/g dry wt remained following removal of α-TEG. In mg_2 recessive strains, 0.3–0.4 mole/g dry yeast was taken up, and all of this was lost during incubation in the absence of α-TEG.

The reversible permeation of 10^{-3} M α-TEG into the 0°C pool, 0.3–0.4 μmole/g dry wt, was therefore in close agreement with that expected for diffusion into the cell-wall volume (0.3 ml/g dry wt). It is thus clear that, of

TABLE 1

UPTAKE OF 10^{-3} M S^{35} α-TEG AT 30°C BY GLUCOSE-GROWN CELLS
OF VARIOUS GENOTYPES

(Data from Okada and Halvorson, 1964a.)

Strain	Genotype	α-TEG μmole/g dry wt		Cytoplasmic concentration of α-TEG M $\times$ 10^3
		Total	Non-washable	
5002–5C	$MG_1MG_2mg_3$	0.83	0.56	0.27
5001–1B	$mg_1MG_2MG_3$	0.91	0.47	0.22
5001–2B	$mg_1mg_2mg_3$	0.35	0.03	0.01
5001–2C	$mg_1MG_2mg_3$	0.65	0.39	0.19
5001–5A	$mg_1MG_2mg_3$	0.72	0.45	0.21
5002–1B	$MG_1mg_2mg_3$	0.29	0.01	0.00
5001–5D	$mg_1mg_2MG_3$	0.31	0.04	0.02

the two α-TEG pools, one involves α-TEG entry into the cell wall and the second *actual* permeation into the cytoplasm of the cell. The penetration of α-TEG into the cytoplasmic volume is specific, as indicated by the fact that mutation in a specific locus on the chromosome led to loss of α-TEG permeation. MG_2 strains are permeable to α-TEG, but mg_2 strains are impermeable to it. The MG_2 gene can, therefore, be considered to control the specific protein for α-TEG transport.

The rate of α-TEG uptake in glucose-grown cells carrying the MG_2 gene shows a substrate dependence characteristic of an adsorption isotherm. A reciprocal plot of uptake rate *vs.* the α-TEG concentration (Fig. 2A) shows

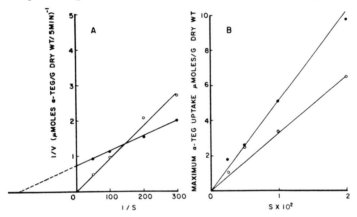

Fig. 2. Effect of external concentration on the initial rate and maximal uptake of α-TEG into glucose-grown cells of 5002-5C ($MG_1MG_2mg_3$). The rate of α-TEG uptake (5 min) and the maximal uptake (120 min) were measured in both the 0°C pool ($\bigcirc$) and the cytoplasmic pool ($\bullet$) (total uptake minus 0°C-pool uptake). (Data from Okada and Halvorson, 1964a.)

that the apparent Michaelis-Menten constant (K_m) for the rate of α-TEG entry into the 0°C pool was infinite, while for entry into the cytoplasmic volume it was 0.05 M. The entry into the 0°C pool was that expected of a simple diffusion process. At equilibrium, the α-TEG concentration in both pools is directly proportioned to the external concentration (Fig. 2B) and in neither case exceeds the external concentration. Thus, α-TEG was not transported against a concentration gradient in glucose-grown cells.

The uptake of α-TEG is energy-independent. In the presence of 10^{-2} M Na azide or 4×10^{-4} M 2,4-dinitrophenol (DNP), the initial rates of α-TEG uptake into the cytoplasmic pool were 93% and 97% of the control rates, respectively.

The entry of α-TEG into glucose-grown cells, therefore, appears to proceed by a process of facilitated diffusion (Stein and Danielli, 1956), rather than by simple diffusion. Not only do the kinetics of entry not fit a simple diffusion model (Fig. 2), but they also show other properties of enzyme reactions, such as competition between similar solutes and a high degree of specificity. For example, both glucose and α-MG competitively inhibit the rate of α-TEG uptake, as well as displace α-TEG from cells.

Induction of an Active-Transport System

When α-TEG-permeable cells (MG_2) are grown in the presence of α-MG or α-TEG, an active-transport system for α-TEG uptake is induced. This induction is shown in Table 2. At equilibrium, the induced cells can accumu-

TABLE 2

CONCENTRATION OF 10^{-3} M S^{35} α-TEG BY INDUCED CELLS
OF VARIOUS GENOTYPES

Cells were induced by growth in nutrient.
(Data from Okada and Halvorson, 1964a.)

Strain	Genotype	α-TEG accumulation μmole/g dry wt	C_n/C_{ex}
5002–5C	$MG_1MG_2mg_3$	23.1	10.8
5001–1B	$mg_1MG_2MG_3$	34.4	16.2
5001–2B	$mg_1mg_2mg_3$	0.4	0.1
5001–2C	$mg_1MG_2mg_3$	27.8	13.0
5001–5A	$mg_1MG_2mg_3$	13.3	6.1
5002–1B	$MG_1mg_2mg_3$	0.3	0.0
5001–5D	$mg_1mg_2MG_3$	0.2	0.0

late more than 100 times the concentration of α-TEG that glucose-grown cells accumulate under the same condition. The accumulated radioactivity was extracted from induced cells and shown to be chromatographically indistinguishable from the synthetic α-TEG. α-TEG was therefore accumulated unchanged in induced cells.

Since active transport obviously requires energy expenditure, it is not unexpected that the process would be sensitive to inhibitors of adenosine triphosphate (ATP) formation. That this is so is shown in Table 3. Active transport of α-TEG in induced cells is inhibited 96% by 4×10^{-3} M NaN$_3$ and 85% by 4×10^{-4} M p-chloromercuribenzoate. Other inhibitors of energy-yielding reactions (monoiodoacetate, arsenate, and arsenite) also partially inhibit α-TEG uptake.

The activation of the accumulation system possesses all the attributes

TABLE 3

EFFECT OF ENERGY INHIBITORS ON THE ACCUMULATION OF S^{35}
α-TEG IN INDUCED CELLS
(Data from Okada and Halvorson, 1964b.)

Inhibitor	Concentration of inhibitor M	Relative rate of accumulation
NaN$_3$	4×10^{-3}	4
NaN$_3$	8×10^{-4}	7
P-chloromercuribenzoate	4×10^{-4}	15
Arsenite	10^{-2}	33
Arsenate	10^{-2}	69
Monoiodoacetate	4×10^{-3}	47
2,4-dinitrophenol	8×10^{-4}	88

of enzyme induction. The active-transport system is induced by both α-TEG and α-MG. As shown in Fig. 3, the induction of α-TEG begins from the moment of addition of the inducer. The differential rate of synthesis (Δ uptake/Δ mg cells) of the active-transport system is constant. Induction is

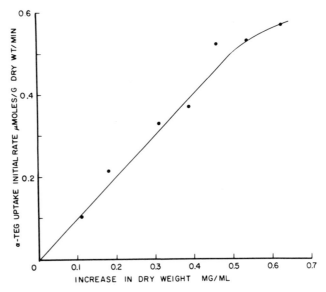

Fig. 3. Kinetics of induction of the α-TEG active-transport system. Cells of 5002-5C ($MG_1MG_2mg_3$) were induced in glucose medium containing 2% α-MG. (Data from Okada and Halvorson, 1963.)

completely inhibited by amino acid analogs or by 10^{-1} M acetate, neither of which has any effect on the function of the active-transport system.

The specificities of the active-transport system and of facilitated diffusion are similar, if not identical. As shown in Fig. 4, α-MG, glucose, maltose, and trehalose are competitive inhibitors of α-TEG accumulation, indicating that they are competing for a common concentrating mechanism. Trehalose and

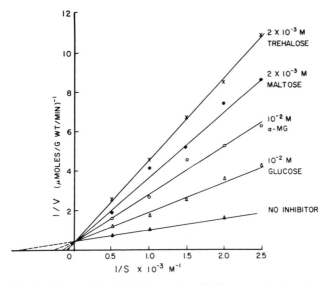

Fig. 4. Competitive inhibition of α-TEG accumulation in induced cells by various sugars. (Data from Okada and Halvorson, 1964b.)

maltose are the most effective inhibitors. Various other β-glucosides and galactosides (melibiose, β-methylglucoside, cellobiose, lactose, and galactose) are inactive. The process is therefore stereospecific and reacts only with α-glucosides. In contrast, the maltose-accumulating system in yeast is induced only by maltose, and only α-MG competes effectively for maltose transport.

Exit Reaction in Induced and Uninduced Cells

Before considering the mechanism of induction of the active-transport process, attention should first be given to the exit reaction in induced and uninduced cells. When either induced or uninduced cells, preloaded with S^{35} α-TEG, are incubated in the absence of exogenous substrate, a slow exponential loss of radioactivity occurs. From the first-order kinetics of the exit reaction, the exit-rate constant (c) can be calculated from the following equation:

$$\ln (G_\infty - G_{in}) = ct \qquad (1)$$

where G_∞ and G_{in} are the internal α-TEG concentrations initially and at any time t. As shown in Table 4, the exit-rate constant is independent of the

TABLE 4

SUMMARY OF EXIT RATES UNDER VARIOUS CONDITIONS

	Equilibrium level G_∞	Entry rate	Exit rate			
			$-\alpha$-TEG		$+10^{-2}$M α-MG	
			Initial rate	Rate constant	Initial rate	Rate constant
Cells grown on	μmole/g cells	μmole/g cells/hr	μmole/g cells/hr	hr^{-1}	μmole/g cells/hr	hr^{-1}
Glucose	0.44	0.36	0.09	0.22	1.58	3.6
α-MG	19.0	18.0	3.42	0.18	73.0	3.84

intracellular concentration of α-TEG. The exit rates in induced cells and in uninduced cells are nearly identical. Therefore, the exit reaction is constitutive, whereas the entry reaction is inducible. The reverse situation has been reported by Horecker et al. (1960) for galactose transport in E. coli. In yeast, the exit reaction for α-TEG is unaffected by 4×10^{-3} M NaN$_3$, an effective inhibitor of the entry reaction (Table 3). The loss of accumulated S^{35} α-TEG, however, can be accelerated by the presence of α-TEG, α-MG, or maltose in the medium. For example, the exit rate in the presence of α-MG increased about 20-fold in both uninduced and induced cells.

Mechanism of α-TEG Permeation

Active-transport processes have been studied extensively in recent years; however, the mechanism is as yet unclear. The mechanism which has been given most serious consideration is a carrier-transport model. The main findings with the α-TEG-transport system also can be explained readily on this basis. According to this scheme, the permeation of α-TEG is dependent upon its reversible combination with a stereospecific carrier which, combined or free, can diffuse across the cytoplasmic membrane. The synthesis of this carrier is controlled by the MG_2 gene; in the recessive state, the carrier is absent and the membrane impermeable.

In active transport the substance is moved against a concentration gradient. It has, therefore, been assumed that active transport involves at least two processes: 1) facilitated diffusion and 2) an energy-dependent accumulation process. Cirillo (1961) has pointed out that a common stereospecific carrier serves for the permeation of both facilitated diffusion and active transport. There are at least two examples to support this hypothesis. One of these is the α-TEG system reported here, and the second is the system for proline transport in *E. coli* described by Kessel and Lubin (1962). These workers observed that a single mutation led to a loss of both an active-transport system at 37°C and an exchange mechanism at 0°C and, therefore, concluded that both were mediated by a common mechanism.

Facilitated diffusion and active transport of α-TEG appear to utilize a common system. They have similar, if not identical, substrate specificities; they are both dependent upon the MG_2 gene; and at temperatures below 20°C they have identical temperature dependences (Okada and Halvorson, 1963). One of the simplest and most attractive models to explain these findings is to assume that the MG_2 gene produces the stereospecific carrier substance for α-TEG. Under conditions favoring induction, α-TEG which has entered the cell via the permeation system can induce an enzyme which couples the carrier substance to the energy-yielding reactions of the cell. Whatever the nature of this coupling, it is thermodynamically possible for α-TEG to be accumulated against a concentration gradient (active transport).

Comparison of the Active-Transport Systems for α-TEG and Maltose

A discussion of the significance of the α-TEG-permeating system to the regulation of enzyme induction would be incomplete without first considering the permeation of another α-glucoside, maltose. From the studies reported by Harris and Thompson (1961), an independent, inducible maltose permeation system has been suggested in yeast. Maltose not only competitively inhibits α-TEG uptake, but also accelerates α-TEG exit (Okada and Halvorson, 1964b). These findings, as well as the isolation by Hawthorne (1958) of $MAmg_2$ strains (maltose-fermenting, α-TEG-impermeable), suggest that not only do yeast cells contain an α-TEG and a maltose permeation system, but that the function of these two may be linked.

The independence of the two systems is evident from an examination of their inducibility. As shown in Table 5, both the maltose active-transport system and the α-TEG-accumulating system are induced by α-MG and re-

TABLE 5

INDUCTION OF MALTOSE AND α-TEG ACTIVE-TRANSPORT SYSTEMS
(Data from Okada and Halvorson, 1963.)

		Entry rate μmole/g cells/hr	
Genotype	Inducer	Maltose	α-TEG
$maMG_1MG_2mg_3$	glucose	0.42	0.36
	maltose	13.6	15.6
	α-MG	27.0	28.2
$mamg_1mg_2mg_3$	glucose	0.40	0.37
	maltose	24.0	0.33

pressed by glucose. The independent function of the two systems is clear from the behavior of the mg_2 recessive strain. When strain 5001-2B was grown on maltose, a maltose-accumulating system was induced without affecting the permeability of α-TEG. Assuming that both maltose and α-TEG accumulations are two-step processes, one can conclude from the above results that independent facilitated diffusion systems exist for maltose and α-TEG penetration. Both are inducible, and in strains having maltose and α-TEG permeation systems, cross-inducibility is observed. As shall be seen later, this cross-inducibility is in contrast to the specificity of induction of the first enzymes active in the metabolism of maltose and α-MG.

The two permeation systems appear to be closely related. Maltose competes for the entry of α-TEG and α-MG (Robertson and Halvorson, 1957), and α-MG inhibits the uptake of maltose in induced cells (Harris and Thompson, 1961). The parallelism between the α-TEG- and the maltose-accumulating systems is even more striking in their inducibility. The two systems are coordinately induced by various sugars (Fig. 5). Over a wide range of differential rates of synthesis, not only do various inducers lead to parallel increases in both maltose- and α-TEG-uptake systems, but also the actual initial rates are identical for both substrates. The induction of the two systems may still be specific, if the accumulated inducer is subject to trans-glucosidation. Thus, α-MG could be converted to maltose, and the reverse. This possibility is ruled out, since coordinate induction was also observed under conditions of gratuity with α-TEG. A more interesting possibility is the following. Maltose and α-TEG are each transported into the yeast cell by separate stereospecific carrier substances. In each case, when an enzyme that couples facilitated diffusion with the energy-yielding reactions is induced, the systems are converted into active-transport processes. Coordinate induction could be explained in either of two ways: the coupling enzymes for the two processes are identical, or the two coupling enzymes are subject to the same regulatory system.

The exact nature of the coordinate induction of the two systems remains to be investigated. It is clear, however, from these results that these two sys-

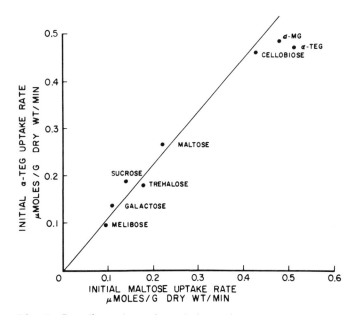

Fig. 5. Coordinate induction of the active-transport systems for α-TEG and maltose. Glucose-grown cultures of the maltose-negative (ma) strain 5002-5C ($maMG_1MG_2mg_3$) were used in these experiments. The inducer concentrations employed were 10^{-2} M for maltose and trehalose and 5×10^{-2} M for all the others indicated. The uptakes of α-TEG and maltose were corrected for the rates of facilitated diffusion in uninduced cells. (Data from Okada and Halvorson, 1963.)

tems interact in the regulation of maltose induction of α-glucosidase and α-TEG induction of isomaltase.

Specificity of Induction of Isomaltase and α-Glucosidase

Yeasts contain two enzymes active against α-MG and maltose. The two enzymes have recently been separated, purified, and partially characterized (Halvorson and Ellias, 1958; Gorman, 1963). In view of the similarity of these two enzymes, and the coordinate induction of the corresponding two active-transport systems, a study of the specificity of induction of isomaltase and α-glucosidase was undertaken.

Isomaltase and α-glucosidase share common substrates, including the chromogenic substrate, p-nitrophenyl α-D-glucopyranoside (α-PNPG). α-Glucosidase hydrolyzes α-MG at only 4% of the rate at which it hydrolyzes maltose (Halvorson and Ellias, 1958), whereas isomaltase is more active against α-MG than against maltose. The specificities of the two are shown in Table 6. Although the two enzymes have similar complexing properties

TABLE 6

COMPLEXING PROPERTIES OF ISOMALTASE AND α-GLUCOSIDASE

	K_i of various substrates against	
Substrate	α-Glucosidase $M \times 10^3$	Isomaltase $M \times 10^3$
P-nitrophenyl-α-glucoside*	20	1.2
Maltose	217	100.0
Sucrose	370	210.0
α-methylglucoside	100	60.0

* K_m.

for various α-glucosides, they show distinct differences. Since both are active against α-PNPG, a method for assaying each in mixtures was required. As shown in Fig. 6, this was possible by the use of specific antisera. Anti-isomaltase antiserum quantitatively precipitated isomaltase, but neither inactivated nor was absorbed by α-glucosidase. Similarily, anti-α-glucosidase antiserum was specific for α-glucosidase. Thus, by the use of both antisera, the two enzymes can be assayed in mixtures with the same substrate, α-PNPG.

The specificities of induction of α-glucosidase and of isomaltase were tested in strains containing both the M_3 gene for α-glucosidase and MG_1MG_2 genes for α-TEG permeation and isomaltase. The cells were grown through several generations in the presence of α-MG, maltose, or glucose, and the enzymes produced in response to each inducer were characterized by the use of specific antisera. The results are shown in Table 7. The units of α-PNPG hydrolysis/mg protein in extracts from maltose-induced cells was 870, from α-MG-induced cells 421, from cells induced by both 430, and from glucose-grown cells 23.1. When $M_3MG_1MG_2mg_3$ was induced by α-MG, 98% of the enzyme activity was due to isomaltase; when the inducer was maltose, 98% of the activity of the hydrolysis of α-PNPG was determined to be due to α-glucosidase. When both maltose and α-MG were used, 46% of the induced enzyme activity was due to α-glucosidase and 54% to isomaltase. In a parallel

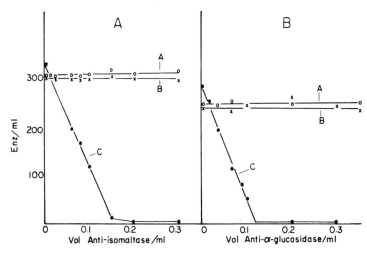

Fig. 6. Antigenic specificity of α-glucosidase and isomaltase. A: Anti-isomaltase serum incubated with α-glucosidase (curve A) or isomaltase (curve C); curve B is α-glucosidase treated with normal serum. B: Anti-α-glucosidase serum incubated with isomaltase (curve B) or α-glucosidase (curve C); curve A is isomaltase treated with normal serum. (Data from Gorman, 1963.)

experiment, α-TEG induced only isomaltase. The product of the MG_1 locus functions only in the induction of isomaltase and functionally recognizes α-MG and α-TEG, not maltose. Similar results were obtained with the MG_3 locus.

When both inducers are employed, the level of α-glucosidase and iso-

TABLE 7

IDENTIFICATION OF ENZYMES INDUCED BY MALTOSE AND α-MG

(Data from Gorman, 1963.)

Genotype	Inducer	Units α-PNPG/ mg protein	Per cent activity removed by antiserum against	
			Isomaltase	α-Glucosidase
$mMG_1MG_2mg_3$	α-MG	440	98	0
$M_6mg_1mg_2mg_3$	maltose	830	0	99
$M_3MG_1MG_2mg_3$	glucose	23.1	90	8
	α-MG	421	98	0
	maltose	870	0	98
	maltose and α-MG	430	54	46

maltase is less than that induced in the presence of the two inducers alone. Whether this finding indicates that each can act as a competitive inhibitor of the induction site of the other remains to be seen. However, the observed inhibition can be explained on the basis of competitive inhibition of inducer uptake. Maltose uptake competes with α-MG uptake (Fig. 4), and, under conditions of the experiment of Table 7, α-MG inhibited the uptake of C^{14} maltose by over 50%.

The Genetic Control of Isomaltase Induction

The induction of isomaltase in acetate medium in strains with various genotypes is shown in Fig. 7. Isomaltase is inducible only in strains

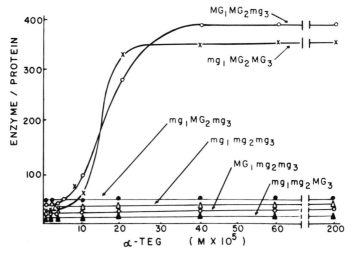

Fig. 7. Induction of isomaltase in acetate medium in strains with various genotypes. (Data from Gorman, 1963.)

$MG_1MG_2mg_3$, $mg_1MG_2MG_3$, and $MG_1MG_2MG_3$. The basal activity in strains carrying various combinations of dominant MG genes or in completely recessive strains ($mg_1mg_2mg_3$) has been shown to be isomaltase (Gorman, 1963). It was, therefore, concluded that MG_1 and MG_3 are regulatory genes. The observation that the genotypes $MG_1mg_2mg_3$, $mg_1mg_2MG_3$, and $mg_1mg_2mg_3$ are not inducible is expected, as the function of the MG_2 is to control facilitated diffusion (Okada and Halvorson, 1964a). For instance, in genotypes recessive for MG_2, exogenous inducer is excluded from the cell, while diffusion is permitted when MG_2 is dominant. The structural gene for isomaltase has not been identified.

The dependence of isomaltase induction on the concentration of inducer is also shown in Fig. 7. These experiments were conducted in 0.5% acetate medium, which inhibits the formation of the active-transport system (Okada and Halvorson, 1964a); therefore, induction of isomaltase is dependent upon facilitated diffusion of α-TEG. At equilibrium, the concentration of α-TEG in the cytoplasm approaches that in the medium. An exogenous concentration of 3×10^{-4} M α-TEG was sufficient to saturate the mechanism of isomaltase synthesis controlled by either the MG_1 or MG_3 gene. Since the maximal level of α-TEG uptake was proportional to the external concentration of α-TEG (Fig. 2), the *internal* concentration of α-TEG required to saturate the induction site is 3×10^{-4} M or less.

From these findings it can be concluded that at concentrations above 3×10^{-4} M α-TEG, facilitated diffusion is sufficient to maintain maximal induction. At α-TEG concentrations less than 3×10^{-4} M, the induction of an active-transport system would be expected to regulate the induction of isomaltase.

Differential Rate of Isomaltase Biosynthesis

Let us now turn to the kinetics of isomaltase synthesis. When the initial rates of induced isomaltase synthesis were observed, it was found that the differential rates of isomaltase synthesis (Δ enzyme/Δ protein) in 10^{-3} M α-TEG were not zero order, but showed an autocatalytic effect (Fig. 8). However, after approximately $1\frac{1}{2}$ cell generations (generation time, 220 min) the differential rate of synthesis reaches a constant value.

A similar phenomenon has been reported in *E. coli* when β-galactosidase induction is carried out with nonsaturating concentrations of inducer (Novick and Weiner, 1957). The differential rate of synthesis shows an accelerating phase which, depending upon the concentration of inducer, slowly reaches a maximum rate. The autocatalytic-type kinetics were shown to be due to a prior induction of a β-galactoside permease which led to a gradual increase in internal accumulation of inducer. In the cryptic or permeaseless strain of *E. coli*, in which inducer enters by diffusion, Herzenberg (1959) demonstrated that the differential rate of β-galactosidase was zero order. The rate of enzyme synthesis was dependent upon the type and concentration of inducer employed.

Yeasts grown on acetate are analogous to the cryptic mutants of *E. coli*. Below 3×10^{-3} M α-TEG, the rate of isomaltase induction is dependent upon internal inducer supplied by the MG_2-mediated facilitated diffusion. In the experiment of Fig. 8, the initial uptake of α-TEG is slow, and, therefore, isomaltase synthesis is limited by a suboptimal concentration of inducer. This is seen more clearly in Fig. 9. During the first 100 min, internal α-TEG

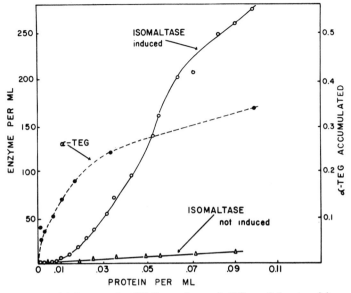

Fig. 8. Initial rate of α-TEG uptake and differential rate of iso-maltase synthesis in strain 5002-5C ($MG_1MG_2mg_3$). Cells were inoculated into peptone-salts medium which contained 0.5% Na acetate and 10^{-3} M α-TEG. (Data from Gorman, 1963.)

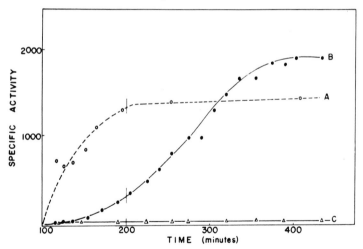

Fig. 9. Kinetics of α-TEG uptake and isomaltose induction in strain 5002-5C ($MG_1MG_2mg_3$). The relative specific activity (enzyme/protein) was determined from the experiment shown in Fig. 8. The specific activity of α-TEG uptake is expressed as μg α-TEG/mg protein. *A*: α-TEG uptake; *B*: induced isomaltase; *C*: basal isomaltase.

is being continually concentrated. During the same interval, the differential rate of isomaltase synthesis displays accelerating kinetics, as predicted for a permeation-limited process (Cohn, 1957). Of particular interest is the fact that, after 100 min, when the internal concentration of α-TEG remains constant, autocatalytic-type kinetics are observed for an additional 170 min. Thus, although the initial rate of enzyme induction can be controlled by the activity of the permeation system, accelerating kinetics of isomaltase synthesis occur under conditions in which the intracellular level of inducer remains constant.

Effect of MG_1 and MG_3 Genes on the Kinetics of Isomaltase Synthesis

Numerous other models for autocatalytic enzyme synthesis have been proposed, based both on a repression phenomenon (Monod and Jacob, 1961) and on replication of enzyme-forming systems (Spiegelman, 1951). The data are insufficient at the present time to characterize the mechanism of the autocatalytic kinetics observed here. One possibility is that a period is required to fully activate the regulatory mechanism for isomaltase synthesis. As previously demonstrated, two regulatory genes, MG_1 and MG_3, govern the inducibility of isomaltase. Autocatalytic expression of enzyme synthesis might be expected if a period of time is required for inducer metabolism or for reversal of the action of an internal repressor. In either case, the kinetics of enzyme synthesis would be expected to be influenced with increasing dosage of the regulatory genes.

In order to further characterize the role of MG_1 and MG_3 in isomaltase synthesis, the dosage effect of these genes on basal and induced enzyme was examined. The results are shown in Table 8. The basal level varies from 11–20, being lowest (11.3) in strains carrying both recessive mg_1 and mg_3 genes, and intermediate (14) in a diploid carrying both dominant and recessive forms of

TABLE 8

EFFECT OF MG GENES ON ISOMALTASE SYNTHESIS
Cells were induced in 10^{-1} M α-MG.

	Units of enzyme/mg protein	
Genotype	Basal	Induced
$MG_1MG_2MG_3$	17.3	2789
$mg_1MG_2MG_3$	20.0	642
$MG_1MG_2mg_3$	18.3	830
$mg_1MG_2mg_3$	11.3	28.1
$MG_1MG_2mg_3/mg_1MG_2MG_3$	14.0	742

the two genes. The induced levels in strains carrying MG_1 or MG_3 are essentially the same. The autonomy of MG_1 and MG_3 is evident from the fact that the same concentration of external inducer (Fig. 7) is required for maximal induction of isomaltase in strains carrying $MG_1MG_2mg_3$ or $mg_1MG_2MG_3$. In the diploid heterozygous for both MG_1 and MG_3, the level of induced isomaltase (742) agrees closely with that predicted from the mean of the induced level of the parental strains (736). Of particular interest is the inducibility in strains carrying both MG_1 and MG_3. If MG_1 and MG_3 were additive in stimulating enzyme synthesis, the expected level of isomaltase should be 1470. However, when the induced level of isomaltase was measured in the haploid $MG_1MG_2MG_3$, an apparently synergistic effect was detected, for the level of induced enzyme was greatly increased (approximately twofold) over that expected from a simple additive effect.

On the other hand, increasing the gene dosage of the MG_2 gene does not increase the rate of α-TEG uptake. As shown in Table 9, the rate of α-TEG

TABLE 9

RATE OF UPTAKE OF α-TEG IN VARIOUS STRAINS OF *S. cerevisiae*
(Data from Gorman, 1963.)

Strain	Genotype	Uptake (μmole/g dry wt/hr)
Y–131	$MG_1MG_2mg_3$	7.00
Y–133	$mg_1MG_2MG_3$	7.01
Y–131/Y–133	MG_1MG_2/MG_2MG_3	7.20
S–1B	$MG_1MG_2MG_3$	7.20

uptake in haploids containing MG_2 was the same as that in a diploid homozygous for MG_2.

In addition to influencing the level of isomaltase (Table 8), the kinetics of isomaltase induction are dramatically dependent upon the number of recessive forms of the two regulatory genes carried by the cell (Fig. 10). The haploids $MG_1MG_2mg_3$ and $mg_1MG_2MG_3$ display accelerating induction kinetics. This same phenomenon occurs in the diploid ($MG_1MG_2mg_3/mg_1MG_2MG_3$) heterozygous for MG_1 and MG_3. Autocatalytic-type kinetics were always observed in diploids containing equal complements of dominant and recessive forms of the two regulatory genes. On the other hand, in the haploid $MG_1MG_2MG_3$, the initial induced differential rate of isomaltase is accelerating only during the first half-generation, corresponding to the time required to saturate the intracellular level of inducer (Fig. 9). Following this, the differential rate is constant. Only when both the recessive mg_1 and mg_3 genes were removed was the typical accelerating kinetics of isomaltase synthesis eliminated.

These findings present an interesting dual behavior of the regulatory genes.

Either MG_1 or MG_3 is required for isomaltase induction, each is specific in its function, and, in each case, inducibility is the dominant form of the gene. On the other hand, the presence of recessive forms of these two genes, mg_1 and mg_3, leads to a reduction in the level of enzyme and a delay in the maximal rate of enzyme synthesis. These findings can be understood by assuming that *both* forms of the regulatory genes (MG and mg) are functional: MG_1 and MG_3 produce products which either activate or react with inducer to promote isomaltase synthesis; the recessive forms of these genes, mg_1 and mg_3, produce

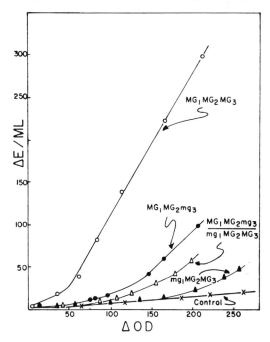

Fig. 10. Initial differential rate of isomaltase synthesis in yeast carrying various MG genes. Cells were induced in nutrient medium containing 10^{-1} M α-MG. (Data from Gorman, 1963.)

inactive products which are similar to the products of MG_1 and MG_3 but compete with the function of the active inducer. Products of mg_1 and mg_3 decrease the basal level of enzyme, lower the induced level of enzyme, and lead to autocatalytic kinetics of enzyme induction due to a delay in reversal by the active inducer.

The search for products of regulatory genes is as yet in its preliminary stages. The fact that MG and mg genes differ by a single mutation suggests that the active and inactive products are closely related. Further examination of the system must await isolation of the structural gene for isomaltase and characterization of the effect of the regulatory genes on its function. What is clear, however, is that the products of the regulatory genes mg_1 and mg_3 can result in autocatalytic-type kinetics of enzyme synthesis.

Conclusions

The essential conclusions to be drawn from the observations in this paper can be summarized as follows.

The induction of the isomaltase in yeast involves initially the uptake of inducer (α-TEG) via a specific permeation system, followed by the interaction or activation of inducer by either of two regulatory systems. In the absence of the permeation systems, the cell is impermeable to the inducers and the inducers are noninducible by isomaltase.

Two mechanisms of α-TEG uptake exist in yeast: facilitated diffusion and active transport. Both are controlled by the MG_2 gene; facilitated diffusion is constitutive, and active transport is inducible. Similar but independent mechanisms exist for maltose accumulation. The two systems are interrelated. They are coordinately induced, and substrates of one will inhibit the activity of the other as well as displace accumulated inducer.

In addition to controlling the specificity of carbohydrase inducibility, the permeation systems can control the kinetics of enzyme synthesis during the initial stages of induction. Autocatalytic-type kinetics of induction, however, are not exclusively the function of permeation systems. In strains carrying either the mg_1 or mg_2 recessive genes, autocatalytic-type kinetics occur under conditions in which the intracellular concentration of inducer is maximal.

REFERENCES

Cirillo, V. P. 1961. *Ann. Rev. Microbiol.* 15: 197.

Cohen, G. N., and J. Monod. 1957. *Bacteriol. Rev.* 21: 169.

Cohn, M. 1957. *Bacteriol. Rev.* 21: 140.

Gorman, J. 1963. Ph.D. Thesis. Univ. of Wisconsin.

Halvorson, H., and L. Ellias. 1958. *Biochim. Biophys. Acta* 30: 28.

Harris, G., and C. C. Thompson. 1961. *Biochim. Biophys. Acta* 52: 176.

Hawthorne, D. C. 1958. *Heredity.* 12: 273.

Herzenberg, L. A. 1959. *Biochim. Biophys. Acta* 31: 525.

Horecker, B. L., J. Thomas, and J. Monod. 1960. *J. Biol. Chem.* 235: 1586.

Kessel, D., and M. Lubin. 1962. *Biochim. Biophys. Acta* 57: 32.

Monod, J., and F. Jacob. 1961. *Cold Spring Harbor Symp. Quant. Biol.* 26: 389.

Novick, A., and M. Weiner. 1957. *Proc. Natl. Acad. Sci. U.S.* 43: 553.

Okada, H., and H. O. Halvorson. 1963. *J. Bacteriol.* 86: 966.

Okada, H., and H. O. Halvorson. 1964a. *Biochim. Biophys. Acta.* In press.

Okada, H., and H. O. Halvorson. 1964b. *Biochim. Biophys. Acta.* In press.

Robertson, J. J., and H. O. Halvorson. 1957. *J. Bacteriol.* 73: 186.

Spiegelman, S. 1951. *Cold Spring Harbor Symp. Quant. Biol.* 16: 87.

Stein, W. D., and J. F. Danielli. 1956. *Discussions Faraday Soc.* No. 21: 238.

Terui, G., H. Okada, and Y. Oshima. 1959. *Tech. Rept. Osaka Univ.* 9: 237.

Cell Potassium and the Regulation
of Protein Synthesis[1]

Martin Lubin

Department of Pharmacology
Harvard Medical School
Boston, Massachusetts

All cells need potassium for growth; all growing cells accumulate potassium. Both statements must be qualified, but they are probably true, and their juxtaposition highlights the problem of the role of potassium in cell growth.

As for the first statement, the requirement of growing cells for potassium has been found whenever sought (Steinbach, 1962a). No exceptions in plant or animal life are known. But the large number of cell species not yet studied makes this generalization necessarily provisional.

Extensive data that support the second statement have been assembled in recent reviews by Steinbach (1962a, b; 1963). The accumulation of K appears to be a universal phenomenon, but the reciprocal exclusion of Na from cells has some exceptions.

For vertebrate cells, the intracellular K range is narrow—100–200 mM—but if other phyla are considered, the range is much larger. For example, in the fresh-water mollusc, *Anodonta*, and in the fresh-water ciliate, *Tetrahymena pyriformis*, cell K is only 15–30 mM—low when compared to frog or man, but high compared to the traces of K in the extracellular environment (Steinbach, 1962b). At the other extreme, *Halobacterium salinarium*,

[1] Support has been received from the U.S. Public Health Service, Grants GM-09552 and GM-06712, and from the National Science Foundation, Grants GB-1150 and G-24163.

which grows well in media containing 4 M NaCl and only a small amount of K, concentrates K to an intracellular level close to 4 M (Christian and Waltho, 1962).

In wild-type *Escherichia coli*, the intracellular K concentration is about 200 mM and remains near that level even if the concentration in the medium is made 1,000-fold less (Lubin and Ennis, 1964; Schultz and Solomon, 1961). Intracellular Na is not so closely regulated in *E. coli*, but rises with the addition of excess NaCl to the growth medium (Schultz and Solomon, 1961). The capacity for active transport of K permits *E. coli* to grow rapidly in media of widely varying K content. Because of this tight control over cell K levels, wild-type bacterial cells are poorly suited for an experimental test of the effects of reducing cell K.

Properties of a Mutant of *Escherichia coli* Defective in K Transport

A direct approach to the problem of the role of intracellular K was facilitated by the isolation of a mutant requiring high K for rapid growth (Lubin and Kessel, 1960). This mutant (strain B207) was derived from *E. coli* B by a modification of the penicillin selection method (Lubin, 1962). The accumulation of K by B207 was defective, and the intracellular K could therefore be set easily and quickly to desired levels. Five other mutants, isolated by the same method from separate clones of *E. coli* B, and a mutant of *Bacillus subtilis* appeared to be similar to B207. Detailed descriptions of the experiments reported here will be published elsewhere (Lubin and Ennis, 1964).

When B207 cells were washed in a Na-salts buffer and resuspended in fresh media containing various concentrations of K, a new level of cell K was reached within 5 min. The relation between the concentration of K in the cells and that in the medium was found to be nonlinear (Fig. 1); for example, a 100-fold decrease of K in the medium caused only a sixfold decrease of K in the cells. Part of the K lost by the cells was replaced by a gain in Na, with the balance of charge presumably made up by gain of H^+ or loss of anions. The large amount of intracellular PO_4 buffer would be expected to keep the intracellular pH nearly constant, in spite of considerable shifts of H^+. Not all the K could be rapidly removed from the cells; in a Na-salts buffer, contaminated with about 0.05 mM K, the cells lost about 95% of their initial K content, leaving a residual intracellular level of about 10 mM.

The biochemical lesion in strain B207 is not known. These cells do not appear to be generally leaky, for experiments have shown that they possess the normal capacity for active transport of amino acids—those tested were glycine, leucine, and proline. When cells were depleted of K, there was no significant change in either the ratio of intracellular water to dry weight or the concentration of cell Mg. Therefore, the change in K and Na concentrations took place sharply and reversibly, and there was no evidence of gross alteration of any other important cell constituents during the brief period needed to deplete the cells of K.

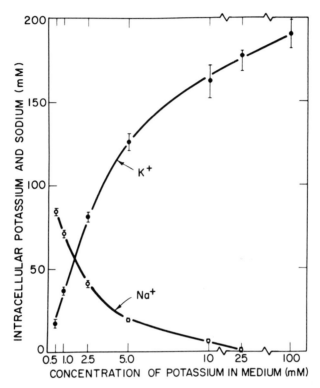

Fig. 1. Dependence of intracellular K and Na concentrations in strain B207 on K and Na in the medium. 100 mM K is the level in the usual growth medium (medium A, Davis and Mingioli, 1950). At lower values of K, Na was substituted mole for mole. K^{42} was used for measurements; details of method are described in Lubin and Ennis, 1964. Bracket shows 1 SE of mean. Intracellular K: ●—●; intracellular Na: ○—○. (From Lubin and Ennis, 1964, *Biochim. Biophys. Acta,* in press.)

Growth Rates of Mutant Cells in Media with Varying K Levels. The rate of division of mutant cells was controlled by the K level in the medium, with about 50% of the maximum growth rate occurring at a K level of 2.5 mM, which corresponds to an intracellular level of about 75 mM (Fig. 2). B207 cells did not grow at all in a Na-salts medium, although even after many

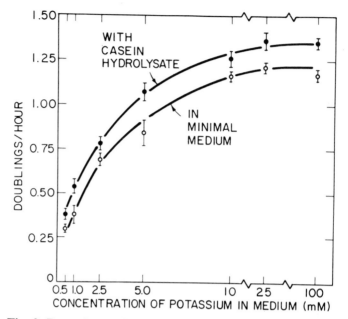

Fig. 2. Dependence of rate of growth of strain B207 on K and Na in the medium. As in Fig. 1, at levels below 100 mM K, Na was substituted mole for mole. Bracket shows 1 SE of mean. Minimal medium: O—O; medium supplemented with 0.1% casein hydrolysate (Sheffield N–Z–Case): ●—●. 37°C. (From Lubin and Ennis, 1964, *Biochim. Biophys. Acta,* in press.)

hours these cells showed no loss of ability to produce colonies on high-K plates. In contrast, wild-type *E. coli* grew rapidly in a Na-salts medium until the traces of K contaminating the medium were exhausted.

A Digression on Enzymes Activated by K

About two dozen intracellular enzymes are known to require K for full activity, and the number will presumably increase as more enzymes are isolated and studied. The list of K-dependent enzymes given in Table 1 was derived from several existing smaller compilations (Glynn, 1957; Dixon and Webb, 1958; Cantoni, 1960; Ussing, 1960), with some additions from the recent literature. For each enzyme listed, K and Na differed in their effects on activity by at least 10- to 20-fold. Enzymes showing only two- or threefold differences in activity in the presence of K or Na have not been listed. Other cations have on occasion been tested; Rb and NH$_4$ in general stimulated

TABLE 1

ENZYMES STRONGLY ACTIVATED BY K

Enzyme	Tissue or organism	Source
Glycolysis and Related Pathways		
Fructokinase	Liver	Parks *et al.*, 1957.
6-phosphofructokinase	Yeast	Muntz, 1953.
Pyruvate phosphokinase	Animal tissues, yeast	Boyer, 1953; Kachmar and Boyer, 1953.
Phospho-transacetylase	*Clostridium*	Stadtman, 1952.
Malic enzyme	*Lactobacillus*	Nossal, 1951.
Acetyl-CoA synthetase	Heart	Von Korff, 1953.
Biosynthesis of Essential Small Molecules		
Inosine 5′ phosphate dehydrogenase	*Aerobacter*	Magasanik *et al.*, 1957.
S-adenosylmethionine synthetase	Yeast, liver	Mudd and Cantoni, 1958.
Deoxyguanylate kinase	*E. coli*	Bessman and Van Bibber, 1959.
Pantothenate synthetase	*E. coli*	Maas, 1952.
AICAR transformylase	Liver	Flax *et al.*, 1957.
Carbamyl phosphate synthetase	Liver	Marshall *et al.*, 1961.
Protein Synthesis		
Tyrosine-activating enzyme	Pancreas, liver	Schweet and Allen, 1958; Holley, 1961.
Phosphodiesterase	*E. coli*	Spahr and Schlessinger, 1963.
Miscellaneous		
5′ adenylic acid deaminase	Erythrocytes	Askari, 1963.
Aldehyde dehydrogenase	Yeast	Black, 1951.
Glycerol dehydrogenase	*Aerobacter*	Lin and Magasanik, 1960.
β-galactosidase	*E. coli*	Cohn and Monod, 1951.
Tryptophanase	*E. coli*	Happold and Struyvenberg, 1954.
γ-glutamylcysteine synthetase	Wheat	Webster and Varner, 1954.
Glutathione synthetase	Wheat	Webster and Varner, 1955.
D-alanyl-D-alanine synthetase	*Streptococcus*	Neuhaus, 1962.
L-threonine dehydrase	Liver	Nishimura and Greenberg, 1961.

activity of the enzymes in Table 1; and Li, like Na, produced little activity or inhibition. Detailed studies of the effect of monovalent cations exist for only a few enzymes.

Similarly, very little is known about the comparative biochemistry of K-dependent enzymes. Pyruvate phosphokinase, taken from sources in several phyla, has been found uniformly to be K-dependent. For S-adenosylmethionine synthetase, the enzymes from both yeast and liver show K dependence; but in *E. coli*, no requirement for K has been noted. β-Galacto-sidase is unusual; the effect of cations depends on the nature of the substrate. When lactose is the substrate of the enzyme, K stimulates activity. When o-nitrophenyl-β-D-galactoside is the substrate, Na stimulates the enzyme more than K does. Deoxyguanylate kinase in *E. coli* is K-dependent, but the analogous enzyme, produced shortly after infection by bacteriophage, is not. Some of the enzymes listed in Table 1, such as β-galactosidase and trypto-phanase, are not likely to be connected with the reason for the slow growth of strain B207 in low K. The enzymes of the glycolytic pathway and of purine biosynthesis are, however, vital for B207 growing in minimal medium with glucose (see Fig. 2).

Because the number of K-dependent enzymes is so large, it is hard to anticipate the specific result of reducing cell K. The paucity of information on the state and activity of these enzymes in cells, relative to the required rate of delivery of their products, also adds to the difficulty of prediction.

Activity of Biosynthetic Pathways in Cells Depleted of K

For many biosynthetic pathways, the possible effect of K deficiency could be assessed by growth tests alone. For example, if the slowing of growth were due to inhibition of arginine synthesis, the addition of arginine would be ex-pected to restore the maximum growth rate promptly. However, as shown in Fig. 2, the addition of a complete mixture of amino acids, most of them known to be readily assimilated by bacterial cells, failed to produce more than a small increase in growth rate when tested over the entire range of K concentrations. This small increase was presumably the result of feedback controls (Davis, 1961), which produce more efficient use of biosynthetic path-ways. In similar experiments, the addition of purines, pyrimidines, or vita-mins failed to restore maximum growth rate to B207 cells in low-K media.

Because the step that limits growth in K-depleted cells was not localized by the experiments reported above, measurements were made of protein and ribonucleic acid (RNA) synthesis. Surprisingly, mutant cells suspended in a Na-salts medium were found to synthesize considerable RNA, but little or no protein (Ennis and Lubin, 1961). Although the incorporation of C^{14} leu-cine into protein was less than a few per cent of the normal rate, RNA syn-thesis proceeded linearly for almost 3 hr, at about 20% of the normal rate (Fig. 3). In enriched medium, RNA synthesis was considerably greater. Chemical measurements of net RNA synthesis gave similar results. The net increase of unbalanced RNA in enriched medium was often 75% or more.

In the absence of a C source—both glucose and glycerol were tested—no RNA was made. If growth conditions were restored by adding K, most of this unbalanced RNA subsequently appeared in stable cell constituents, including ribosomes (Ennis and Lubin, unpublished data).

In many bacterial strains, such as *E. coli* B, changes in the rates of RNA and protein synthesis are usually closely coupled (Neidhardt and Magasanik, 1960; Neidhardt and Fraenkel, 1961). Almost any change of medium that slows division (e.g., shifting from glucose to glycerol as a C source, or from an NH₄ salt to an amino acid as N source) results in a decrease in both RNA and protein synthesis. If any nutrient essential for growth is completely withheld, both RNA and protein synthesis stop.

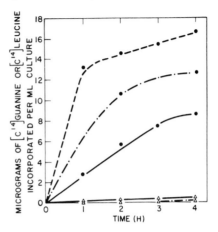

Fig. 3. Incorporation of C¹⁴ guanine (●) into RNA and C¹⁴ leucine (△) into protein by B207, under conditions of K depletion, in either minimal medium (————) or enriched medium (—·—·—). Data are also given for cells in high-K medium containing chloramphenicol (— — —). (From Ennis and Lubin, 1961, *Biochim. Biophys. Acta* 50:399.)

A well-known exception to the close coupling of RNA and protein synthesis occurs as a result of the addition of chloramphenicol to growing cultures. This drug blocks protein synthesis but not RNA synthesis (Fig. 3). The site of action is at a late stage in protein synthesis, beyond the formation of aminoacyl-s-RNA—somewhere in the complex process involving transfer of amino acid to polypeptide, in the presence of ribosomes and messenger (Davis and Feingold, 1962). Therefore, the observation that RNA but not protein is synthesized in K-depleted B207 cells leads to the expectation that the rate-limiting step in protein synthesis would be found at or near the step blocked by chloramphenicol.

This increase in RNA must have required the activity of a number of enzymes, including those involved in mononucleotide synthesis. For example, the adenosine triphosphate (ATP) level in *E. coli* is only 2–4% of the amount needed for a 50% increase of cellular RNA (Goldstein *et al.*, 1960; Franzen and Binkley, 1961). The observed rapid synthesis of RNA in K-depleted cells implies that the enzymes of nucleotide biosynthesis and of the glycolytic pathway and the deoxyribonucleic acid (DNA)–RNA polymerase must have been functioning with at least moderate efficiency.

Protein Synthesis in the Polyuridylic Acid System

Stimulation of protein synthesis by K in a cell-free system derived from liver was first reported by Sachs (1957). An optimum concentration of about 50 mM has been used for the now classical polyuridylic acid system, both by Nirenberg and Matthaei (1961) and by Lengyel *et al.* (1961). We have studied the activity of this system (referred to below as the poly-U system) over a wide range of K and Na concentrations, measuring the incorporation into

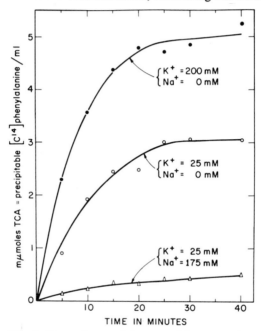

Fig. 4. Dependence of the rate of incorporation of C^{14} phenylalanine, in the cell-free system, on K and Na concentrations. Each ml of reaction mixture contained, in μmoles: 100 Tris (*p*H 7.8), 13 Mg acetate, 6 mercaptoethanol, 50 sucrose, 1.0 disodium-ATP, 0.03 trisodium guanosine triphosphate (GTP); 6 disodium-creatine phosphate; and 20 μg creatine phosphokinase; 40 μg polyuridylic acid; 1 mg s-RNA; 36 mμ moles C^{14} phenylalanine, 0.08 μc; S30 fraction (Nirenberg and Matthaei, 1961) (4 mg protein); and additions of K or Na as specified. 37°C. (From Lubin and Ennis, 1964, *Biochim. Biophys. Acta,* in press.)

polypeptide of counts originating either in C^{14} phenylalanine or in C^{14} phenylalanyl-s-RNA.

The system of Nirenberg and Matthaei was used, with only minor modifications. Creatine phosphate and creatine phosphokinase were substituted for phosphoenolpyruvate and pyruvate phosphokinase because of the dependence of the latter enzyme on K (Table 1). In Fig. 4, the kinetics of synthesis of polyphenylalanine are shown for two concentrations of K. At 200 mM K, more polyphenylalanine was synthesized than at 25 mM, although

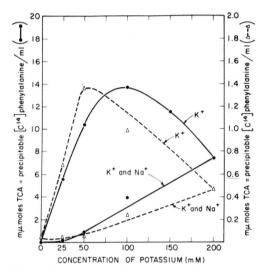

Fig. 5. Dependence of the extent of incorporation of C^{14} phenylalanine on K and Na. Reaction components were the same as for Fig. 4, except as follows: no s-RNA supplement ($\triangle$—$\triangle$); s-RNA present at 0.4 mg/ml ($\bullet$—$\bullet$). Note the increased efficiency of incorporation in the presence of s-RNA. 37°C. (From Lubin and Ennis, 1964, *Biochim. Biophys. Acta,* in press.)

with other batches of extract, 25 and 200 mM K often produced similar stimulation of synthesis. A large inhibition produced by Na is evident.

A similar antagonism between K and Na is illustrated in Fig. 5. Data are plotted from two experiments, and the values show the final level of incorporation reached. For each pair of lines (dashed or solid), the upper curve shows the effect of K concentration alone, with no Na present other than the small amount contributed by the salts of ATP and creatine phosphate. The optimum concentration, as others have also found, was between 50 and

100 mM. At levels of K higher than 200 mM, incorporation fell off steeply.

The lower curve of each pair shows the effect of varying the proportiosn of K and Na, keeping the sum of the two cations constant at 200 mM. The curve did not pass through a maximum, but incorporation fell progressively

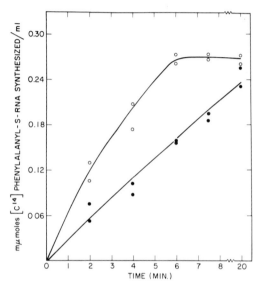

Fig. 6. Kinetics of synthesis of C^{14} phenyl-alanyl-s-RNA. Each ml of reaction mixture contained, in μmoles: 100 Tris (*p*H 7.2), 13 Mg acetate, 1.0 disodium-ATP, 6 disodium-creatine phosphate, 4.0 reduced glutathione; and 20 μg creatine phosphokinase; 0.4 mg bovine albumin; 1 mg stripped s-RNA; 10 mμmoles C^{14} phenyl-alanine, 0.25 μc; 0.002 ml of supernatant (S100) (Nirenberg and Matthaei, 1961) from extract of B207; and either 100 μmoles KCl (○—○) or 100 μmoles NaCl (●—●). 30°C. (From Lubin and Ennis, 1964, *Biochim. Biophys. Acta,* in press.)

as the proportion of Na increased. This is the pattern produced in cells of B207 with increasing replacement of K by Na.

Synthesis of Phenylalanyl-s-RNA. The preceding results showed that some part of the poly-U system distinguishes decisively between K and Na. Therefore, the poly-U system was examined in parts.

Of the three well-recognized steps in protein synthesis, 1) the formation of amino acid adenylate, 2) transfer of amino acid to a specific acceptor s-RNA, and 3) transfer of amino acid from aminoacyl-s-RNA to polypeptide, the first two are catalyzed by an activating enzyme, with at least one enzyme specific for each amino acid. The effect of K and Na on the rate of synthesis of aminoacyl-s-RNA was tested for 16 of the 20 amino acids (the omissions were isoleucine, glutamine, asparagine, and cysteine). In all cases, the rates of synthesis of C^{14} aminoacyl-s-RNA were only slightly influenced (at most, two- to threefold) by the choice of Na or K as an addition to the reaction mixture.

For the synthesis of C^{14} phenylalanyl-s-RNA, the rate in K was twice as fast as the rate in Na (Fig. 6). This difference is not sufficient to account for the large effect of K on synthesis in the poly-U system.

The Effect of K on the Transfer of Amino Acid from Aminoacyl-s-RNA to Polypeptide. In the presence of polyuridylic acid, this transfer step was found to be markedly K-dependent. In the experiment shown in Fig. 7, the rate of synthesis of polyphenylalanine in the presence of K was about 20 times greater than that in the presence of Na. Antagonism of K by Na also occurred, as expected. The reaction proceeded rapidly and in optimum K was finished in about 5 min. The results of many other experiments similarly showed a large difference between the effects of K and Na on both rate and extent of incorporation.

The step in protein synthesis that becomes rate-limiting in the presence of low K appears, therefore, to be at the stage of transfer from aminoacyl-s-RNA to polypeptide, as predicted from observations of unbalanced RNA synthesis in K-depleted B207 cells.

Further Localization of the Step Requiring Optimum K. The transfer of labeled amino acid from aminoacyl-s-RNA into polypeptide is complex, and it is not yet clear how many components or steps are involved. The following experiments resolved this process of transfer into two parts.

A distinction was sought between two possibilities: either that K was needed in optimum concentration for some part of the process of transfer—for example, an initial step—or that K was needed for the entire sequence of transfer of amino acid into polypeptide. Experiments were designed to provide K at optimum concentration for only a short period of time, followed by a rapid change in cation concentration before polypeptide synthesis could be completed. In practice, rapid removal of K was not feasible, and as an alternative, the addition of Na or Li was used to antagonize the effect of K.

The use of two experimental conditions made the results discernible. First, the incorporation of counts originating in C^{14} phenylalanine was measured (in preference to measurement of the aminoacyl-s-RNA transfer step, which proceeds very rapidly), so that the course of incorporation could be followed over a period of 15–20 min. Second, concentrations of antagonistic cations were selected to provide efficient incorporation with K alone, but sizable inhibition if Na or Li were added at the start of the reaction.

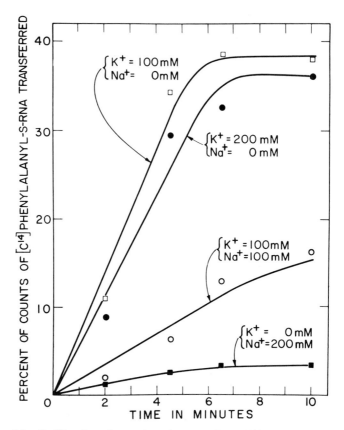

Fig. 7. Kinetics of transfer of counts from C^{14} phenylalanyl-s-RNA into polypeptide precipitable by trichloroacetic acid, at various K and Na concentrations. Each ml of reaction mixture contained, in μmoles: 100 Tris (*p*H 7.4), 13 Mg acetate, 6 mercaptoethanol, 50 sucrose, 0.3 trisodium-GTP, 1.0 disodium-ATP, 6 disodium-creatine phosphate; and 20 μg creatine phosphokinase; 80 μg polyuridylic acid; 0.0075 μc C^{14} phenyl-alanyl-s-RNA (spec. activity 210 mc/mmole); and S30 fraction (Nirenberg and Matthaei, 1961) (4 mg protein). 37°C. (From Lubin and Ennis, 1964, *Biochim. Biophys. Acta,* in press.)

In the experiment of Fig. 8, incorporation proceeded efficiently in the presence of 50 mM K. If Li was added at zero time, incorporation was strongly inhibited. But if the addition of Li was delayed 3.3 min, incorporation proceeded over the next 15 min, with evidence of only slight inhibition due to the addition of Li. The effect of monovalent cations on the early part of the incorporation reaction seems to differ from that on the later part.

This result not only localizes the requirement for optimum K, but, in addition, suggests the existence of at least two distinguishable steps in the

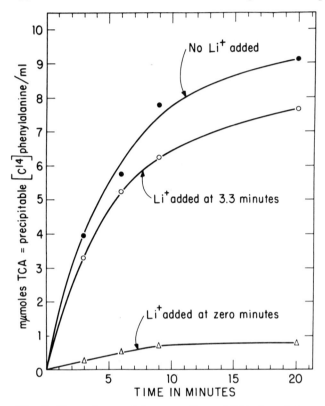

Fig. 8. Dependence of incorporation of C^{14} phenylalanine on the time of addition of LiCl. Reaction mixture similar to that in Fig. 4. Each ml contained 50 μmoles KCl. LiCl (150 μmoles) was added at zero time ($\triangle$—$\triangle$), after 3.3 min ($\bigcirc$—$\bigcirc$), or not at all ($\bullet$—$\bullet$). 37°C. (From Lubin, 1963, *Biochim. Biophys. Acta* 72: 345.)

transfer of amino acid from aminoacyl-s-RNA to polypeptide. Some of the components necessary for this first step, or "priming reaction," have been determined. Further details appear in another report (Lubin, 1963); and it appears that the priming reaction also involves messenger RNA and ribosomes.

Recent experiments reported by Nakamoto *et al.* (1963) show that a complex structure is formed from aminoacyl-s-RNA, messenger, and ribosomes, in the presence of optimum Mg and either K or NH_4. They found no indication of a requirement for an enzyme, although the possibility was not excluded that an enzyme firmly bound to washed ribosomes might participate in the reaction. In a system derived from reticulocytes, Arlinghaus *et al.* (1963) also reported the presence of two steps at this stage of protein synthesis, both apparently requiring enzymes. The evidence strongly suggests that the product of the "priming reaction" and the structure studied by Nakamoto *et al.* are identical.

Some Further Experiments on Intact Cells

In the poly-U system, the addition of NH_4 was found to be two- to threefold more effective in stimulating incorporation than was K. This raises the possibility that in the intact cell, NH_4 rather than K stimulates protein syn-

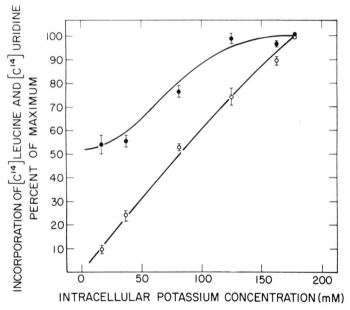

Fig. 9. Incorporation of C^{14} leucine into protein (O—O) and C^{14} uridine into RNA (●—●) at various levels of intracellular K. Intracellular levels computed from data of Figs. 1 and 2. Each point shown represents a rate of synthesis. Bracket shows 1 SE of mean. All values expressed as per cent of rate at highest K level. (From Lubin and Ennis, 1964, *Biochim. Biophys. Acta,* in press.)

thesis. Data derived from other kinds of experiments make this unlikely. First, the addition of NH$_4$ salts to B207 cells in low-K medium did not stimulate growth (Lubin and Ennis, 1964). Second, the intracellular concentration of NH$_4$ was measured and found to lie between 5 and 10 mM (Lubin and Ennis, 1964); in the cell-free system, this low level of NH$_4$ stimulated polyphenylalanine synthesis only slightly. Therefore, K, not NH$_4$, appears to be the more important cation for protein synthesis in intact cells.

The experiments described to this point have largely focused on the effects of extreme changes in K concentration. Even a modest decrease in cell K can be shown, under special conditions, to have a differential effect on protein and RNA synthesis. To demonstrate this, B207 cells were grown in minimal medium, washed in Na salts, and transferred to enriched medium in parallel flasks containing various levels of K. The incorporation of C^{14} uridine or C^{14} leucine was measured over a 15-min period, and the rates were plotted as a function of intracellular K concentration (Fig. 9). The results show that as the level of cell K fell, the rate of protein synthesis decreased faster than the rate of RNA synthesis.

Summary and Speculation

The results may be summarized as follows: Mutants of E. coli B that lack the normal capacity to concentrate K from low levels in the medium were isolated (Lubin and Kessel, 1960). With these mutants, cell K could be set easily and quickly to a predetermined level. A loss in cell K was partly replaced by a gain in Na, but other cell constituents were apparently conserved. After severe K depletion from a normal intracellular level of 200 mM to a final level of about 10 mM, cells synthesized considerable RNA but no protein (Ennis and Lubin, 1961). This dissociation of RNA and protein synthesis was similar to the effect of chloramphenicol on growing cells; the observation suggested that K depletion produced a block at a late stage in protein synthesis. These results were consistent with those obtained from experiments on the cell-free poly-U system. The step in the cell-free system that was most markedly dependent on K was found to be the transfer of amino acid from aminoacyl-s-RNA to polypeptide. Optimum K appeared to be required for a "priming reaction," involving Mg, messenger RNA, ribosomes, and perhaps other components (Lubin, 1963).

Although the results of experiments on cells and on the cell-free system are consistent, there are several loose ends. First, the effect of K on the release of completed protein from the ribosomes could not be determined, because most of the polyphenylalanine remains stuck to the ribosome (Haschemeyer and Rich, 1962). Second, the possible connection between the requirement of protein synthesis for K and the K-dependent phosphodiesterase (Spahr and Schlessinger, 1963), to which messenger is sensitive, is obscure. Third, RNA synthesis in K-depleted cells was considerably slower than RNA synthesis produced by the addition of chloramphenicol; the reason for this is not known.

The provocative title of this symposium—the cellular functions of membrane transport—has encouraged the advancement of a few speculative ideas. K is known to stimulate protein synthesis in extracts of mammalian cells. If the cells of higher organisms resemble *E. coli*, a direct effect of cell K on protein synthesis may be one of the mechanisms that link extracellular regulators to cell growth.

In general, K and Na levels probably do not vary widely among the cells of a given species. However, two curious examples of atypical patterns are known. In the mature erythrocytes of some mammals, including the cat and dog, K levels are low and Na high (Steinbach, 1962b). But erythrocytes do not make protein, and it would be of interest to find out if the precursor reticulocytes, which do synthesize hemoglobin, have much higher levels of cell K.

The nucleus of the frog egg has been reported in two independent studies to have a much higher concentration of Na—0.3 M—than does the cytoplasm (Abelson and Duryee, 1949; Naora *et al.*, 1962). K also appears to be unusually high in the nucleus of this cell (Naora *et al.*, 1962). These high levels of Na and K may be far removed from the optimum concentrations for protein synthesis. It seems plausible that a rapid shift of nuclear cations toward levels more favorable for protein synthesis may occur very shortly after fertilization.

Finally, the widespread occurrence in nature of high levels of cell K remains puzzling. For cells living in a high-Na environment, the activity of a Na–K pump may be required, as suggested by Wilson (1954), Leaf (1956), and Tosteson (1963), for maintenance of constant cell volume. But many cell species prosper in environments containing a wide spectrum of K and Na concentrations, and some of these, like *E. coli*, are protected from distortion by rigid cell walls. Moreover, microorganisms possess a remarkable capacity for discarding unnecessary biochemical appendages, through mutation and selection.

On teleonomic grounds (Davis, 1961), therefore, it seems reasonable to seek other explanations for the universal occurrence of high cell K. An alternative possibility was suggested by the results described in this paper and by the related results of Nakamoto *et al.* (1963). In *E. coli*, the step in protein synthesis that requires high levels of K involves the interaction of three components containing RNA. A K requirement for protein synthesis has also been found for extracts from liver (Sachs, 1957), pancreas (Gazzinelli and Dickman, 1962), yeast (Simpson, personal communication), and sea urchin eggs (Hultin, 1961).

Although the ability to distinguish between closely related small molecules has usually been the prerogative of enzymes, it seems possible that the precise fit of three molecules containing RNA may be unusually sensitive to the K and Na composition of the environment. The configuration of nucleic acid is less susceptible to change by mutation than is that of protein. These arguments suggest that the requirement for K in the formation of the complex of s-RNA, ribosomes, and messenger may account for the persistence of high levels of intracellular K throughout evolution.

REFERENCES

Abelson, P. H., and W. R. Duryee. 1949. *Biol. Bull.* 96: 205.

Arlinghaus, R., G. Favelukes, and R. Schweet. 1963. *Biochem. Biophys. Res. Commun.* 11: 92.

Askari, A. 1963. *Science* 141: 44.

Bessman, M. J., and M. J. Van Bibber. 1959. *Biochem. Biophys. Res. Commun.* 1: 101.

Black, S. 1951. *Arch. Biochem. Biophys.* 34: 86.

Boyer, P. D. 1953. *J. Cellular Comp. Physiol.* 42: 71.

Cantoni, G. L. 1960. In *Comp. Biochem.*, Vol. 1. New York: Academic Press, Inc. P. 234.

Christian, J. H. B., and J. A. Waltho. 1962. *Biochim. Biophys. Acta* 65: 506.

Cohn, M., and J. Monod. 1951. *Biochim. Biophys. Acta* 7: 153.

Davis, B. D. 1961. *Cold Spring Harbor Symp. Quant. Biol.* 26: 1.

Davis, B. D., and D. S. Feingold. 1962. In *The Bacteria*, Vol. 4. New York: Academic Press, Inc. P. 343.

Davis, B. D., and E. S. Mingioli. 1950. *J. Bacteriol.* 60: 17.

Dixon, M., and E. C. Webb. 1958. *Enzymes.* New York: Academic Press, Inc.

Ennis, H. L., and M. Lubin. 1961. *Biochim. Biophys. Acta* 50: 399.

Flax, J. G., M. J. Erwin, and J. M. Buchanan. 1957. *J. Biol. Chem.* 229: 603.

Franzen, J. S., and S. B. Binkley. 1961. *J. Biol. Chem.* 236: 515.

Gazzinelli, G., and S. R. Dickman. 1962. *Biochim. Biophys. Acta* 61: 980.

Glynn, I. M. 1957. *Progr. Biophys. Chem.* 8: 241.

Goldstein, D. B., B. J. Brown, and A. Goldstein. 1960. *Biochim. Biophys. Acta* 43: 55.

Happold, F. C., and A. Struyvenberg. 1954. *Biochem. J.* 58: 379.

Haschemeyer, A. E. V., and A. Rich. 1962. *Biochim. Biophys. Acta* 55: 994.

Holley, R. W. 1961. *J. Biol. Chem.* 236: 197.

Hultin, T. 1961. *Exptl. Cell Res.* 25: 405.

Kachmar, J. F., and P. D. Boyer. 1953. *J. Biol. Chem.* 200: 669.

Leaf, A. 1956. *Biochem. J.* 62: 241.

Lengyel, P., J. F. Speyer, and S. Ochoa. 1961. *Proc. Natl. Acad. Sci. U.S* 47: 1936.

Lin, E. C. C., and B. Magasanik. 1960. *J. Biol. Chem.* 235: 1820.

Lubin, M. 1962. *J. Bacteriol.* 83: 696.

Lubin, M., 1963. *Biochim. Biophys. Acta* 72: 345.

Lubin, M., and H. L. Ennis. 1964. *Biochim. Biophys. Acta.* In press.

Lubin, M., and D. Kessel. 1960. *Biochem. Biophys. Res. Commun.* 2: 249.

Maas, W. 1952. *J. Biol. Chem.* 198: 23.

Magasanik, B., H. S. Moyed, and L. B. Gehring. 1957. *J. Biol. Chem.* 226: 339.

Marshall, M., R. S. Metzenberg, and P. P. Cohen. 1961. *J. Biol. Chem.* 236: 2229.

Mudd, S. H., and G. L. Cantoni. 1958. *J. Biol. Chem.* 231: 481.

Muntz, J. A. 1953. *Arch. Biochem. Biophys.* 42: 435.

Nakamoto, T., T. W. Conway, J. E. Allende, G. J. Spyrides, and F. Lipmann. 1963. *Cold Spring Harbor Symp. Quant. Biol.* 28. In press.

Naora, H., H. Naora, M. Izawa, V. G. Allfrey, and A. E. Mirsky. 1962. *Proc. Natl. Acad. Sci. U.S.* 48: 853.

Neidhardt, F. C., and D. G. Fraenkel. 1961. *Cold Spring Harbor Symp. Quant. Biol.* 26: 63.

Neidhardt, F. C., and B. Magasanik. 1960. *Biochim. Biophys. Acta* 42: 99.

Neuhaus, F. C. 1962. *J. Biol. Chem.* 237: 778.

Nirenberg, M. W., and J. H. Matthaei. 1961. *Proc. Natl. Acad. Sci. U.S.* 47: 1588.

Nishimura, J. S., and D. M. Greenberg. 1961. *J. Biol. Chem.* 236: 2684.

Nossal, P. M. 1951. *Biochem. J.* 49: 407.

Parks, R. E., Jr., E. Ben-Gershom, and H. A. Lardy. 1957. *J. Biol. Chem.* 227: 231.

Sachs, H. 1957. *J. Biol. Chem.* 228: 23.

Schultz, S. G., and A. K. Solomon. 1961. *J. Gen. Physiol.* 45: 355.

Schweet, R. S., and E. H. Allen. 1958. *J. Biol. Chem.* 233: 1104.

Spahr, P. F., and D. Schlessinger. 1963. *J. Biol. Chem.* 238: PC2251.

Stadtman, E. R. 1952. *J. Biol. Chem.* 196: 527.

Steinbach, H. B. 1962a. *Perspectives Biol. Med.* 5: 338.

Steinbach, H. B. 1962b. In *Comp. Biochem.*, Vol. 4. New York: Academic Press, Inc. P. 677.

Steinbach, H. B. 1963. *Biol. Bull.* 124: 322.

Tosteson, D. C. 1963. *Federation Proc.* 22: 19.

Ussing, H. H. 1960. In *Handbuch der Experimentellen Pharmakologie*, Ergan-zungswerk, Vol. 13, ed. O. Eichler and A. Farah. Berlin: Springer-Verlag. P. 1.

Von Korff, R. W. 1953. *J. Biol. Chem.* 203: 265.

Webster, G. C., and J. E. Varner. 1954. *Arch. Biochem. Biophys.* 52: 22.

Webster, G. C., and J. E. Varner. 1955. *Arch. Biochem. Biophys.* 55: 95.

Wilson, T. H. 1954. *Science* 120: 104.

Role of the Membrane

in Secretory Phenomena

Structure and Function of the Intestinal Absorptive Cell

T. Hastings Wilson

Department of Physiology
Harvard Medical School
Boston, Massachusetts

During this symposium, there has been discussion of the role of membrane transport in the regulation of a variety of cellular functions—metabolism, osmotic behavior, conduction, and contraction. This paper will discuss a cell whose special mission in life is transport *per se*. The columnar absorptive cell of the small intestine must transport from the lumen of the intestine all of the nutrients required for the survival of all of the cells of the animal body. The variety and complexity of transport processes in this cell is quite staggering. One could name 25 transport systems from available data (see Wilson, 1962), and there may well be an equal number more. The plasma membrane of this versatile cell possesses the potential for virtually every type of transport mechanism known. A few of these mechanisms will be illustrated in this brief review.

A few introductory remarks concerning the morphological appearance of this tissue might be useful. Figure 1 shows normal villi, which may be seen with a simple hand lens. Three villi are shown at higher magnification in Fig. 2. The columnar epithelial cells lining these villi are predominantly absorptive cells, with a minor fraction mucus-secreting cells. The cells of the crypts of Lieberkühn are, not absorptive, but immature cells which will migrate up the sides of the villi and be extruded from the tips into the lumen. During this ascent, the cells mature, increasing their content of hydrolytic enzymes and transport machinery. Figure 3 shows an electron micrograph of the absorptive cell of the golden hamster (Strauss, 1963). The most striking morphologic feature of this cell is the long, slender, finger-like projections on the luminal border of the cell, called microvilli. The collection of microvilli has been known to the light-microscopist as the brush border. The second membrane of the cell which concerns us is the endoplasmic reticulum,

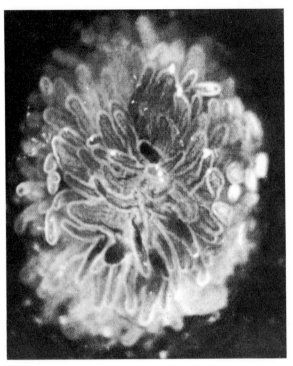

Fig. 1. Villi of human jejunum. Unstained biopsy specimen taken from a normal adult. ×9.4. (From Rubin *et al.*, 1960, *Gastroenterology* 38: 28.)

which may be identified in Fig. 3 as vesicular structure in the apical portion of the cell. As we shall see, this membrane is extremely important in the transport of lipids and proteins across the cell.

Now let us consider some of the general permeability properties of this cell. As in all living cells, the plasma membrane of the absorptive cell has the general properties described by Overton in 1899. It is permeable to many lipid-soluble substances, regardless of molecular weight, and permeable to water and to very small water-soluble, lipid-insoluble compounds. The pore size has been estimated by Lindemann and Solomon (1962) to be about 4 Å in diameter.

Many important nutrients cannot diffuse into the cell, either because they are too large to enter the pores (such as vitamin B_{12}) or because they are highly charged (such as Ca). For these substances, special mechanisms have been evolved for their transport across the cell.

One type of transport is the familiar phenomenon commonly classified as "active transport." One of the simplest examples is the intestinal absorption

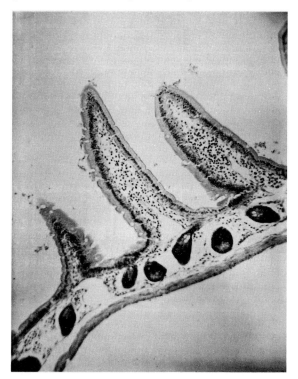

Fig. 2. Villi of hamster jejunum. Hematoxylin and eosin. ×8.3.

of sugars against a concentration gradient. Two general methods are available for the study of these cells *in vitro:* those which measure net transport across the cell, and those which measure accumulation within the epithelial cells. One of the *in vitro* methods available for study of net transport across the epithelial cells is the everted-sac technique which was developed in collaboration with Dr. Wiseman (Wilson and Wiseman, 1954) at the University of Sheffield. The small intestine of a rat or hamster is turned inside out, and a small sac is prepared containing Krebs-Ringer solution (Fig. 4). This everted sac is incubated in 5 or 10 ml of the same medium, and the flask gassed with 95% O_2, 5% CO_2. The following simple experiment may be performed with this preparation. Tissue was incubated with the same glucose-containing solution on both sides of the intestinal wall. At the end of 1 hr of incubation, the concentration on the mucosal side fell to about 70 mg%, while that on the opposite side rose to about 700 mg% (Fig. 5). As there was little fluid movement in this experiment, the concentration changes indicate a net movement of sugar across the full thickness of the tissue against a final concentration

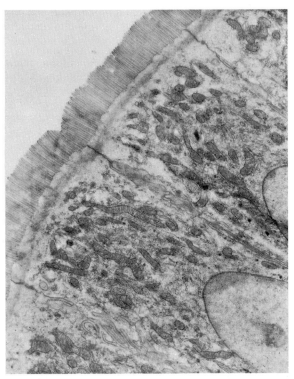

Fig. 3. Electron micrograph of absorptive cells of a villus from the golden hamster. ×4,050. (From Strauss, 1963, *J. Cell Biol.* 17: 597.)

ratio of tenfold. It is quite easy to demonstrate a 100-fold concentration ratio. The maximum gradient has never been determined.

The specificity of this sugar-transport system is perhaps the most carefully studied of any transport system. Through the work of Crane and Krane (1956, 1959) and our own laboratory (Wilson and Vincent, 1955; Wilson and Crane, 1958; Wilson and Landau, 1960; Landau *et al.*, 1962), more than 70 compounds have been tested. The essential features of the glucose molecule required for transport by the hamster intestine are as follows: a D-pyranose ring structure, at least 6 carbon atoms, and an OH⁻ group at carbon 2 of

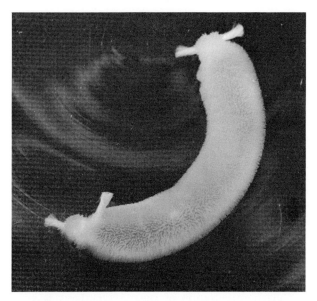

Fig. 4. Everted sac of hamster jejunum. ×1.35.

the configuration found in glucose (Fig. 6). This study of specificity has made untenable the classical phosphorylation-dephosphorylation hypothesis of Wilbrandt and Laszt (1933). The modern version of this hypothesis (Kalckar, 1937; Krogh, 1937) states that glucose is phosphorylated by hexokinase at the luminal border of the cell to glucose-6-phosphate, which diffuses across the cell, where it is dephosphorylated by phosphatase. The free glucose enters the blood, and the inorganic PO_4 is recycled in the cell. The finding of Crane and Krane (1956) that 6-deoxyglucose was actively transported by the glucose-transport system eliminated hexokinase as an enzyme involved in sugar transport. Although phosphorylation of the OH^- at carbon 2 has not been specifically excluded, glucose-2-phosphate has not been isolated from the gut during absorption. It is our own working hypothesis that sugars are adsorbed to membrane carrier molecules without the formation of covalent bonds. According to this view, the sugar-carrier

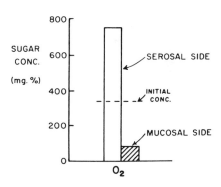

Fig. 5. Active transport of glucose by the everted sac of hamster intestine. (From data of Wilson and Wiseman, 1954.)

complex moves across the osmotic barrier, and the sugar is released on the inner boundary of the membrane.

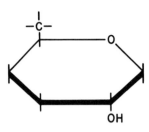

Fig. 6. Minimum structural requirements for intestinal transport of sugars. (From Crane, 1960, *Physiol. Revs.* 40: 789; Wilson *et al.*, 1960, *Federation Proc.* 19: 870.)

An extremely important question is the exact location of the sugar pump within the cell. It has been known from the work of Fisher and Parsons (1953) and of Crane and Mandelstam (1960) that the intestinal tissue accumulates the sugars which it transports. Among the various hypotheses which might be advanced, there are two which can be distinguished experimentally. Hypothesis A states that the active-transport mechanism of the cell is localized at the basal membrane of the cell. This would result in a high concentration of sugar immediately below the base of the cell. Hypothesis B states that the "pump" mechanism is localized in the brush border region of the cell. The consequence of this localization would be a high intracellular concentration of sugar. Hypothesis B was consistent with inhibitor data of Newey *et al.* (1959) and microdissection data of McDougal *et al.* (1960). The radioautographic technique, however, would give a decisive answer to this question. Dr. Kinter (1961), in our department (now at the University of Syracuse), had experience in radioautographic methods with water-soluble compounds, and he undertook the experiment. Identical results were obtained for both sugars (galactose, 3-O-methylglucose, and 6-deoxyglucose) and amino acids (L-methionine and L-valine); Fig. 7 illustrates results for an amino acid. An everted sac of hamster intestine was incubated for 30 sec with C^{14}-labeled L-methionine. The tissue was then dropped into a freezing mixture and subsequently sectioned on a microtome at $-20°C$, care being taken not to thaw the section at any time. Alternate sections were exposed to photographic film at $-20°C$, and the others stained with hematoxylin-eosin. After 4 days' exposure of the photographic emulsion to the frozen section, the film was developed and compared with the adjacent stained section (Fig. 7). It is clear that the darkening of the film corresponds to the layer of columnar absorptive cells lining the villus. The belief that this radioactivity was associated with freely diffusible methionine and not protein was supported by the fact that thawing of the section for 1–2 sec followed by refreezing led to very marked diffusion of radioactivity from the cells. When the technique was modified to retain the tissue section on the photographic emulsion, it was possible with phase contrast microscopy to visualize both tissue and radioautograph simultaneously. In these experiments, it was quite clear that the radioactivity within the cell was greater than that in the lumen or the lamina propria. These data demonstrate the presence of an active-transport system in the region of the brush border of the cell.

Another interesting area of investigation has been recently opened up by Miller and Crane (1961) who devised an ingenious method for the preparation and purification of the brush border. They homogenized the mucosa in distilled water to which they added a trace of versene. The cells apparently swell and rupture, the nuclei and mitochondria disappear (apparently also

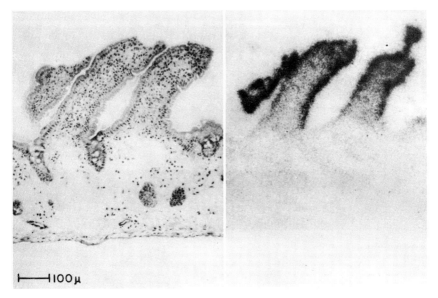

├────┤100 μ

Fig. 7. Autoradiograph of a section of hamster intestine absorbing L-methionine. Everted sac of hamster jejunum was incubated 30 sec in presence of C^{14}-labeled L-methionine, frozen in isopentane at $-160°C$, and sectioned in a cryostat at $-20°C$. Alternate sections were stained with hematoxylin and eosin (left) or exposed to photographic film (right). (From Kinter, 1961, *Proc. 12th Ann. Conf. Nephrotic Syndrome,* ed. J. Metcoff. P. 59.)

by osmotic means), and the brush border remains intact. An electron micrograph of the resulting preparation is shown in Fig. 8. The isolated brush border contains all or most of the cell's invertase, maltase, lactase, and phosphatase, and some of the peptidases. This is one of the very few cases where the plasma membrane may be studied separately from the other organelles of the cell. Undoubtedly, this preparation will be extensively investigated during the next few years.

Let me turn now to another type of membrane transport which may be found in the absorptive cell—membrane vesiculation, or pinocytosis. One of the clearest examples of pinocytosis in animal cells is that responsible for gamma globulin absorption in the newborn of certain species. This remarkable process of intestinal absorption of antibodies allows a variety of animals to obtain passive immunity during the newborn period. The process in the pig, cow, and horse offers a dramatic example of the phenomenon. These animals are born virtually devoid of serum gamma globulins, but following a single feeding of colostrum, enough gamma globulin is absorbed to bring the blood level to that of the adult. The transport of intact protein across the epithelial cell occurs only once in the postnatal life of these animals. Payne and Marsh (1961a, b) have fed fluoroscein-labeled gamma globulin

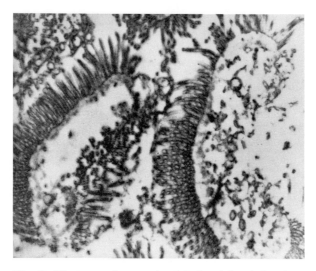

Fig. 8. Electron micrograph of isolated brush borders. ×6,250. (From Miller and Crane, 1961, *Biochim. Biophys. Acta* 52: 281.)

to newborn pigs and shown that spherical droplets of protein appear in the apical cytoplasm of the cell shortly after exposure of the cells to labeled material (Figs. 9 and 10). The protein is apparently within the endoplasmic reticulum. Absorption continues until about the fifth hour, during which time the protein is seen to accumulate in large amounts. So much accumulates at the capillary pole of the cell that the nucleus is actually displaced to the opposite end of the cell. Between the 5th and 12th hours, fluoroscent gamma globulin can be seen leaving the epithelial cells and entering the lymphatics. This continues until the 18th hour, when all of the gamma globulin has disappeared from the cells and lymphatics. These cells are never again able to absorb appreciable quantities of intact protein molecules.

Considerable evidence has accumulated that the mechanism of protein absorption of the newborn animal involves the formation of vesicles in the columnar absorptive cells. Feeding of protein stimulates vesicle formation, and the time of cessation of protein absorption in different species corresponds exactly to the time of loss of vesicular appearance of the cells. Clark (1959) has recently made a careful study of the ultrastructure of the absorptive cells during protein absorption in the rat and mouse. Figure 11 shows the large number of vesicles of all sizes found in the apical cytoplasm of an

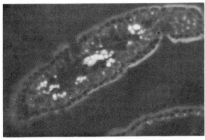 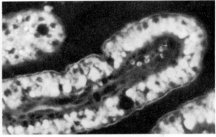

Fig. 9. Photomicrograph (UV) of intestinal tissue of the newborn pig before administration of gamma globulin. ×53. (Kindly provided by Dr. L. C. Payne.)

Fig. 10. Photomicrograph (UV) of intestinal tissue 8 hrs after administration of fluorescein-labeled gamma globulin. × 53. (Kindly provided by Dr. L. C. Payne.)

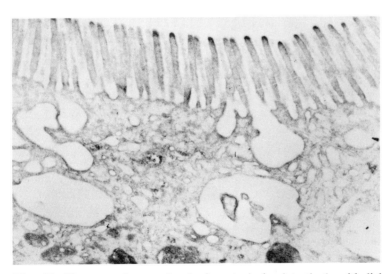

Fig. 11. Electron micrograph of pinocytosis by intestinal epithelial cell of the suckling rat. ×15,200. (From Clark, 1959, *J. Biophys. Biochem. Cytol.* 5: 41.)

absorptive cell of the suckling rat. One of the vesicles in the figure clearly communicates with the lumen of the intestine. Although there is strong evidence for the entry of gamma globulin into the cell by pinocytosis, the mode of exit from the cell has not been studied in any detail.

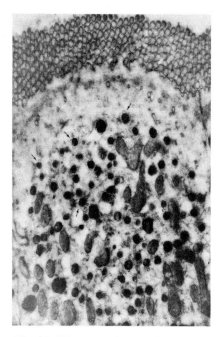

Another transport phenomenon seen in these cells also involves the participation of both plasma membrane and the endoplasmic reticulum. This is triglyceride absorption. Palay and Karlin (1959) have published electron micrographs of the sequence of events in fat absorption in the rat. About 20 min after feeding 1.5 ml of corn oil, the osmium-fixed tissue shows small droplets of fat (about 50 mμ in diameter) in the spaces between the microvilli. Soon thereafter, droplets begin to appear in the apical cytoplasm, enclosed in membranes apparently identical with the endoplasmic reticulum (Fig. 12). Figure 13 shows a higher magnification of these droplets surrounded by membranes. At the level of the nucleus, these droplets are extruded from the cell into the extracellular space between the columnar epithelial cells. Figure 14 shows a cross-

Fig. 12. Electron micrograph of apical cytoplasm of intestinal epithelial cell 75 min after feeding corn oil to a rat. ×15,700. (From Palay and Karlin, 1959, *J. Biophys. Biochem. Cytol.* 5: 373.)

section of such cells, with the many droplets of triglyceride devoid of membrane lying between the cells. The sequence of events is summarized in Fig. 15. There is, at present, a difference of opinion concerning the mechanism by which lipid enters the cell. Palay and Karlin (1959) favor the uptake of particulate lipid by pinocytosis. Hogben (1960), on the other hand, points out that the mixture of fatty acids, mono-, di-, and triglycerides, might enter the cell by simple passive diffusion if they were in molecular form at the surface of the cell. Regardless of the mode of entry into the cell, there is little doubt that the endoplasmic reticulum is the site of resynthesis of triglyceride from the absorbed fatty acids and lower glycerides. Senior and Isselbacher (1960) have shown that activation of long-chain fatty acids occurs in the microsome fraction (endoplasmic reticulum) of the cell. The secretion of the triglyceride particle from the cell has not been studied

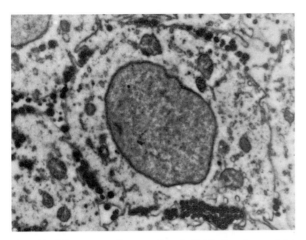

Fig. 13. Electron micrograph of lipid droplets within the endoplasmic reticulum of absorptive cell of the rat. ×18,500. (From Palay and Karlin, 1959, *J. Biophys. Biochem. Cytol.* 5: 373.)

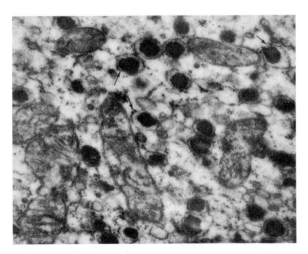

Fig. 14. Extracellular position of lipid at the level of the nucleus of an absorptive cell of the rat. Note that the extracellular lipid droplets are devoid of their membranous envelopes. ×8,000. (From Palay and Karlin, 1959, *J. Biophys. Biochem. Cytol.* 5: 373.)

in much detail but appears to be similar to zymogen-granule secretion by the pancreatic acinar cell.

Just to stimulate the incredulity of the reader, let us consider briefly one process which is extremely poorly understood, namely, vitamin B_{12} absorption. This vitamin, with a molecular weight of about 1,200, cannot be ab-

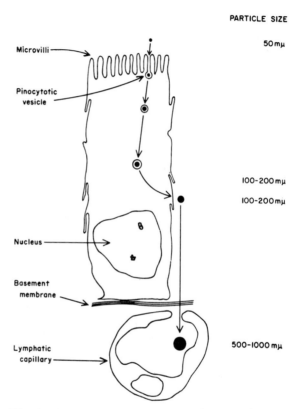

PARTICLE SIZE

Microvilli

50 mμ

Pinocytotic vesicle

100-200 mμ

100-200 mμ

Nucleus

Basement membrane

Lymphatic capillary

500-1000 mμ

Fig. 15. Summary of morphological aspects of lipid absorption. This figure illustrates the pinocytosis hypothesis of lipid entry into the cell. (From Wilson, 1962, *Intestinal Absorption*. Philadelphia: W. B. Saunders Co.)

sorbed without the simultaneous presence of a specific protein produced in the stomach, called gastric intrinsic factor (IF), with a molecular weight of about 100,000 (see review by Castle, 1953). An *in vitro* experiment may illustrate this point. Two everted sacs were incubated with radioactive vitamin— one in the presence and one in the absence of IF. Figure 16 shows that B_{12} uptake was stimulated 20-fold (Strauss and Wilson, 1960). It is quite possible

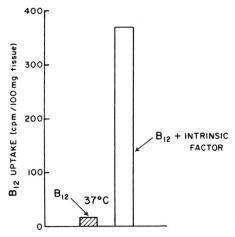

Fig. 16. Stimulation by intrinsic factor of B_{12} uptake by everted sacs of hamster ileum. (From Strauss and Wilson, 1960, *Am. J. Physiol.* 198: 103.)

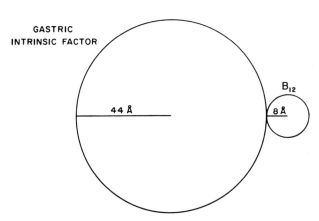

Fig. 17. Approximate molecular dimensions of intrinsic factor and vitamin B_{12}. (From Wilson, 1963, *Physiologist* 6, No. 1: 11.)

to obtain a 100-fold stimulation by IF. The relative sizes of these molecules are shown in Fig. 17. Clearly, they could not enter via the pore route.

According to current views, vitamin B_{12} is freed from dietary proteins during digestion and then tightly bound to gastric IF in the lumen of the intestine. There is some evidence that it may enter the cell bound to IF (Wilson, 1963; Boass and Wilson, unpublished observations). The mechanism of this transport is not known. If it must be one of the well-recognized mechanisms, then perhaps a logical candidate would be pinocytosis (which is known to be able to take up protein). There is, however, no direct evidence to support this view.

This has been a bird's-eye view of some of the functions of the intestinal absorptive cell. There is certainly no doubt that this cell is one of the most versatile pieces of transport machinery available to the experimentalist.

REFERENCES

Castle, W. B. 1953. *New England J. Med.* 249: 603.

Clark, S. L., Jr. 1959. *J. Biophys. Biochem. Cytol.* 5: 41.

Crane, R. K. 1960. *Physiol. Revs.* 40: 789.

Crane, R. K., and S. M. Krane. 1956. *Biochim. Biophys. Acta* 20: 568.

Crane, R. K., and S. M. Krane. 1959. *Biochim. Biophys. Acta* 31: 397.

Crane, R. K., and P. Mandelstam. 1960. *Biochim. Biophys. Acta* 45: 460.

Fisher, R. B., and D. S. Parsons. 1953. *J. Physiol. (London)* 119: 224.

Hogben, C. A. M. 1960. *Ann. Rev. Physiol.* 22: 381.

Kalckar, H. M. 1937. *Enzymologia* 2: 47.

Kinter, W. B. 1961. In *Proc. 12th Ann. Conf. Nephrotic Syndrome*, ed. J. Metcoff. P. 59.

Krogh, A. 1937. *Scand. Arch. Physiol.* 76: 60.

Landau, B. R., L. Bernstein, and T. H. Wilson. 1962. *Am. J. Physiol.* 203: 237.

Lindemann, B., and A. K. Solomon. 1962. *J. Gen. Physiol.* 45: 801.

McDougal, D. B., Jr., K. D. Little, and R. K. Crane. 1960. *Biochim. Biophys. Acta* 45: 483.

Miller, D., and R. K. Crane. 1961. *Biochim. Biophys. Acta* 52: 281.

Newey, H., B. J. Parsons, and D. H. Smyth. 1959. *J. Physiol.* 148: 83.

Overton, E. 1899. *Vierteljahresschr. Naturforsch. Ges. Zuerich* 44: 88.

Palay, S. L., and L. J. Karlin. 1959. *J. Biophys. Biochem. Cytol.* 5: 373.

Payne, L. C., and C. L. Marsh. 1962a. *Federation Proc.* 21: 909.

Payne, L. C., and C. L. Marsh. 1962b. *J. Nutr.* 76: 151.

Rubin, C. E., L. L. Brandborg, P. C. Phelps, and H. C. Taylor, Jr. 1960. *Gastroenterology* 38: 28.

Senior, J., and K. J. Isselbacher. 1960. *Biochim. Biophys. Acta* 44: 399.

Strauss, E. W. 1963. *J. Cell Biol.* 17: 597.

Strauss, E. W., and T. H. Wilson. 1960. *Am. J. Physiol.* 198: 103.

Wilbrandt, W., and L. Laszt. 1933. *Biochem. Z.* 259: 398.

Wilson, T. H. 1962. *Intestinal Absorption.* Philadelphia: W. B. Saunders Co.

Wilson, T. H. 1963. *Physiologist* 6, No. 1: 11.

Wilson, T. H., and R. K. Crane. 1958. *Biochim. Biophys. Acta* 29: 30.

Wilson, T. H., and B. R. Landau. 1960. *Am. J. Physiol.* 198: 99.

Wilson, T. H., and T. N. Vincent. 1955. *J. Biol. Chem.* 216: 851.

Wilson, T. H., and G. Wiseman. 1954. *J. Physiol. (London)* 123: 116.

Wilson, T. H., E. C. C. Lin, B. R. Landau, and C. R. Jorgensen. 1960. *Federation Proc.* 19: 870.

Hydrochloric Acid Secretion, Ion Gradients, and the Gastric Potential[1]

Warren S. Rehm

Department of Physiology and Biophysics
University of Louisville School of Medicine
Louisville, Kentucky

The gastric mucosa can transport both H^+ and Cl against their respective electrochemical potential gradients (Rehm, 1950; Hogben, 1951). The minimum free energy ΔG necessary for the transport of a monovalent ion across a tissue is given by the well-known equation:

$$\Delta G_{\pm} = nRT \log \frac{a_1}{a_2} \mp nF \Delta \Psi \qquad (1)$$

where n is the number of moles transported, R the gas constant, T the absolute temperature, a_1 and a_2 the activities of the ion in the fluids bathing the tissue, F the Faraday, and $\Delta \Psi$ the potential difference between the two fluids. For the dog's stomach (Rehm, 1950), with the values given in Fig. 1, the ΔG for the transport of one mole of H^+ is

$$\Delta G_{\mathrm{H}} = 1400 \times 6.5 - 1400 = 1400\,(6.5 - 1) \qquad (2)$$

and for one mole of Cl is

$$\Delta G_{\mathrm{Cl}} = 1400 \times 0.18 + 1400 = 1400\,(0.18 + 1) \qquad (3)$$

[1] Part of the work reviewed was supported by grants G-3505 and 2G-583 from the National Institutes of Health and by grant G-5592 from the National Science Foundation.

The ratio of $\Delta G_{Cl}/\Delta G_H$ is 0.21 (1.18/5.5). In other words, the ΔG for Cl is about 20% of that for the H^+. Neglecting the force of the electric field leads one to the erroneous conclusion (Bull and Gray, 1945) that the minimum work needed for the transport of the Cl is only a very small fraction of that for the H^+; i.e., the ratio of $\Delta G_{Cl}/\Delta G_H = 0.028$ (0.18/6.5).

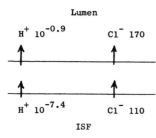

Fig. 1. Typical values for H^+ (activities) and Cl (concentration, mM) in the gastric juice and ISF of the dog. The ISF is approximately 60 mv positive to the lumen fluid. In the calculations in equations (2) and (3), it was assumed that the ratio of the activity coefficients of the Cl is unity and $\Delta\Psi = 60$ mv.

During secretion of gastric juice, H^+ and Cl account for about 95% of the ions transported, and Na plus K for about the remaining 5%. Only trace amounts of other ions appear in gastric juice (Babkin, 1950). During secretion, Na and K move down their electrochemical potential gradients. However, under certain conditions, there is probably a small amount of "uphill" transport of Na and K. The uphill Na transport is directed from lumen to interstitial fluid (ISF) (Bornstein et al., 1959), while that for K is directed from ISF to lumen (Edelman and Harris, 1958).

The free-energy calculations for H^+ and Cl tell us that some force or forces, other than those arising from the electrochemical potential gradients, must be available for the transport of these ions. The only forces that one can easily conceive of as playing a role in this transport are those arising from the force of attraction between molecules. In other words, there must be an attraction between the substance transported and some substance or substances in the cell. Furthermore, for a net transport of an ion against its electrochemical potential gradient, there must be a cyclic change in the force of this attraction, otherwise a net transport of the ion could not be accomplished.

The above is what I mean when I talk about the "carrier" concept, and I will use the term "carrier" to denote the substance (or substances) that attracts the ion being transported, without regard to the details of how the carrier-ion complex moves across the membrane (Patlak, 1956).

There are essentially three ways that an ion can be transported against its electrochemical potential gradient. In Fig. 2, these three ways are illustrated for Cl. They are 1) the simultaneous transport of Cl and a cation by a single carrier between cytoplasm and external fluid; 2) a forced exchange between Cl and another anion, A^-, from cytoplasm to external fluid; and 3) mechanisms in which there is a net transport of charge across the membrane. These latter mechanisms would give rise to an electromotive force in the absence of ion gradients between the cytoplasm and external fluid, and are referred to as electrogenic mechanisms. With the first two mechanisms, it would not be mandatory for an electromotive force to be present, and they

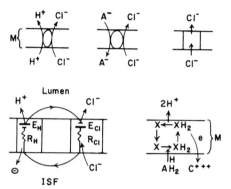

Fig. 2. Schemes for Cl transport.

are referred to as nonelectrogenic mechanisms. Any electromotive force that would result from the nonelectrogenic mechanisms would arise indirectly as a result of the establishment of ion gradients between the cytoplasm and external fluid. In an electrogenic mechanism, the net transport of charge in the membrane could occur by the transport of either electrons or ions. Figure 2 (right lower diagram) illustrates a possible mechanism for the transport of H^+ in which the net transport is by electrons (Rehm and Dennis, 1957). Figure 3 illustrates a possible mechanism for the transport of Cl in which the charge is carried through the membrane by a cation.

On the basis of a substantial amount of experimental work, a theory of gastric HCl was formulated in which it was postulated that both H^+ and Cl mechanisms are electrogenic and hence are secreted at separate sites in the membrane (Rehm, 1950). This theory will be referred to as the separate-site theory. An equivalent

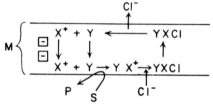

Fig. 3. Possible electrogenic mechanism for Cl transport in which charge is carried by cation. $S \rightarrow P$ represents substrate to product and is the source of energy for the synthesis of YX^+ which has strong affinity for Cl. On lumen side, it is assumed that an enzyme is present that cleaves YXCl to $X^+ + Y + Cl$. The cation X^+ moves across the membrane via fixed negative charges in membrane.

circuit illustrating this theory is shown in Fig. 2 (lower left). It can be shown that the electromotive force, E, for the Cl electrogenic scheme shown in Fig. 3 would be given by the following equation:

$$E = E_0 - \frac{RT}{F} \ln \frac{a_L}{a_C} \qquad (4)$$

where a_L and a_C are the Cl activities in the lumen and cytoplasm, respectively. When $a_L = a_C$, $E = E_0$. It is to be emphasized that in the separate-site theory, the type of electrogenic mechanism is not specified, i.e., whether the net transport of charge is by electrons or by ions. If the separate-site theory is correct, then ion gradients between the cytoplasm and external fluids would not be essential for the maintenance of the gastric potential difference (PD). It is to be emphasized that the operation of electrogenic mechanisms would undoubtedly result in a redistribution of ions, so that electromotive forces dependent on ion gradients between the cytoplasm and the external fluids would also be present.

On the other hand, if the transport processes are entirely nonelectrogenic, then the gastric PD would be completely dependent upon ion gradients between cytoplasm and bathing fluids. This paper will be primarily concerned with the problem of whether the Cl and H^+ mechanisms are electrogenic or nonelectrogenic.

Methods

Most of the work in this field has been performed on the *in vivo* dog stomach and on the *in vitro* stomachs of the frog and mouse. A technique for the *in vitro* frog stomach is illustrated in Fig. 4 (Rehm, 1962). A technique for the dog stomach was used which was essentially the same, except that an intact blood supply was maintained (Rehm, 1945). With the studies on both the frog and dog stomachs, two pairs of electrodes were used, one pair for sending current across the mucosa and the other pair for measuring the PD. The resistance was determined as the ratio of the change in PD per unit of applied current. In the technique for the frog stomach, illustrated in this figure, the H^+ secretory rate was measured by the pH-stat technique which was introduced into this field by Durbin and Heinz (1958). With this method, the pH of the fluid on the secretory side is automatically maintained constant by the injection of a NaOH solution, and the rate of NaOH injection is taken as a measure of the rate of H^+ secretion.

Results and Discussion

I am not going to review most of the older findings that led to the original formulation of the separate-site theory, since they have been adequately reviewed before (Rehm and Dennis, 1957; Rehm, 1959). Nor am I going to present certain recent findings that were reviewed at the Buffalo Symposium

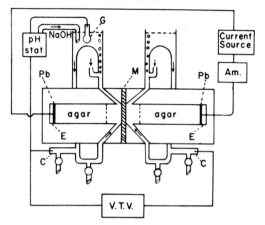

Fig. 4. Diagram of apparatus for measurement of H+ secretory rate of frog stomach. *C*: calomel electrodes; *G*: glass electrode. *G* and electrode *C* on secretory side are connected to *p*H stat. *VTV*: vacuum tube voltmeter; *Am*: microammeter; *M*: gastric mucosa; *E*: current-sending electrodes; *Pb*: lead disc. Pb acetate agar adjacent to Pb disc; layers of agar made of secretory solution and nutrient solution extend from Pb acetate agar to dotted lines. Secretory and nutrient solutions between dotted lines and stomach. (From Rehm, 1962, *Am. J. Physiol.* 203: 63.)

(Rehm, in press). However, I would like to mention briefly one finding that was primarily responsible for the formulation of the separate-site theory. This is illustrated in Fig. 5. On the basis of the separate-site theory, it would be predicted that the sending of current from ISF to the lumen would in-

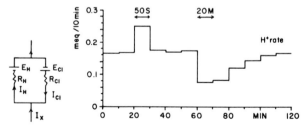

Fig. 5. Effect of electric current on H+ secretion. During period labeled *50 S*, 50 ma of current was sent across the dog stomach from serosa to mucosa (area, 20 cm²), and during period labeled *20 M*, 20 ma sent from mucosa to serosa.

crease the flow of current in the H^+ limb of the circuit, and, hence, the rate of H^+ secretion and the sending of current in the opposite direction would have the opposite effect. As seen in this figure, this prediction was borne out. The current sent from ISF to lumen (labeled *50 S*) results in a substantial increase in H^+ rate, and the sending of current in the opposite direction results in a decrease in H^+ rate. The details of this finding have been presented and discussed repeatedly (Rehm, 1945, 1959; Rehm and Dennis, 1957), and I am not going to say anything more about them other than to point out that this finding is difficult to explain adequately on the basis of the nonelectrogenic theories.

As pointed out above, one way to test the separate-site theory is to determine whether or not the gastric PD is dependent on ion gradients between cytoplasm and external bathing fluids. We will approach the problem by assuming that the separate-site theory is incorrect and that the transport mechanisms are nonelectrogenic, and attempt to determine which ion gradients between the cytoplasm and bathing fluids are necessary for maintenance of the gastric PD. If we find that the gastric PD is not dependent on ion gradients between cytoplasm and external fluids, it follows that there must be at least one electrogenic mechanism present in the mucosa.

I am somewhat appalled by the large amount of experimental data accumulated on this aspect of the subject. However, I am more appalled by the large number of obvious experiments that have not as yet been performed. For the sake of simplicity and brevity, I will be somewhat dogmatic in my interpretation of the findings. Space does not permit a detailed examination of many second-order assumptions.

Since the nutrient side of the gastric mucosa is positive, the PD must originate, on the basis of the ion-gradient hypothesis, from one or more of the four classes of gradients shown in Fig. 6A, i.e., 1) cation gradients from lumen to cell, 2) anion gradients from cell to lumen, 3) anion gradients from ISF to cell, and 4) cation gradients from cell to ISF. The role of a given ion gradient could be assessed by determining the effect on the PD of changing the concentration of the ion in one of the bathing fluids. Many such experiments were performed. However, in order to condense the presentation, I have chosen a number of key experiments. One such experiment is shown in Fig. 6C (Rehm, 1962). The secretory fluid and nutrient fluid had the composition shown in Fig. 6B. The secretory fluid contained Mg and Cl as the only ions; sucrose was used to make up the osmotic deficit. The nutrient contained Cl as the only anion, and both sides were gassed with 100% O_2. The arrow labeled *H* (Fig. 6C) indicates the addition of histamine, which resulted in the establishment of the secretory state. This experiment shows that, under these conditions, the PD and short-circuit current were maintained in both the resting and secretory states. The open-circuit PD was measured during a momentary opening of the circuit. Assuming that Mg cannot penetrate the secretory surface, then the gradient labeled *1* (Fig. 6A) cannot account for the gastric PD. The Cl concentration in the lumen in this experiment was 100 mM. Davenport and Alzamora (1962) and others have shown that the cellular Cl of the gastric mucosa is relatively high but is less than 100 mM. In other words, the Cl gradient is in the wrong direction to account for the nutrient being positive. However, there may be other cellular anions whose gradients into the lumen might account for the gastric PD. In other experiments, we have tested this hypothesis by replacing the Cl with HCO_3, acetate, lactate, and other anions and have found that the presence of these ions does

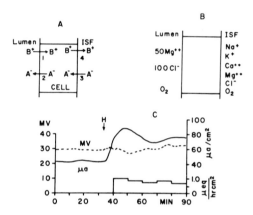

Fig. 6. A and B: see text. C: represents experiment in which resting frog gastric mucosa was short-circuited; at time indicated by arrow (*H*), histamine was added to nutrient solution and H^+ secretion was established. PD was measured during momentary opening of circuit. See text.

not abolish the PD (Dennis and Rehm, 1958; Rehm, unpublished). In fact, the PD is usually higher with these other anions. On the basis of the known anions present in cells, it is difficult to believe that there is an anion that could account for the gastric PD. Another piece of evidence that makes it improbable for the PD to be dependent on an anion gradient from cell to lumen (Fig. 6A, *2*) is the finding that in the dog's gastric juice, Cl is essentially the only anion present (Babkin, 1950). If the PD were dependent on an anion gradient, the anion ought to appear in gastric juice, especially under conditions of maximal secretory rates, when the velocity of flow in the lumen is quite high.

We see, then, that it is difficult to account for the origin of the gastric PD on the basis of ion gradients between the cell and lumen fluid. Let us now take a look at the third possibility, that is, an anion gradient from ISF to cell (Fig. 6A, *3*). Since we have only the Cl present in the nutrient fluid in this experiment, only a Cl gradient from the ISF into the cell could account for the gastric PD. Our analysis has eliminated gradients *1*, *2*, and *3*, except for a Cl gradient from the ISF to the cell. Now let us take a look at the gradient labeled *4* (Fig. 6A). Only K and Na will be considered. Na in the ISF was 104 mM, and this is higher on the basis of the finding of Davenport and Alzamora (1962) than the Na concentration in the cells. Therefore, the Na gradient would be in the wrong direction and, hence, could not account for the positivity of the nutrient fluid.

We have left two possibilities; i.e., the PD may arise from a K gradient from cell to ISF and a Cl gradient from ISF to cell or a Cl gradient from ISF to cell alone. I will first present the analysis of the Cl-gradient hypothesis, but in a very condensed form. Our goal is to attempt to explain the finding that the cellular Cl is less than the bathing fluid Cl on the basis of the pumping out of Cl from the cell by nonelectrogenic mechanisms. The Cl could be pumped out of the lumen via a forced-exchange mechanism with another anion from the lumen. But in the experiment shown in Fig. 6C, there is no other anion in the lumen; hence, this possibility is eliminated. It might be argued that the Cl is transported to the lumen with a cation via a single carrier. But Hogben (1955) has shown that the net transport of Cl into the lumen is greater than that of the H^+ by an amount equal to the short-circuit current. To account for this finding, essentially all of the transported cation would have to diffuse back into the cell. This cation could not be Na or K under the conditions of the experiment shown in Fig. 6C. Similar considerations for the transport of Cl from cell to ISF via nonelectrogenic mechanisms indicate that this is not consistent with the facts. It is, therefore, concluded that a Cl gradient from ISF to cell cannot account for the gastric PD on the basis of nonelectrogenic mechanisms.

We have left for our consideration the possibility that the gastric PD is dependent on a K gradient from cytoplasm to ISF. Studies on the effect of increasing the K in the nutrient and secretory fluids (Na replaced by K) support the hypothesis that a K gradient from cell to ISF accounts for the gastric PD. Increasing the K on the secretory side, apart from transient changes, results in very little change in the magnitude of the PD, while increasing the K on the nutrient side results in a decrease in PD (Davies and Ogston, 1950; Harris and Edelman, 1959; Simon *et al.*, 1959). The PD decreases, not by 58 mv, but by about 30 mv per tenfold increase in the K concentration in the nutrient fluid. These findings, together with the findings of Davenport and Alzamora (1962) of a high intracellular K, support the hypothesis that the gastric PD is primarily dependent on a K gradient across the nutrient membrane.

In other words, it appears at this juncture that the explanation of the gastric PD may be similar to the explanation offered by Ussing (1960) for the origin of the PD of the frog skin. However, it is possible that the K concentration in the cytoplasm may be quite low and that most of the cellular K is compartmentalized in structures such as mitochondria. Let us see what happens to the PD when all of the Cl is replaced with SO_4.

Figure 7 shows such an experiment. Instead of the PD increasing, as it does in the frog skin, it inverts; and this is difficult to reconcile with the K-gradient hypothesis. One might suggest that the mechanism of K accumulation may not be similar to that apparently present in other cells and that in the absence of Cl, the K may leak out of the cell. In unpublished work

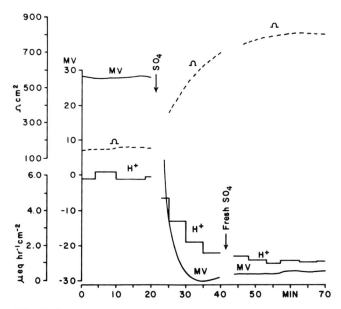

Fig. 7. PD, resistance, and H^+ rate of *in vitro* frog gastric mucosa. At time of first arrow (SO_4), SO_4 bathing solutions (Cl-free) replaced regular Cl bathing solutions. At time of second arrow, both secretory and nutrient sides washed several times with SO_4 solutions.

from my laboratory, D. Keesee and F. Bajandas found that the K content of the mucosa, after the inversion of the PD, is within normal limits. The simplest explanation is that most of the K is not floating free in the cytoplasm. Recent evidence indicates that the K may be tightly compartmentalized (Davis *et al.*, 1963a; unpublished work by D. Keesee, F. Bajandas, T. Davis, J. Rutledge, and W. S. Rehm). Removal of K from the bathing solutions results in a decrease in the H^+ rate to zero but in only a small reduction in the K content of the mucosa. The simplest interpretation is that K is necessary for H^+ secretion and that with zero K in the bathing solutions, the K concentration in certain regions is markedly decreased, while in other regions it remains high. The regions that still have a high K content do not liberate K at a high enough rate to prevent the H^+ rate from falling to zero. Support of the concept that under these conditions the membranes are still permeable to K is found in the observation that after the H^+ rate is reduced to zero, the introduction of a secretory solution with a high K results in re-establishment of the H^+ secretion.

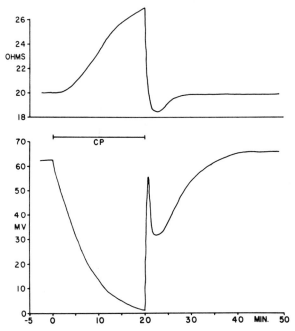

Fig. 8. Effect of interruption of blood flow, by clamping pedicle (*CP*) of dog stomach, on PD and resistance.

The foregoing experiments make it difficult to account for the gastric PD on the basis of ion gradients between the cytoplasm and the external bathing fluids. On the other hand, these facts may be explained readily on the basis of the separate-site theory. Referring to the equivalent circuit of Fig. 2, it is obvious that the elimination of Cl would result in an inversion of the PD, since the electromotive force of the H^+ pump would be unmasked.

There is the possibility that the absence of the Cl results in some unknown way in a change in permeability properties of the gastric mucosal membranes, so that a K gradient from cell to lumen fluid is responsible for the inverted PD. We will return to a consideration of this assumption after a look at the effects of anoxia on the PD, resistance, and H^+ secretory rate. Red blood cells continue to transport ions in the absence of O_2 (Maizels, 1949). In sharp contrast, removal of O_2 from the gastric mucosa results in a reduction of the H^+ rate and PD to zero and a marked increase in electrical resistance. This was demonstrated by Davies (1957) and colleagues for the frog stomach and by our group (Rehm *et al.*, 1953) for the dog stomach.

We thought, at one time, that the anoxia experiments might be decisive with respect to the problem of whether or not the gastric PD was dependent on ion gradients between the cytoplasm and external media. Figure 8 shows an experiment on the resting dog stomach (Bornstein *et al.*, 1957). The blood

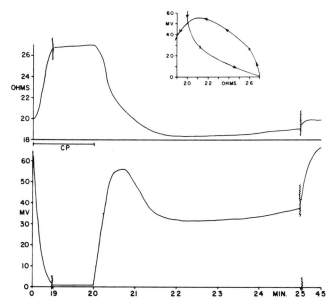

Fig. 9. Same as Fig. 8, except expanded time-scale covering period of re-establishment of blood flow. Inset: PD *vs.* re-sistance during interruption and re-establishment of blood flow.

flow was interrupted during the period labeled *CP*, and this resulted in a decrease of the PD to about zero and a marked increase in the resistance. These effects are those expected on the basis of the separate-site theory. Anoxia eliminates the source of energy for ion transport and, hence, would result in a decrease in PD and an increase in resistance. Re-establishment of the blood flow by unclamping the pedicle results in an increase in PD within about 1 sec. The PD increases at rates as high as 4 mv/sec. This is seen better in Fig. 9, in which the time-scale has been expanded during the period of the re-establishment of blood flow. On the basis of nonelectrogenic theories, one might assume that the decline in PD is due to a wiping out of ion gradients.

However, one is then faced with a dilemma. It is difficult to believe that the ion gradients can be re-established fast enough to account for the rapid increase in PD. However, within the framework of the nonelectrogenic theories, one might assume that the ion gradients are not wiped out by anoxia, but that the permeabilities of the membranes are changed in such a way that the PDs across the nutrient and luminal membranes are of equal magnitude but oppositely oriented.

Similar experiments were performed on the frog gastric mucosa, with particular attention to the rate of increase in PD following the readmission of O_2. The results were qualitatively similar to those obtained on the dog stomach, except that the rate of increase in PD of the frog stomach was about one-fifth of that of the dog stomach. This would be expected because of the longer diffusion pathway in an *in vitro* preparation.

Similar experiments were also performed on the frog skin. I thought that these experiments would serve as sort of a control, since, on the basis of Ussing's model (1960), readmission of O_2 might not result in a rapid restoration of the PD. I was wrong. Anoxia depressed the PD, but not to zero; instead, it went to a relatively steady-state level of about 15 mv; and readmission of O_2 resulted in as rapid a rise in the PD as it did in the frog gastric mucosa. In some experiments, about 5 min before the readmission of O_2, the bathing fluids were replaced anaerobically with fluids that contained no K. Under these conditions, readmission of O_2 resulted in a typical rapid increase in PD. However, the subsequent behavior of the PD was different in the absence of K. It is assumed that under these conditions, there would be relatively little K in the extracellular spaces and, hence, the rapid increase in PD could not be due to a rapid re-establishment of the K gradient.

The anoxia experiments taken by themselves are not decisive for deciding between electrogenic and nonelectrogenic mechanisms. On the basis of the ion-gradient hypothesis, anoxia would gradually change the permeability of the membranes, and readmission of O_2 would very rapidly restore their original permeability. In order to explain the decrease to zero for the gastric mucosa, it must be emphasized that the permeability properties have to be changed in a rather precise way; otherwise, we would not expect to obtain a zero PD. The anoxia experiments tell us that H^+ secretion and the PD are both dependent on oxidative metabolism. Since there is a substantial rate of anaerobic glycolysis in the stomach (Davies, 1957), there should be an appreciable amount of adenosine triphosphate (ATP) produced during anoxia. In an attempt to explain these findings, many workers in this field have suggested that both high-energy phosphate and oxidative metabolism are essential for gastric secretion. I might add that the conclusion that high-energy phosphate is needed for gastric secretion is based more on the prevailing fashions in biochemistry than on experimental evidence.

I would now like to return to the problem of the inverted PD in Cl-free solutions. Heinz and Durbin (1959) pioneered in this work. They found that in the absence of Cl, the gastric mucosa could still secrete H⁺, but at a lower level, and that the short-circuit current was essentially equal to the H⁺ rate. This is substantial evidence in favor of the idea that the inverted PD is essential to H⁺ secretion. We have extended the findings of Heinz and Durbin, and I would like to review briefly our findings with Cl-free preparations. The Cl was replaced with SO_4, and sucrose was used to make up the osmotic deficit. In Fig. 10, the effect of histamine on the PD and resistance of a resting stomach in SO_4 solutions is given. It can be seen that, as results of histamine administration, H⁺ secretion was established, the PD changed, the nutrient became negative by about 20 mv, and the resistance decreased. We confirmed Heinz and Durbin; i.e., during short-circuiting, the H⁺ secretory

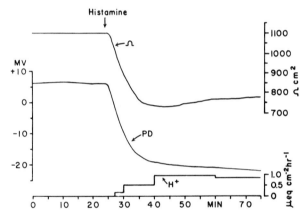

Fig. 10. Effect of histamine administration to nutrient fluid of *in vitro* resting frog gastric mucosa bathed in Cl-free solutions.

rate expressed as current was essentially equal to the short-circuit current. Actually, as indicated in the data of Heinz and Durbin, the H⁺ current was slightly less than the short-circuit current, so that there may be a small amount of transport of cations from secretory to nutrient fluid or anions from nutrient to secretory fluid. Hogben (1961) has reported a net transport of SO_4 under these conditions toward the secretory side.

If the inverted PD is essential to H⁺ production, then various procedures that inhibit the H⁺ rate should also decrease the magnitude of the inverted PD. For example, it is well known that thiocyanate markedly inhibits the rate of H⁺ production, and one would predict that the inverted PD would markedly decrease after thiocyanate administration. This is essentially what is found, as illustrated in Fig. 11 (Rehm et al., 1963). Thiocyanate was added to the secretory side, and this resulted in a marked decrease in the absolute magnitude of the PD and a decrease of the H⁺ rate to about zero. The thiocyanate gradient would by itself tend to make the nutrient more negative, while the fact is that the nutrient became more positive; i.e., the inverted PD was almost wiped out.

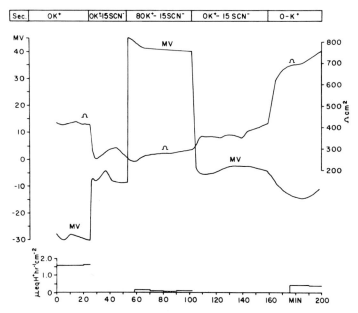

Fig. 11. Effect of addition of thiocyanate and of thiocyanate plus 80 mM K to secretory fluid of *in vitro* frog mucosa bathed in SO_4 solutions. *Sec.*: K and thiocyanate content of secretory fluid.

All the evidence indicates that H⁺ secretion is dependent on aerobic metabolism, and in Fig. 12, the effects of anoxia are shown in SO_4 experiments (Rehm *et al.*, 1962). It can be seen that anoxia results in a rapid decrease in the production of H⁺ and an increase in the PD, i.e., a decrease in the absolute magnitude of the PD. The resistance also increases. It can be seen that following the readmission of O_2, H⁺ secretion is re-established and the PD and resistance both return to approximately their original levels. The initial spike of the PD upon the readmission of O_2 is of interest. This spike is seen when O_2 is readmitted simultaneously to both sides or when O_2 is readmitted only to the secretory side. As seen in Fig. 13, this spike is not seen when O_2 is readmitted first to the nutrient side. The spike seen in this figure (arrow labeled ΔS) resulted from the addition of a small amount of O_2 to the secretory side. The tentative conclusion is that there is a transport process located near the secretory surface which is dependent on aerobic metabolism. It, by itself, would make the nutrient positive; however, its potency is not as great

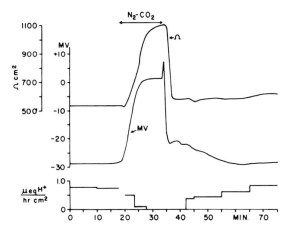

Fig. 12. Effect of anoxia (95% O_2–5% CO_2 to 95% N_2–5% CO_2 and back again) on *in vitro* frog gastric mucosa bathed in SO_4 solutions.

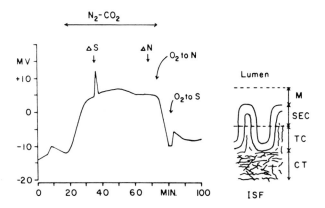

Fig. 13. Left: similar to Fig. 12, except at time indicated by Δ S, a small amount of O_2 admitted to secretory chamber during N_2–CO_2 period. At Δ N, fresh nutrient fluid, and at O_2 to N, O_2–CO_2 readmitted to nutrient, but N_2–CO_2 still on secretory side. At O_2 to S, O_2–CO_2 readmitted to secretory side. Right: diagrammatic sketch of the mucosa. *M*: mucus coat; *SEC*: surface epithelial cells; *TC*: tubular cells; *CT*: connective tissue. Findings indicate that surface epithelial cells possess ion-transport mechanism that may be similar to that of frog skin.

as the H^+ mechanism, so when both are restored, there is an inverted orientation of the PD. It is tempting to believe that the surface epithelial cells are similar to the frog skin, i.e., capable of transporting NaCl from lumen to ISF, and that the tubular cells are the site of H^+ and Cl secretion.

Another line of evidence supporting the concept that the inverted PD is essential for H^+ secretion is found in studies of LeFevre and Rehm (1963) on the effect of 2,4-dinitrophenol (DNP). Added in increasing amounts to ordinary Cl preparations, DNP resulted in a suppression of the H^+ rate to zero before there was a substantial decrease in the PD. On the basis of the separate-site theory, the explanation is that DNP knocks out the H^+ pump before it knocks out the Cl pump. With higher concentrations, the PD is eventually reduced to zero. In a conversation with Dr. Peter Curran, he pointed out that it would be interesting to see whether or not the inverted PD in SO_4 preparations could be dissociated from the H^+ rate, just as it is in the Cl experiments. In sharp contrast to the effects of DNP in the Cl solutions, addition of this substance to SO_4 preparations always resulted in a suppression of the PD when the H^+ secretory rate was inhibited. In other words, it was not possible to dissociate the inverted PD from the H^+ rate.

Another way of suppressing the H^+ rate is to remove the K from the nutrient solution, and this results in a suppression of the secretory rate to zero and a decrease in the absolute magnitude of the PD. In fact, the PD invariably becomes positive by a few mv (Davis *et al.*, 1963a). The K content of the mucosa is again about 70% of the control value when the H^+ rate is reduced to zero.

These experiments on the SO_4 preparations strongly support the concept that the inverted PD is intimately linked with the H^+ mechanism. They all can be explained easily on the basis of the separate-site theory. To rule out nonelectrogenic mechanisms, one could again attempt to show that the inverted PD is not dependent on ion gradients between the cytoplasm and external fluids. Space does not permit another systematic exploration of possible gradients, so I will confine myself to a consideration of the inverted PD originating from Na and/or K gradients.

If both Cl and Na are replaced by SO_4 and choline in the bathing fluids, the PD and H^+ rate are at about the same levels as they are in the Na_2SO_4 experiments (unpublished observations). It is, therefore, difficult to believe that the inverted PD is due to a Na gradient.

In the remaining space, let us turn our attention to the problem of whether the inverted PD is due to a K gradient. In SO_4 preparations, the mucosal K content is within normal limits. Increasing the K on the nutrient side results in an increase in negativity of the nutrient, with a PD–log K slope of about 25, just as in the Cl preparations. On the other hand, increasing the K content of the secretory solution in the SO_4 preparations, in contrast to the effects in the Cl preparations, results in an increase in positivity of the

nutrient, with a PD–log K slope of about 25. In other words, removal of Cl
from the bathing solutions changes the apparent permeability of the secretory
surface. The secretory membrane becomes essentially like the nutrient surface
from the point of view of their relative permeabilities to K and Na. Therefore,
the K diffusion potentials across the two membranes would be equal and
oppositely oriented and should cancel out. If this be the case, then increasing
the K concentration on both sides to levels comparable to K levels in the

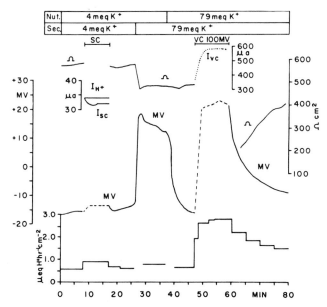

Fig. 14. Effect of increasing secretory K to 79 mM and nutrient K to 79 mM on *in vitro* frog gastric mucosa bathed
in SO$_4$ solutions. Voltage was clamped at 100 mv (nutrient
positive) during period indicated. During voltage-clamping,
open-circuit PD measured during momentary opening of
circuit. *SC*: short-circuiting; *Nut.*: K content of nutrient
fluid; *Sec.*: K content of secretory fluid. (From Davis
et al., 1963b, *Am. J. Physiol.* 205: 873.)

cells should not wipe out the inverted PD. Figure 14 shows an experiment
with Na$_2$SO$_4$-Ringer's (Davis *et al.*, 1963a). The K concentration was increased on the secretory side from 4 to 70 mM (Na replaced by K), and
this resulted in a restoration of the PD to its normal orientation. When the
high K was maintained on the secretory side and the K on the nutrient side
was increased to the same level, the PD returned to approximately its original
level. This finding illustrates the fact that the K permeability relative to other
ions is essentially the same for both membranes. This makes it very difficult

to explain the inverted PD on the basis of a K gradient. With a high K concentration on both sides, clamping the voltage with the nutrient positive results in a very marked increase in the H^+ secretory rate. This finding, together with certain other findings (Davis et al., 1963b) which I do not have space to consider, essentially eliminates the possibility that H^+ secretion results from a forced exchange with K. I might add, in this connection, that the experiments of Davenport (1963) and our experiments in which Na is replaced with choline (in which H^+ secretion is maintained) effectively eliminates the possibility that H^+ secretion results from a forced exchange with Na.

The last finding that I will present is concerned with the problem of whether the permeability of the secretory surface in SO_4 preparations is changed after thiocyanate inhibition. The results shown in Fig. 11 clearly show that after thiocyanate inhibition, increasing the secretory K concentration results in a marked increase in the positivity of the nutrient. In other words, the decrease in the absolute magnitude of the inverted PD cannot be explained by a decrease in the relative permeability of the secretory membrane to K.

Summary

A systematic attempt was made to explain the origin of the gastric PD on the basis of ion gradients resulting from nonelectrogenic mechanisms. A K gradient from cell to ISF was the only ion gradient that justified detailed consideration. The K-gradient hypothesis was supported by 1) the finding that the steady-state PD was not changed significantly when K replaced Na on the secretory side, 2) the finding that replacing Na with K on the nutrient side reduced the PD, and 3) the finding by many workers of a high cellular K in the gastric mucosa. On the other hand, the finding that the PD of the secreting mucosa inverted when Cl was replaced by SO_4 cannot be explained easily on the basis of the K-gradient hypothesis, particularly in light of the finding that the mucosal K content is not decreased by this procedure. The inversion of the PD in SO_4 preparations raised the possibility that the major portion of the intracellular gastric K is not free K in the cytoplasm. Davenport's (1963) and our studies with zero K in the bathing fluids support the concept that the K is compartmentalized.

The results of anoxia experiments were not decisive as far as the origin of the PD is concerned, but they do narrow the possibilities either to electrogenic pumps or to the hypothesis that ion gradients are maintained during anoxia and that the permeability properties of the membrane are a function of oxidative metabolism.

The experiments with the SO_4 bathing solutions demonstrate that the inverted PD is intimately associated with H^+ secretion. The finding that the PD is still inverted with high K on both sides and also with choline sulfate solutions make it extremely difficult to explain the inverted PD upon the basis of either a K or Na gradient. In closing, I would like to point out that all of the findings are explained easily on the basis of the separate-site theory.

REFERENCES

Babkin, B. P. 1950. *Secretory Mechanism of the Digestive Glands*, 2nd Ed. New York: P. B. Hoeber.

Bornstein, A., W. H. Dennis, and W. S. Rehm. 1957. *Physiologist* 1: 13.

Bornstein, A., W. H. Dennis, and W. S. Rehm. 1959. *Am. J. Physiol.* 197: 332.

Bull, H. B., and J. S. Gray. 1945. *Gastroenterology* 4: 175.

Davenport, H. W. 1963. *Am. J. Physiol.* 204: 213.

Davenport, H. W., and F. Alzamora. 1962. *Am. J. Physiol.* 202: 711.

Davies, R. E. 1957. In *Metabolic Aspects of Transport Across Cell Membranes*, ed. Q. R. Murphy. Madison: Univ. of Wisconsin Press. P. 273.

Davies, R. E., and A. G. Ogston. 1950. *Biochem. J.* 46: 324.

Davis, T. L., J. R. Rutledge, and W. S. Rehm. 1963a. *Physiologist* 6: 165.

Davis, T. L., J. R. Rutledge, and W. S. Rehm. 1963b. *Am. J. Physiol.* 205: 873.

Dennis, W. H., and W. S. Rehm. 1958. *Am. J. Physiol.* 195: 15.

Durbin, R., and E. Heinz. 1958. *J. Gen. Physiol.* 41: 1035.

Edelman, I. S., and J. B. Harris. 1958. *Federation Proc.* 17: 39.

Harris, J. B., and I. S. Edelman. 1959. *Am. J. Physiol.* 196: 1266.

Heinz, E., and R. Durbin. 1959. *Biochim. Biophys. Acta* 31: 246.

Hogben, C. A. M. 1951. *Proc. Natl. Acad. Sci. U.S.* 37: B93.

Hogben, C. A. M. 1955. In *Electrolytes Biol. Systems, Symp. Marine Biol. Lab., Woods Hole, Mass., 1954*, ed. A. M. Shanes. Washington: *Am. Physiol. Soc.* P. 176.

Hogben, C. A. M. 1961. *Federation Proc.* 20: 139E.

LeFevre, M. E., and W. S. Rehm. 1963. *Federation Proc.* 22: 213.

Maizels, M. 1949. *J. Physiol.* (*London*) 108: 247.

Patlak, C. S. 1956. *Bull. Math. Biophys.* 18: 271.

Rehm, W. S. 1945. *Am. J. Physiol.* 144: 115.

Rehm, W. S. 1950. *Gastroenterology* 14: 401.

Rehm, W. S. 1959. *Am. J. Digest. Diseases* 4: 194.

Rehm, W. S. 1962. *Am. J. Physiol.* 203: 63.

Rehm, W. S. In *Gastric Potential and Ion Transports, Symp. Am. Physiol. Soc.* In press.

Rehm, W. S., and W. H. Dennis. 1957. In *Metabolic Aspects of Transport Across Cell Membranes*, ed. Q. R. Murphy. Madison: Univ. of Wisconsin Press. P. 303.

Rehm, W. S., C. Chandler, T. Davis, E. Gohmann, Jr., and A. Bashirelahi. 1962. *Biophys. Soc. Abstracts* TD8.

Rehm, W. S., T. L. Davis, C. Chandler, E. Gohmann, Jr., and A. Bashirelahi. 1963. *Am. J. Physiol.* 204: 233.

Rehm, W. S., H. Schlesinger, and W. H. Dennis. 1953. *Am. J. Physiol.* 175: 473.

Simon, M. A., W. J. Kilgour, C. Chandler, and W. S. Rehm. 1959. *Physiologist* 2: 108.

Ussing, H. H. 1960. *J. Gen. Physiol.* 43: 135.

Mechanism of Action of Antidiuretic Hormones on Epithelial Structures

Jack Orloff and Joseph S. Handler

Laboratory of Kidney and Electrolyte Metabolism
National Heart Institute
National Institutes of Health
Bethesda, Maryland

Our purpose is to summarize some of the current knowledge concerning the role of neurohypophyseal hormones in the regulation of water balance in both mammals and amphibia. This will necessarily include a survey of the pertinent properties of those epithelial membranes whose permeability to water is altered by these hormones, as well as a discussion of the possible mode of action of the responsible agents.

In the normal mammal, the osmotic pressure of the fluids of the body is maintained relatively constant despite wide variations in the intake of solute and water. Dr. Tosteson (1964) has discussed the mechanism of the maintenance of the ionic content of the cell which involves precise and adjustable alterations in both active transport and diffusional processes across the plasma membrane. This view may be defined by referring to it as the "pump-leak" hypothesis. Although the total content of the major ions within the cell is apparently set by this mechanism, the cells are still capable of acting as osmometers, and will shrink and swell in response to changes in the effective osmotic pressure of the surrounding medium. In order that cell volume and osmotic pressure be maintained relatively constant, the organism must either 1) limit or accelerate its uptake of water when overhydration or dehydration prevails or 2) dissipate the excess solute or water in the form of a hypertonic or hypotonic solution. The regulation of water balance in the mammal involves the latter process, the excretion of urine of varying tonicity. It depends in large measure on a neurohypophyseal-renal system which responds to alterations in the effective osmotic pressure of the extracellular environment. As with many significant advances in science, the fundamental observations stem from the combined and persistent pursuit of the problem by clinicians, mammalian pharmacologists, and physiologists; only later did the cell physiologists attempt an explanation of the important phenomena at the so-called cellular level. Thus, in the early 1900's, it was known that destructive processes involving the pituitary gland in man resulted in the unremitting excretion of copious volumes of dilute urine (Goetsch et al., 1911). The effect was clearly the result of a deficiency of a hormone whose main effect was to limit the excretion of urine. It has since been established, largely owing to the work of the English pharmacologist Verney (1947), that an increase in the effective osmotic pressure of the extracellular compartment, whether due to excess intake of solute or to a deficiency of water, promotes the secretion of an antidiuretic substance from the posterior pituitary gland and that the hormone, now known to be the octapeptide, arginine vasopressin, in man (Du Vigneaud, 1956), acts on the kidney to conserve water by reducing urine flow. Conversely, a reduction in the effective osmotic pressure of the extracellular fluid interferes with the secretion of hormone and permits the kidney to excrete large volumes of dilute urine.

This is a reasonable summary of the state of knowledge of mammalian osmoregulation 20 to 25 years ago. The intrinsic renal mechanisms involved in the elaboration of a dilute or concentrated urine, so essential to the maintenance of osmotic pressure, were not understood, and only within the past ten years or so has an adequate explanation evolved.

It had not been difficult to account for the elaboration of a dilute urine. This merely required the removal of solute without water from isosmotic glomerular filtrate. The elaboration of urine more concentrated than plasma, on the other hand, was a puzzling process. Since glomerular filtrate is isosmotic with plasma (Walker et al., 1941), the formation of a hyperosmotic solution appeared to require active transport of water out of the filtrate into the surrounding blood, a process which defied known physiochemical principles and which exceeded the ingenuity of even the "irreversible thermodynamicists." The problem was resolved when Henry Wirz rediscovered a fact known and forgotten or rejected for 50 years, namely, that the deeper portions of the kidney interstitium are hypertonic to plasma. He suggested, in association with the physical chemists, Hargitay and Kuhn (1951), who had proposed a similar scheme on theoretical grounds, some time earlier, that osmotic flow of water out of the tubule lumen into the hypertonic surrounding tissue was all that was necessary to account for the process of urinary concentration.

Wirz proposed that alterations in urine osmotic pressure are effected by variable reabsorption of water along osmotic gradients in response to vasopressin-induced changes in the permeability of the limiting membrane to water. His views, as modified and extended by Gottschalk (1961), Ullrich *et al.* (1961), Berliner *et al.* (1958), and others, are illustrated in an oversimplified fashion in Fig. 1. This is a schematic diagram of the nephron. For simplicity, the kidney has been divided into two anatomical areas: an outermost one, the cortex, and an innermost one, containing the medulla and papilla through which the final urine flows. The cortex is isosmotic with

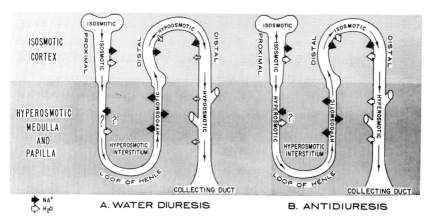

Fig. 1. Schematic diagram of the nephron. (Modified from *Metabolic Diseases of the Kidney,* ed. John B. Stanbury, James B. Wyngaarden, and Donald S. Fredrickson. Copyright 1960. McGraw-Hill Book Company. Used by permission.)

plasma, whereas the deeper portions of the kidney are hyperosmotic to plasma.

In the left-hand panel of Fig. 1, the nephron is excreting a dilute urine, which is the situation when vasopressin secretion is in abeyance. In the normal mammal, about 20% of the plasma which perfuses the kidney is filtered at the glomerulus. The ultrafiltrate so formed is then reduced in volume in the proximal convolution by reabsorption of about 80–85% of the fluid. The fluid remaining retains the same osmolality as the parent filtrate. Na and associated anions are reabsorbed by a process involving the active transport of Na, and the water follows passively along the resultant osmotic gradient. Residual isosmotic urine is then delivered to the descending limb of the loop of Henle, where water without appreciable solute is lost to the surrounding hypertonic interstitium. The concentrated fluid then flows upward into the ascending limb and distal convolution, where active transport of salt without water occurs, diluting the urine in the process. The membrane in the ascending limb, unlike that in the proximal convolution, is relatively impermeable to water under all circumstances; the membrane in the distal convolution is impermeable to water only in the absence of vasopressin. Thus, despite the osmotic gradient established by solute removal, little or no water leaves by osmotic flow in the distal convolution. Although further alterations in solute and water content occur in the collecting duct, the dilute urine formed in the distal convolution may be considered to be excreted virtually unchanged.

In contrast, when the antidiuretic hormone vasopressin is present, hypertonic urine is excreted. Under these circumstances, though the sequence of events differs markedly in the distal portions of the nephron, it is probably unaltered elsewhere in the kidney. This is illustrated in the right-hand panel of Fig. 1. The hormone increases the permeability of both the distal convolution and collecting duct to water. Consequently, although urinary dilution is still effected by electrolyte abstraction in the ascending limb and first portion of the distal convolution, water now flows along the osmotic gradient in the terminal portions of the distal convolution until equilibrium is achieved. The small volume of residual isosmotic urine is then delivered to the collecting duct, where, once again, water without solute leaves by osmotic flow across the now permeable membrane, and the resultant hypertonic urine is excreted.

Just one word about the genesis of the hypertonicity in the medullary-papillary region. It is now agreed that the deposition of salt, urea, and other solutes in excess of water, derived from the ascending limb and collecting duct, respectively, into an area of low effective blood flow accounts for the development and maintenance of the hypertonicity.

The vasopressin-induced alteration in the permeability to water of the renal tubular epithelium is now an established fact. This view of the action of the hormone derives from studies utilizing amphibian skin and bladder. Most of the available information stems from the work of the Copenhagen group led by Ussing, Zerahn, Koefoed-Johnsen, and others (Ussing, 1960). With few exceptions, their conclusions from studies in frog skin have been confirmed and extended by similar studies in amphibian bladder by Bentley (1958), Leaf (1960), Rasmussen et al. (1960), and Sawyer (1961). At the risk of offending everyone, we will rely heavily on Ussing's published data and make the reasonable assumption that at least in so far as the gross or qualitative changes are concerned, the skin model will serve as a prototype for the other two major tissues which respond to vasopressin, namely, toad bladder and the pertinent portions of the renal tubule.

The epithelial cells of frog skin differ functionally and anatomically from many of the cells discussed thus far in the symposium. Unlike the red cell, for example, these cells are capable of effecting the net transfer of NaCl and water across the entire tissue. The cells are polar, or oriented. In contrast to the red cell, they are not surrounded by a homogeneous or uniform membrane, but possess, at the very least, two distinct diffusion barriers. This is illustrated in Fig. 2, which is a schematic drawing based on a model proposed by Koefoed-Johnsen and Ussing (1958). One barrier separates the cell interior from the outside environment, which, for skin, is the pond, and for both bladder and tubule, is the urine. The other membrane separates the cell interior from the extracellular space and blood. The properties of these barriers differ and provide the cell with a mechanism both for the maintenance of the steady-state concentration of electrolytes within the tissue and for the net reabsorption of NaCl and water across the tissue.

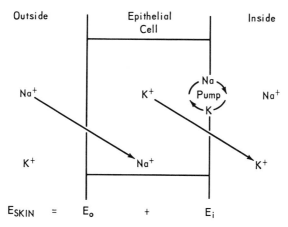

Fig. 2. Frog-skin model of Koefoed-Johnsen and Ussing. Outside: pond surface; inside: blood surface.

The capability of the skin to abstract salt from vanishingly low concentrations in pond water was first demonstrated in 1937 by Ussing's predecessor, Krogh (1937), who used an intact frog perched in a water bottle. He recognized that the process had considerable physiological significance, since it afforded a mechanism for reconstituting the Na content of the body during starvation, when urinary losses of salt continue unabated in frogs. Since then, Ussing and Zerahn's (1951) short-circuit technique, a simpler measure of Na transport, has provided investigators with a tool to reconfirm the fundamental observation that Na is actively transported across the skin. Furthermore, a potential difference can be measured across the structure, which is so oriented that the blood surface is electrically positive to the outside.

Koefoed-Johnsen and Ussing (1958), until recently, considered this potential difference to be the sum of two diffusion potentials, one due to passive movement of Na across the outer border and the other due to the passive movement of K across the inner border. Their evidence, which had always seemed incontrovertible, was the demonstration that the outer membrane is impermeable to K and, under appropriate circumstances, acts as a relatively pure Na electrode and that the inner membrane is relatively impermeable to Na and acts as a K electrode. They suggested that the active-transport system which ejects Na from the cell and is localized in the inner membrane is a linked 1:1 Na–K exchange pump which, by definition, is neutral and incapable of accounting for the net charge transfer observed. Clearly, the passive penetration of Na down its electrochemical gradient into the cell, demonstrated by direct analysis in bladder by Frazier and his colleagues (Frazier, 1962; Frazier et al., 1962), and its ejection by the pump into the blood, coupled with the passive movement of Cl along its electrochemical gradient through the cell, readily accounted for the capabilities of the skin for the net movement of NaCl. In this view, the inner membrane is similar to the plasma membrane of nonpolar tissues, in that linked exchange of Na and K in series with a "leak" of Na, in this instance from either side, is responsible for the maintenance of the steady-state ionic composition of the tissues.

Recently, this simple hypothesis has been challenged. Two groups of investigators, including Ussing himself, have suggested that the pump may be electrogenic and therefore capable of actively transporting Na alone across the tissues without the interposition of a counter-ion. Bricker, Biber, and Ussing (1963) argued that elimination of the K diffusion gradient by elevation of the K concentration of the inner solution should erase net charge transfer, if the pump were neutral as originally suggested. The persistence of active Na transport and charge transfer under such circumstances in frog skin led them to conclude that the pump may well be electrogenic. Their data are inconclusive, in that they did not establish that the diffusion gradient for K was, in fact, eliminated.

Frazier and Leaf (1963) arrived at similar conclusions. They not only noted the persistence of Na transport across toad bladder when the K concentration of the inner solution was elevated, but also were able to demonstrate the continued presence of an apparently normal positive potential step across the inner membrane under these circumstances. Similar criticisms apply to their studies as to those of Bricker et al., however, since they have not established the absence of a K diffusion gradient, either. On the other hand, Essig and Leaf (1963) were able to show unequivocally that, although optimal Na transport requires the presence of K in the inner bathing solution, no constant ratio of linkage, if any at all, exists between Na efflux and K influx. They believe that the reduction in Na transport associated with elimination of K from the inner bathing solution is not, as had been contended by others, evidence for a linked Na–K exchange pump. On the contrary, they have made the interesting suggestion that the removal of K from the inner solution diminishes the permeability of the outer membrane to Na, thereby restricting the rate of entry of Na to the postulated electrogenic pump.

This conclusion is based on an observed decrease in the uptake of Na^{22} into tissue water when the isotope is added to the mucosal solution and K is simultaneously removed from the serosal bath. This presupposes that the Na^{22} concentration in tissue water is a reflection of the size of a so-called Na-transport pool and that isotopic exchange across the serosal border is inconsequential. The data are difficult to interpret, since the concentration of Na in tissue water rose, despite a fall in so-called Na^{22}-pool size. Furthermore, the postulated effect of K on the permeability of the outer membrane to Na is inconsistent with the results obtained in nonpolar tissues such as red cells. In these, a similar decrease in Na efflux induced by reduction in K concentration of the medium is mediated by a direct effect on the active-transport system. Despite these objections to the views of Bricker et al. and Leaf and his associates, it is clear that the model proposed by Koefoed-Johnsen and Ussing requires re-evaluation and modification in order to account for many of the more recent observations.

Whatever the intimate details are found to be, it is still reasonable to view the inner membrane as being permeable to K and relatively impermeable to Na and to consider it as a "pump-leak control" system. This inner membrane is also permeable to water, since MacRobbie and Ussing (1961) have shown that cell volume changes in response to alterations in the tonicity of the inner bathing solution. This is not the case for the outer membrane. Osmotic flow of water is limited through this barrier in the absence of hormone, though Na, but not K, can penetrate relatively freely. The low permeability of the outer membrane to water is obviously important to the frog, with respect to osmoregulation. It prevents the rapid flow of water from the pond into the animal which would occur were the cells freely permeable to water.

The addition of neurohypophyseal hormone to the intact frog, on the other hand, does alter the permeability of the skin to water, and rapid swelling occurs in response to this manipulation. This was first demonstrated by Brunn in 1921. The observation was apparently ignored for years, despite its clear-cut implication with respect to osmoregulation in the amphibian. Thus, Krogh, who together with Hevesy and Hofer examined the characteristics of net water flow and heavy water diffusion across frog skin in 1935 (Hevesy et al., 1935), seems to have been unaware of this observation. It is remarkable that Krogh's monograph on osmoregulation in the aquatic animal, published in 1939, has no mention of the effect of "pituitrin." Admittedly, the amphibian, which has a relatively constant source of water from the pond, would seem to have no need for a hormone which would, in effect, cause it to gain water. In contrast to the mammal, the frog must be able to excrete water rapidly at all times to remain in osmotic balance, and this it does by elaborating a dilute urine. On the other hand, Krogh's apparent neglect of Brunn's observation is the more surprising since another classic monograph published at approximately the same time as Krogh's, *The Physiology of the Kidney*, by

Homer Smith (1937), contains a clear and concise description of osmoregulation in the mammal and the role of vasopressin. Furthermore, Smith, a one-
time amphibian physiologist, as was Krogh, was aware of the paper of
Steggerda and Essex (1934) on the induction of water uptake across intact
frog skin by pituitary extract, but he somehow—which was unusual for him—
neglected to grasp its significance. Apparently, Krogh either did not concern
himself with mammalian physiologists or considered pharmacology a repre-
hensible practice. Krogh may also have been prejudiced regarding the role of
pituitrin, since he and Rehberg (1922), a renal physiologist, had proposed
that pituitrin was of importance for the maintenance of vascular tone in
the frog.

Returning to the subject at hand, years after Brunn's discovery, a more
precise analysis of the effects of neurohypophyseal hormone on the permeability characteristics of isolated amphibian skin was begun by Ussing and
his colleagues. They and many others have established unequivocally that
the addition of neurohypophyseal hormone to the inner surface of the isolated skin produces two characteristic effects: 1) an increase in the permeability to water, as manifested by an increase in the net flow of water along
an osmotic gradient; and 2) an increase in net Na transport. The water effect
is illustrated in Table 1, taken from a study utilizing the isolated toad bladder

TABLE 1

EFFECT OF VASOPRESSIN ON OSMOTIC FLOW OF WATER
Osmotic gradient $= 165$ mOs/kg H_2O.

Medium	Mg/min
Ringer's	0.8
Vasopressin	26.5
Ringer's	1.1

sac, according to the method of Bentley (1958). Net water movement along
an osmotic gradient is estimated in this preparation by measuring the weight
loss of the sac at appropriate time intervals. Observe that despite an osmotic
gradient, there is negligible flow of water across the bladder in the absence of
hormone. Addition of vasopressin to the inner bathing medium results in a
rapid and reversible increase in net flow. Koefoed-Johnsen and Ussing (1953)
measured the unidirectional diffusional permeability to water of the skin,
using D_2O, and observed that the net flow along an osmotic gradient was
considerably greater than that predicted were water moving by diffusion
alone across the structure. A similar discrepancy between the predicted diffusional net flow and the observed osmotic net flow in the absence of hormone had been reported by Hevesy et al. in 1935.

These observations have led to a spate of publications by the "irreversible thermodynamicists" in an effort to resolve the problem. We do not propose to review them. However, stated in less rigorous terms, without the superstructure of irreversible thermodynamics, the problem was as follows: if water moves by random movement of the particles or, in other words, by diffusion, then the flux of water (M) in one direction will be proportional to the activity of water (α) on the side of origin:

$$M_{1 \to 2} = k(\alpha_1) \tag{1}$$

and the opposing flux across the membrane will be proportional to the activity on the opposite side:

$$M_{2 \to 1} = k(\alpha_2) \tag{2}$$

This, in essence, is a restatement of Fick's law of diffusion. It then follows that the ratio of the two fluxes will be equal to the ratio of the corresponding activities:

$$\frac{M_{1 \to 2}}{M_{2 \to 1}} = \frac{\alpha_1}{\alpha_2} \tag{3}$$

or, rearranging terms:

$$\Delta M = \frac{M_{1 \to 2}(\Delta \alpha)}{\alpha_1} \tag{4}$$

This equality of the ratios has not been observed in biological membranes. In fact, the flux ratio for water greatly exceeds its activity ratio, indicating that the equations are not an adequate description of the process. Stated in another fashion, the net movement of water along an osmotic gradient is considerably greater than that calculated on the basis of free diffusion from the observed unidirectional flux and the known activities of the water in both phases. Clearly, the assumption of random diffusional movement as the mechanism of osmotic flow of water across biological membranes is an error, and water must move in large part by a nondiffusional process, best visualized as hydrodynamic or bulk flow through aqueous channels or pores in the membrane. Koefoed-Johnsen and Ussing (1953) observed in skin and Hays and Leaf (1962) in toad bladder that, though the addition of vasopressin to the inner surface of the tissue results in a marked increase in the net flow of water, the diffusional permeability to water is increased only slightly. These authors concluded, as did Sawyer and Schisgall (1956), that the hormone must enlarge the radius of pores within the membrane, thereby permitting an increase in laminar flow through aqueous channels in response to an osmotic gradient. Additional support for the view that net movement is accomplished largely by bulk flow through aqueous channels was provided by Andersen and Ussing (1957). They were able to show that when equal concentrations of certain permeant substances, such as acetamide, were placed on both sides of frog skin, there being no driving force for the net movement of the acetamide under these circumstances, the imposition of an osmotic gradient plus vasopressin resulted in an acceleration of the flux of acetamide that was greater in the direction of net water movement than in the reverse direction. This phenomenon has been termed "solvent drag." In view of these observations, most workers now subscribe to the thesis that vasopressin exerts its effect in kidney, in skin, and in bladder either by increasing the number of pores in the structure or by enlarging the radius of existing aqueous channels.

It is of interest that, although the hormone increases water movement only when applied to the inner surface of the responsive membrane, both MacRobbie and Ussing (1961) and Maffly et al. (1960) have established that the resultant increase in permeability occurs on the outer surface. This is a reasonable concept, since virtual impermeability of the outer membrane to water in the absence of hormone protects the cell from violent volume changes in response to alterations in urine and pond tonicity. However, when water is demanded in response to dehydration, the outer surface can become as permeable as the inner surface, and bulk inward movement of water through the enlarged pores will occur. Leaf and Hays (1962) have also presented evidence in support of an earlier suggestion of Andersen and Ussing (1957) that the outer membrane may consist of at least two barriers in series. The fixed permeability of one barrier determines which molecules reach the second. The second barrier is assumed to be the porous structure the permeability of which is altered by the hormone.

The inequality of the flux and activity ratios for water and the phenomenon of solvent drag have now come to be accepted as evidence not only of nondiffusional flow, but also of the presence of pores in biological membranes. The universal truth of these criteria has been questioned by Sidel and Hoffman (1961). They re-examined the problem by studying the permeability characteristics of a system involving a liquid phase membrane, mesityl oxide, separating two aqueous solutions. The membrane selected is certainly nonporous and unresponsive to hormone. Sidel and Hoffman then repeated the studies of Hevesy et al. (1935), by measuring the net flux of water along an osmotic gradient, as well as the unidirectional flux in both directions, with tritiated water. As did Hevesy and coworkers in skin, they observed that the flux ratio markedly exceeded the activity ratio and, further, that solvent drag for urea occurred across the mesityl oxide membrane. The least that one can conclude on the basis of their studies is that these criteria for the presence of pores in a living membrane are not absolute and that an inequality of the flux and activity ratios and the presence of solvent drag can occur in the absence of pores. However, that flow along an osmotic gradient is predominantly nondiffusional is incontrovertible, and the aqueous-channel thesis should not be discarded until some other reasonable suggestion to account for nondiffusional flow can be conceived.

The augmentation in Na transport afforded by vasopressin was first observed by Fuhrman and Ussing (1951). The effect conceivably could be due either to direct stimulation of the inner Na pump or to an increase in the permeability of the outer surface to Na, which would allow more Na to reach an unsaturated pump and be ejected. The latter hypothesis, a unitary effect of neurohypophyseal hormone on the permeability to both Na and water, was suggested by Ussing (1955) on the basis of electrical measurements in which the so-called driving force for Na was noted to be unaltered by hormone, despite an increase in net flux, whereas the internal resistance to Na fell. More recently, Frazier *et al.* (1962) have offered support for the unitary view, since they observed that vasopressin caused greater accumulation in the so-called Na-transport pool of Na^{22} derived from the outer bathing solution. The rate-limiting step in Na transport, in their view, is the penetration of Na through the outer barrier, which, though downhill, is said to have some of the characteristics of a carrier-mediated process, that is, saturation kinetics.

The contrary view, that stimulation of Na transport and the increase in the permeability to water are separate and independent effects of vasopressin, has been suggested by Bourguet and Maetz (1961), who reported that certain analogs of vasopressin which yield equal changes in water movement across the skin of the *Rana esculenta* have unequal effects on Na transport. Their studies are subject to the criticism that the alteration in water movement and Na transport were not measured simultaneously nor in the same tissues. A clear-cut separation of the effects of vasopressin on Na and water movement is afforded by the addition of Ca in high concentrations to the inside bathing medium. Bentley (1959, 1960) observed that an increase in the Ca content of the inner bathing solution interfered with the effect of hormone on water transport but not with its effect on Na. This has been confirmed by Petersen and Edelman (1963). Although difficult to explain at the moment, since the independent effects of Ca are quite complicated, the results of both studies are not inconsistent with the view that vasopressin has two separate effects and that Na and water may not penetrate through the same channels on the outer border.

The structural requirements for hormone action have been investigated extensively, and much important information has been obtained (Jard *et al.*, 1960; Sawyer, 1960; Rasmussen *et al.*, 1963). These studies will not be reviewed here. Instead, we should like to conclude by discussing some of the current views concerning the possible mode of action of the hormone. At present, there are at least two views. The first, proposed by Schwartz, Rasmussen, and their colleagues (1960), involves a mechanical model in which interaction of the hormone with tissue receptors is thought to initiate directly a structural change within the membrane. The second, proposed by Dr.

Handler and myself (Orloff and Handler, 1961, 1962), involves an intracellular intermediate adenosine 3′,5′-monophosphate (cyclic AMP), whose concentration within the tissue is thought to be regulated by vasopressin.

Schwartz, Rasmussen, and their associates have suggested that the hormone first attaches to the membrane at at least two sites, the most important of which involves a covalent linkage between the disulfide group of the octapeptide and free sulfhydryl groups on the membrane. This latter reaction, it is postulated, then initiates a series of disulfide-sulfhydryl interchanges that ultimately results in a mechanical opening of pores or aqueous channels in the mucosal membrane. The hypothesis is based on the following observations: Tritiated vasopressin is firmly "bound" to both toad bladder and kidney, as evidenced by accumulation of radioactivity in treated tissues. It should be noted that it is necessary to assume that the "bound" radioactivity is still resident in the octapeptide, since this has not been established rigorously. On the other hand, the fixation of radioactivity to the tissue is thought to have many of the characteristics of a linkage involving the disulfide group of the hormone. Furthermore, the extent of fixation correlates with the physiological effect of vasopressin or its analogs (Rasmussen et al., 1960). Thus, manipulations which interfere with the responses of the tissue to hormone limit or prevent "binding." Pretreatment of the bladder with N-ethylmaleimide, a potent sulfhydryl inhibitor, interferes with both "binding" and the permeability effect. Similarly, acidification limits both the physiological response and "binding," and cysteine, which is thought to reduce the disulfide bridge of the hormone, also prevents the response of the tissues to the hormone. Finally, they have excluded a metabolic basis for the action of vasopressin, since they have been unable to demonstrate inhibition of the effect of vasopressin on the permeability of the toad bladder to water with a variety of potent metabolic inhibitors, including 2,4-dinitrophenol (DNP), iodoacetamide, etc. These results are at variance with those reported by Bentley (1958) and recently confirmed in our laboratory. In our hands, as well as in those of Bentley, DNP and iodoacetamide, as well as other inhibitors, effectively interfere with the action of a variety of agents, including vasopressin, on the permeability of the toad bladder to water.

It seems to us that none of the observations reported by Schwartz and Rasmussen and their associates are germane to the main thesis, in that they provide no evidence favoring the postulated mechanical opening of pores by a series of disulfide-sulfhydryl interchanges. On the other hand, they may be directed at an elucidation of the nature of the critical attachment of the vasopressin molecule to its receptor organ. It is certainly reasonable to interpret the "binding" data as supporting the view that the hormone must first attach to, or at least interact with, a receptor site in a specific manner before it can initiate its physiological effect. However, the inhibitory effect of N-ethylmaleimide on both "binding" and the physiological response may be of no pertinence to the argument. As pointed out elsewhere, N-ethylmaleimide alters the viability of the tissue in an irreversible fashion (Orloff and Handler, 1962; Sawyer, 1961). It lowers O_2 consumption and Na transport of the toad bladder and also interferes with the action of nondisulfide-containing agents on water movement. Similarly, cysteine and thioglycollate, though considered by many to be specific inhibitors of the action of antidiuretic hormone (ADH), also interfere with the response of the toad bladder to theophylline, a nondisulfide-containing compound, whereas they do not alter the response to cyclic AMP (Handler and Orloff, 1964) which, we will show, effectively mimics ADH in all respects. And, finally, an alternative explanation for the acidification effect will be considered below.

In an effort to approach the problem in a different manner, we have investigated the possibility that vasopressin initiates a series of biochemical changes within the tissue which ultimately results in a change in permeability. The hormone is known to increase O_2 consumption and the rate of glycolysis in skin and bladder (Leaf and Renshaw, 1957; Leaf and Dempsey, 1960). However, these effects are unrelated to the changes in water permeability, since they do not occur in the absence of Na in the bathing medium, though the hormone is still capable of eliciting changes in water movement under these circumstances. Some time ago, Haynes (1958) and Sutherland and Rall (1960) suggested that cyclic AMP exerts a central role in the action of a variety of hormones. They have shown that adrenocorticotrophic hormone (ACTH), glucagon, and other hormones have in common the property of stimulating the production of cyclic AMP in their respective receptor tissues. The addition of cyclic AMP to the adrenal gland promotes the release of cortisol, as does ACTH, and the addition of cyclic AMP to liver promotes the release of glucose, as does glucagon. Sutherland and Rall (1960) proposed that cyclic AMP alters the activity of certain enzyme systems within receptor tissues, finally yielding the physiologically recognizable effect of the various hormones. Subsequently, Hilton, Bergen, and coworkers (Hilton et al., 1959; Bergen et al., 1960) observed that vasopressin mimics ACTH in the adrenal and glucagon in the liver of the dog.

In view of these and other observations, we proposed that vasopressin may stimulate the production of cyclic AMP in responsive epithelial tissues and that cyclic AMP in some unknown fashion may be responsible for the modification of the permeability of these structures to water and to Na (Orloff and Handler, 1961, 1962). This is illustrated in Fig. 3. In the toad bladder and kidney, for example, adenosine triphosphate (ATP) is converted to cyclic AMP. In our view, this enzymatic process is accelerated by vasopressin. The physiologically recognizable response of the tissue to hormone is, we think, mediated by cyclic AMP. It is important to the argument to note that cyclic AMP is degraded to an inactive derivative, 5'-AMP, and that this degradation is inhibited by methyl xanthines, such as theophylline

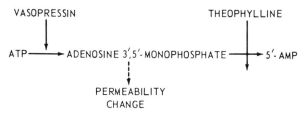

Fig. 3. Role of cyclic AMP in action of neurohypophyseal hormones.

(Butcher and Sutherland, 1962). Support for our hypothesis was afforded by the observation that the response of the toad bladder to cyclic AMP and to theophylline is indistinguishable from the response to vasopress'n (Table 2). All three agents increase the permeability of the toad bladder to water, as

TABLE 2

OSMOTIC FLOW OF WATER
Osmotic gradient = 165 mOs/kg H_2O.

Initial medium	Mg/min	Final medium	Mg/min
Ringer's	1.0	Cyclic AMP	26.7
Ringer's	0.6	Theophylline	18.2
Ringer's	0.8	Vasopressin	26.5

evidenced by an increase in osmotic flow, and all three stimulate Na transport. Furthermore, as with vasopressin, both cyclic AMP and theophylline exert their effects only if applied to the inner surface of the bladder. Bentley (1958), and later Rasmussen and Schwartz and their coworkers (Rasmussen *et al.*, 1960), had demonstrated that acidification of the bathing medium interferes with the response of the toad bladder to vasopressin. The latter workers have interpreted this observation as reflecting interference with a critical attachment of the hormone by its disulfide bridge to a sulfhydryl receptor site on the membrane. The results are also consistent with an alternative explanation. Table 3 illustrates the effect of acidification on the permeability response to vasopressin, theophylline, and cyclic AMP. It is apparent that acidification does interfere with the response to vasopressin. However, theophylline, which cannot bind to the tissue by a dilsulfide linkage, is also ineffective in an acid medium, whereas cyclic AMP exerts its usual effect under these circumstances. These observations lend support to our thesis, since the conversion of ATP to cyclic AMP is minimal at *p*H 6.5 (Sutherland *et al.*, 1962). Consequently, if endogenous cyclic AMP cannot be formed in the

TABLE 3

EFFECT OF pH ON RESPONSE OF THE BLADDER

Osmotic gradient = 165 mOs/kg H_2O.

Medium	Mg/min	
	pH 7.6	pH 6.5
Vasopressin	10.4	1.2
Theophylline	11.1	1.7
Cyclic AMP	9.4	10.4

tissues, neither vasopressin nor theophylline could be expected to alter permeability. In contrast, the effect of exogenous cyclic AMP should be unaltered by acidification.

Further evidence in support of the cyclic-AMP view is provided by the following studies. In other tissues, cyclic AMP is known to activate phosphorylase, an enzyme which accelerates the conversion of glycogen to glucose-1-phosphate. Hormones which are thought to exert their effect through the intermediacy of cyclic AMP generally enhance phosphorylase activity in their receptor tissues (Sutherland and Rall, 1960). A similar phenomenon occurs in toad bladder and kidney following addition of vasopressin (Handler and Orloff, 1963). As is illustrated in Table 4, incubation

TABLE 4

STIMULATION OF PHOSPHORYLASE ACTIVITY IN TOAD BLADDER

Ringer medium	Activity (μM P_1/min/g)	
	Control	Vasopressin
pH 7.4	1.91	+0.22 ± 0.05
pH 6.5	2.00	+0.08 ± 0.08
Choline-Ringer's	2.81	+0.96 ± 0.13

of toad bladder with a number of neurohypophyseal hormones results in a significant increase in phosphorylase activity in the tissues. It is noteworthy that acidification, which prevents the permeability effects of the hormone, also interferes with the phosphorylase effect. These observations, while lending support to our thesis, admittedly do not contribute to an understanding of the mechanism of the permeability changes. Vasopressin, as indicated, does stimulate glycogenolysis in toad bladder, which conceivably could involve phosphorylase activation. However, the stimulation of glycogenolysis is dependent on the presence of Na in the bathing medium, and yet phosphorylase activation by hormone (in contrast to the changes in glycogenolysis) is demonstrable in the absence of Na, as is the effect on the permeability to water. Of greater significance are recent observations relating to the production of cyclic AMP by kidney and toad bladder. Brown *et al.* (1963) were able to demonstrate direct stimulation by vasopressin of cyclic-AMP production in dog kidney. This has been confirmed in kidney and in toad bladder in preliminary studies with Drs. Sutherland and Butcher.

In view of the physiological studies and the biochemical evidence, it is not unreasonable to conclude that vasopressin exerts its effect on amphibian bladder and skin and renal tubules by stimulating the production and/or accumulation of cyclic AMP in these tissues. The important question that remains unresolved is the nature of the precise physical and biochemical events initiated by cyclic AMP which alter membrane structure and permit accelerated flow of water and Na across the cells.

REFERENCES

Andersen, B., and H. H. Ussing. 1957. *Acta Physiol. Scand.* 39: 228.

Bentley, P. J. 1958. *J. Endocrinol.* 17: 201.

Bentley, P. J. 1959. *J. Endocrinol.* 18: 327.

Bentley, P. J. 1960. *J. Endocrinol.* 21: 161.

Bergen, S. S., Jr., R. Sullivan, J. G. Hilton, S. W. Willis, Jr., and T. B. Van Itallie. 1960. *Am. J. Physiol.* 199: 136.

Berliner, R. W., N. G. Levinsky, D. G. Davidson, and M. Eden. 1958. *Am. J. Med.* 24: 730.

Bourguet, J., and J. Maetz. 1961. *Biochim. Biophys. Acta* 52: 552.

Bricker, N. S., T. Biber, and H. H. Ussing. 1963. *J. Clin. Invest.* 42: 88.

Brown, E., D. L. Clarke, V. Roux, and G. H. Sherman. 1963. *J. Biol. Chem.* 238: PC852.

Brunn, F. 1921. *Z. Ges. Exptl. Med.* 25: 170.

Butcher, R. W., and E. W. Sutherland. 1962. *J. Biol. Chem.* 237: 1244.

Du Vigneaud, V. 1956. *Proc. Intern. Congr. Biochem., 3rd, Brussels, 1955.* P. 49.

Essig, A., and A. Leaf. 1963. *J. Gen. Physiol.* 46: 505.

Frazier, H. S. 1962. *J. Gen. Physiol.* 45: 515.

Frazier, H. S., and A. Leaf. 1963. *J. Gen. Physiol.* 46: 491.

Frazier, H. S., E. F. Dempsey, and A. Leaf. 1962. *J. Gen. Physiol.* 45: 529.

Fuhrman, F. A., and H. H. Ussing. 1951. *J. Cellular Comp. Physiol.* 38: 109.

Goetsch, E., H. Cushing, and C. Jacobson. 1911. *Bull. Johns Hopkins Hosp.* 22: 165.

Gottschalk, C. W. 1961. *Physiologist* 4: 35.

Handler, J. S., and J. Orloff. 1963. *Am. J. Physiol.* 205: 298.

Handler, J. S., and J. Orloff. 1964. *Am. J. Physiol.* In press.

Haynes, R. C., Jr. 1958. *J. Biol. Chem.* 233: 1220.

Hays, R. B., and A. Leaf. 1962. *J. Gen. Physiol.* 45: 905.

Hevesy, G., E. Hofer, and A. Krogh. 1935. *Scand. Arch. Physiol.* 72: 199.

Hilton, J. G., L. F. Scian, C. D. Estermann, and O. R. Kruesi. 1959. *Science* 129: 971.

Jard, S., I. Maetz, and F. Morel. 1960. *Compt. Rend.* 251: 788.

Koefoed-Johnsen, V., and H. H. Ussing. 1953. *Acta Physiol. Scand.* 28: 60.

Koefoed-Johnsen, V., and H. H. Ussing. 1958. *Acta Physiol. Scand.* 42: 298.

Krogh, A. 1937. *Scand. Arch. Physiol.* 76: 60.

Krogh, A. 1939. *Osmotic Regulation in Aquatic Animals.* London: Cambridge University Press.

Krogh, A., and P. B. Rehberg. 1922. *Compt. Rend. Soc. Biol.* 87: 461.

Leaf, A. 1960. *J. Gen. Physiol.* 43: 175.

Leaf, A., and E. Dempsey. 1960. *J. Biol. Chem.* 235: 2160.

Leaf, A., and R. M. Hays. 1962. *J. Gen. Physiol.* 45: 921.

Leaf, A., and A. Renshaw. 1957. *Biochem. J.* 65: 82.

MacRobbie, E. A. C., and H. H. Ussing. 1961. *Acta Physiol. Scand.* 53: 348.

Maffly, R. H., R. M. Hays, E. Lamdin, and A. Leaf. 1960. *J. Clin. Invest.* 39: 630.

Orloff, J., and J. S. Handler. 1961. *Biochem. Biophys. Res. Commun.* 5: 63.

Orloff, J., and J. S. Handler. 1962. *J. Clin. Invest.* 41: 702.

Petersen, M. J., and I. S. Edelman. 1963. *Federation Proc.* 21: 146.

Rasmussen, H., I. L. Schwartz, M. A. Schoessler, and G. Hochster. 1960. *Proc. Natl. Acad. Sci. U.S.* 46: 1278.

Rasmussen, H., I. L. Schwartz, R. Young, and J. Marc-Aurele. 1963. *J. Gen. Physiol.* 46: 1171.

Sawyer, W. H. 1960. *Endocrinology* 66: 112.

Sawyer, W. H. 1961. *Pharmacol. Rev.* 13: 225.

Sawyer, W. H., and R. M. Schisgall. 1956. *Am. J. Physiol.* 187: 312.

Schwartz, I. L., H. Rasmussen, M. A. Schlessler, L. Silver, and C. T. O. Fong. 1960. *Proc. Natl. Acad. Sci. U.S.* 46: 1288.

Sidel, V. W., and J. F. Hoffman. 1961. *Federation Proc.* 20: 137.

Smith, H. W. 1937. *The Physiology of the Kidney.* London: Oxford University Press.

Steggerda, F. R., and H. E. Essex. 1934. *Proc. Soc. Exptl. Biol. Med.* 32: 425.

Sutherland, E. W., and T. W. Rall. 1960. *Pharmacol. Rev.* 12: 265.

Sutherland, E. W., T. W. Rall, and T. Menon. 1962. *J. Biol. Chem.* 237: 1220.

Tosteson, D. C. This volume.

Ullrich, K. J., K. Kramer, and J. W. Boylan. 1961. *Progr. Cardiovascular Diseases* 3: 395.

Ussing, H. H. 1955. *The Relation Between Active Ion Transport and Bioelectric Phenomena. Publ., Inst. Biophys., Univ. of Brazil,* Rio de Janeiro.

Ussing, H. H., and K. Zerahn. 1951. *Acta Physiol. Scand.* 23: 110.

Ussing, H. H., P. Kruhoffer, J. H. Thaysen, and N. A. Thorn. 1960. In *Handbuch der Experimentellen Pharmakologie.* Berlin: Springer-Verlag. P. 112.

Verney, E. B. 1947. *Proc. Roy Soc. (London) Ser. B* 135: 25.

Walker, A. M., P. A. Bott, J. Oliver, and M. C. MacDowell. 1941. *Am. J. Physiol.* 134: 580.

Wirz, H., B. Hargitay, and W. Kuhn. 1951. *Helv. Physiol. Pharmacol. Acta* 9: 196.

The Structure and Function
of the Cerebrospinal Fluid

David P. Rall

Laboratory of Chemical Pharmacology
National Cancer Institute
National Institutes of Health
Bethesda, Maryland

It is appropriate, in this, the last presentation of this symposium, that the cerebrospinal fluid (CSF) be discussed. This fluid has been recently defined as the backwater of modern physiology. Perhaps this is correct. In fact, the main thesis I want to present is the concept that the CSF *is* the water, if not the backwater, of the brain; that it, call it extracellular fluid if you will, is a somewhat brackish pool within the brain which provides not only a highly controlled *milieu intérieur* within the *milieu intérieur* as far as ions and other compounds are concerned, but also an escape route for agents which might be potentially noxious but which are so polar as to pass through lipoid membranes with difficulty.

Let us first consider the membranes which separate the CSF from the blood and then the attributes and activities of these membranes, to provide a basis for proposing potential functions for this system.

It should be clear at the outset that we are dealing with a three-compartment system (Fig. 1). Three potential barriers are represented. The membrane separating CSF from blood directly is the choroid plexus; that separating CSF from brain and therefore indirectly from blood is the ependyma; the third is the blood-brain barrier. I will present evidence that the second barrier, that between CSF and brain, is less of a barrier than has been realized; for the present, it will be ignored. Therefore, CSF is separated from blood by two main barriers: the choroid plexus and the blood-brain barrier. The

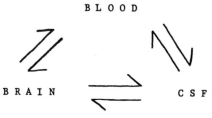

Fig. 1. The three-compartment system.

choroid plexus in simple but typical form is shown in Fig. 2; this is from *Squalus acanthias*, the spiny dogfish. The solid layer of cuboidal cells is apparent. In electron micrographs of the choroid plexus, the walls of adjoining cells are seen to be highly interfolded and interdigitated in the area near the capillary (Wislocki and Ladman, 1958). In this and other ways, these cells resemble those of the proximal renal tubule. This is a solid cellular barrier, and substances must pass through the cells, not between them. The blood-brain barrier is another story. Electron micrographs of brain capillaries show that the capillary itself is not unusual; what seems to represent the barrier is the solid investment of cells, glia, and even neurones, around each capillary. Substances, to gain entrance into the CSF, must pass through, not between, cells. Much evidence from studies on the passage of drugs into CSF and brain indicates that such a concept is likely to be correct (Davson, 1960; Rall and Zubrod, 1962; Schanker, 1962). Lipoid-soluble, un-ionized compounds enter brain and CSF freely and rapidly. Lipoid-insoluble, highly ionized substances enter brain and CSF slowly and incompletely, a state of affairs consistent with the existence of a solid cellular barrier isolating the CSF.

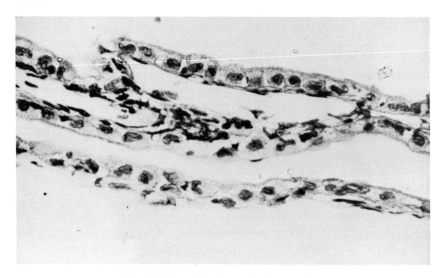

Fig. 2. Choroid plexus of *S. acanthias*.

The volume of CSF is relatively large, ranging from around 120 ml in man to 12 ml in the dog. Figure 3 shows the location of CSF within and surrounding the brain. CSF is formed by the choroid plexi of the lateral ventricles, the third ventricle, and the fourth ventricle. It flows out of the ventricular system via the lateral foramina of Luschka and the medial foramen of Magendie into the subarachnoid space. Here, it may flow down the spinal cord or up and around the convexities of the brain. The CSF exits from the subarachnoid space alongside the nerve roots of spinal or cranial nerves as well as out the

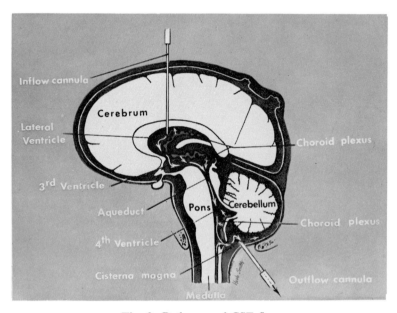

Fig. 3. Pathways of CSF flow.

arachnoid villi. These arachnoid villi have recently been called the "valves of the cerebrospinal fluid" by Welch and Friedman (1960). Evidence has been presented that these arachnoid villi are valves and that they are sensitive to pressure. When the CSF pressure is higher than venous sinus pressure, the leaf-like valves open, and spinal fluid flows into the dural sinuses. When the venous sinus pressure exceeds that of the spinal fluid, the valves close, and blood cannot back up into the cerebrospinal fluid. This, then, provides a mechanism by which spinal fluid can be returned to the blood with considerable rapidity. In fact, the rate of formation of CSF is approximately 0.5%/min. In man, therefore, this represents about 30 ml/hr or 720 ml/day. This may not be a diuresis, but it is a respectable amount of fluid. In other species, the rate is approximately proportional to choroid plexus weight (Oppelt et al., 1964).

Table 1 shows the composition of the CSF, and it is apparent from the excess of Na and Cl that either of these ions might be involved in the production of this fluid. Held and coworkers (1963) have shown that there is a potential difference (PD) between CSF and the extracellular space of the

TABLE 1

COMPARISON OF CONCENTRATION OF SUBSTANCES
IN CSF AND PLASMA

Substance	CSF/Plasma
Cl	1.15
Na	1.08
Mg	1.3
K	0.60
Ca	0.50
HCO_3	0.93
Protein	0.003

body. This difference is a function of the pH of the blood, and this theoretical relationship is shown in Table 2. If one calculates the distribution of Cl be-

TABLE 2

BLOOD pH AND CL CONCENTRATION RATIO
PD: Held et al., 1963; Cl ratio: Nernst equation.

pH Blood	PD mv	$\dfrac{Cl_{CSF}}{Cl_{Bl}}$
7.1	+10	1.7
7.3	+ 5	1.3
7.5	0	1.0

tween blood and CSF as a function of the PD, it is apparent that for normal arterial pH of about 7.3, the PD can account for the observed Cl concentration ratio. One might suggest, then, that Cl may be passively distributed between the plasma and CSF. However, recently, Friedman et al. (1963), working in my laboratory, have made dogs hypochloremic by gastric drainage. Since these animals are alkalotic, there should be a ratio of approximately unity for Cl between CSF and blood. In fact, as can be seen in Table 3, the CSF to plasma Cl ratio is significantly increased. One would suggest, therefore, that this provides satisfactory evidence that the movement of Cl is likely not to be passive. The movement of Na seems not to be passive for essentially similar reasons.

TABLE 3

EFFECT OF HYPOCHLOREMIC ALKALOSIS ON CL AND NA
IN PLASMA AND CSF
The figures are the means of the results from three dogs.
(Data from Friedman *et al.*, 1963.)

	pH		Cl		Na	
	Pl	CSF	Pl	Ratio	Pl	Ratio
Control	7.41	7.40	113	1.16	146	1.04
Hypochloremic	7.64	7.51	53	1.68	126	1.02

The mechanisms involved in the movement of these ions are not well understood. In many studies, inhibitors of various enzymes have been perfused through the ventriculocisternal system, and the production of CSF has been measured. These are summarized in Table 4. The data are clear as far

TABLE 4

EFFECT OF INHIBITORS ON CSF PRODUCTION
(References: Davson and Pollay, 1963; Vates and Bonting, 1963;
Oppelt *et al.*, 1964.)

	Cat	Rabbit	Dog
Acetazolamide	↓	↓	↓
2,4-dinitrophenol	—	↓	—
Ouabain	↓ ↓	0	0

as the carbonic anhydrase inhibitors are concerned. Given either parenterally or in the ventriculocisternal perfusion fluid, acetazolamide causes a consistent decrease in CSF production (Pollay and Davson, 1963). The magnitude of this decrease, about 50%, is quite constant for the various species (Tschirgi *et al.*, 1954; Maren and Robinson, 1960). There is one report that 2,4-dinitrophenol (DNP) is able to reduce CSF production in the rabbit (Pollay and Davson, 1963). The results with ouabain as an inhibitor of (Na + K)-activated adenosine triphosphatase (ATPase) are intriguing. Vates and Bonting (1963) and their coworkers have shown very clearly that when ouabain is perfused through the ventriculocisternal system, there is a reduction in CSF production in the cat, amounting to a 70–80% decrease. Working in the same laboratory, Oppelt and coworkers (Oppelt *et al.*, 1964), however, have been unable to show any decrease in CSF production in the dog. Davson and Pollay (1963) have not shown any decrease in CSF production in the rabbit. Thus, carbonic anhydrase certainly is involved in the production of CSF, and, while it is possible that (Na + K)-activated ATPase is involved, certainly more data and studies on other species are mandatory.

As shown in Table 1, K and Ca are present in a lower concentration in CSF than in plasma, whereas Mg is higher. If I may simply summarize a number of experiments involving the concentration of K (Bekaert and Demeester, 1952), Mg (Oppelt et al., 1963a), and Ca (Oppelt et al., 1963b) in the CSF, it is fair to say that, in spite of wide variations in the plasma concentrations of these three cations, the CSF concentration is held within rigid limits. Figure 4 shows an experiment in which Mg was perfused intravenously

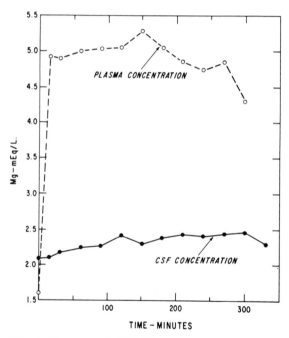

Fig. 4. Plasma and CSF Mg concentrations during continuous infusion of Mg in the dog.

in the dog so as to increase the plasma concentration approximately threefold. This infusion was maintained for 5 hr. The CSF concentration during that period of time, however, increased less than 10%. This is typical of the ability of the membranes surrounding the CSF to maintain a relatively constant concentration of the cations in CSF in the face of plasma variations. Similar experiments could be shown with K or Ca.

This discussion has been concerned with the formation of CSF and the fact that there must be active processes, as yet not defined, which maintain the cationic composition reasonably constant. Although K, Mg, and Ca are held constant, under certain circumstances H^+ concentration can change considerably. In respiratory acidosis, CSF pH follows blood pH closely, while in metabolic acidosis, CSF pH tends to remain unchanged, and large pH gradients develop between CSF and blood (Rall et al., 1958; Robin et al., 1958). The reasons for this are as follows. Changes in arterial pCO_2 are reflected quite rapidly in CSF pCO_2 (Table 5). Changes in plasma HCO_3 are

TABLE 5

PARADOXICAL pH CHANGES IN ACIDOSIS FROM HCL INFUSION
(Data from Robin et al., 1958.)

	pH		CO_2 (mm Hg)		HCO_3 (mEq/l)	
	Control	HCl	Control	HCl	Control	HCl
Art. blood	7.30	7.20	54	46	25.8	18.0
CSF	7.22	7.41	64	42	24.2	24.4

very slowly reflected in CSF HCO_3. After HCl infusion, the compensatory hyperventilation lowers pCO_2 in CSF as well as in blood, but the CSF HCO_3 remains relatively unchanged. Thus, on occasion, CSF pH can rise slightly while blood pH falls.

Another interesting aspect of these membranes which separate the CSF from the rest of the body is that they are able to transport a number of substances out of the CSF and back into the general circulation against an electrochemical gradient. The substances that, so far, are known to be transported in this way are iodopyracet, p-amino hippurate, phenol red, hexamethonium, decamethonium, n-methylnicotinamide, thiocyanate, and iodide. The characteristics of the system that extrudes weak acids (Pappenheimer et al., 1961; Rall and Sheldon, 1961) and weak bases (Schanker et al., 1962) out of the CSF are similar to the characteristics of the comparable system in the proximal renal tubule. Saturation phenomena exist, competition exists, and a source of energy is required.

In addition to this system, Davson and Pollay (1963) have shown that iodide and thiocyanate are actively removed from the CSF. Thus, there exist, within the epithelial membrane separating the spinal fluid from the general tissues of the body, specialized processes for removing a number of polar substances.

Streicher (1961) showed that the brain/plasma concentration ratio of thiocyanate is proportional to the plasma concentration of the thiocyanate ion, as shown in Table 6. This relationship is consistent with a saturable extrusion mechanism. Since it is thought that this mechanism is located in the choroid plexus, one obvious implication is that the thiocyanate in the brain is in communication with the CSF. This serves to introduce the question of the rela-

TABLE 6

EFFECT OF PLASMA CONCENTRATION ON BRAIN PLASMA
CONCENTRATION RATIO FOR THIOCYANATE IN RATS
(Data from Streicher, 1961.)

Dose CNS⁻ mM/kg	CNS⁻ in Plasma mM/l	$\frac{CNS^- \text{ in Brain}}{CNS^- \text{ in Plasma}}$
1	1.8	0.042
2	4.1	0.089
5	8.4	0.152

tionship between the CSF and the extracellular fluid of the brain, as well as the question of the extent of the extracellular space in the brain.

About 15 years ago, there seemed to be no question concerning the existence or the extent of extracellular space in brain. The Cl and Na spaces occupied approximately 35% of the area, and this seemed in agreement with the picture, seen by light microscopy, of large spaces surrounding the neural elements. However, in the 1950's, with the advent of electron microscopy, this picture suddenly and drastically changed. Electron micrographs showed there is essentially no space between the cellular elements of the brain. What light microscopists considered to be open spaces is the watery cytoplasm of the supporting glial cells. More recently, a space between the various cell membranes has been observed, but it is only about 150–200 Å wide (cf. Davson, 1960; Rall and Zubrod, 1962; Schanker, 1962). For the whole brain, this represents an extracellular space of perhaps 4%.

Such a small extracellular space in the brain has a number of implications. First, there need not be any specialized barrier between the capillaries of the brain and the brain cells. Substances which are unable to penetrate cellular membranes simply are prevented from gaining access to a very large volume of the brain, because the great bulk of the brain is intracellular. Secondly, in terms of the nourishment of the neuronal cells, the lack of an extracellular space adequate for diffusion of metabolites implies that glial cells must be involved in some rather specific way in supporting the nutrition of the neuronal cells. As Van Harreveld et al. (1961) emphasized, there are problems concerning the impedance of neuronal tissue if the entire brain is an intracellular compartment. Oppelt, Patlak, and I (Rall et al., 1962) have recently reported experiments which cast doubt upon the limited size of the extracellular space in the brain, and, further, tend to suggest 1) that the extracellular space in the brain is in free communication with the CSF and 2) that the extracellular fluid of the brain must be very similar to the CSF.

Because of the critical nature of this problem, I would like to describe in some detail the experiments that we performed. We perfused the ventriculocisternal system of dogs with an artificial CSF containing C^{14}-labeled inulin. The locations of the cannulae are shown in Fig. 3. This perfusion lasted for 2–7 hr. At the end of the perfusion, the animal was killed, and the brain was removed rapidly and chilled on dry ice. Coronal sections approximately 2 mm thick were taken. From each of these sections, small blocks of tissues were taken at right angles to the surface of the ventricular cavities. This tissue was rapidly placed in a tarred scintillation counting bottle and weighed, scintilla-

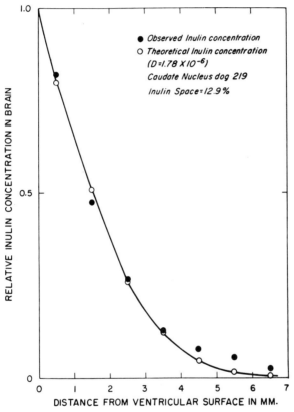

● *Observed Inulin concentration*
○ *Theoretical Inulin concentration*
   (D =1.78 X 10⁻⁶)
Caudate Nucleus dog 219
Inulin Space = 12.9 %

Fig. 5. Inulin in brain as related to distance from ventricular surface after perfusion for 4 hr.

tion medium was added, and the radioactivity was measured. The results are shown in Fig. 5. The ordinate is the concentration of the inulin in the brain tissue (on a weight basis) as the per cent of the inulin concentration of the perfusion fluid, and the abscissa is the mean distance of each piece of tissue from the ventricular surface. The experimental points are represented by solid circles, and the theoretical points (assuming free diffusion of inulin in an aqueous medium) by open circles. Because of the shape of the curve assuming free diffusion, it is possible to extrapolate the first two or three points in a linear fashion to the origin. This gives a reasonable estimate for the inulin space of the particular tissue being studied. Shown in Table 7 are the data

TABLE 7

EXTRACELLULAR SPACE IN BRAIN USING INULIN AND SUCROSE

	Caudate nucleus Mean ± SE	Pons Mean ± SE
Inulin (18 dogs)	12.8 ± 0.7	11.8 ± 0.9
Sucrose (5 dogs)	17.3 ± 2.3	19.4 ± 4.3

for inulin and sucrose in caudate nucleus and pons. It seems clear that the inulin space, or the extracellular space, is at least this order of magnitude. We were concerned, however, because of the disagreement between results of this method, which shows a considerable amount of space available for diffusion of a molecule as large as inulin, and the results of electron microscopy. We tried one further experiment, which was to perform the identical perfusion and sampling technique in a dead dog. Table 8 shows the results

TABLE 8

INULIN SPACE IN LIVE AND DEAD DOGS

	Caudate nucleus Mean ± SE	Pons Mean ± SE
Live dogs (18)	12.8 ± 0.7	11.8 ± 0.9
Dead dogs (6)	5.8 ± 0.7	4.4 ± 0.7

obtained in these same tissues in the dead dog. The space is very much lower and, in fact, very close to the 4% figure observed by the electron microscopist. One wonders if the diffusional characteristics are the same in the dead animal as in the live animal. Figure 6 shows the similarity of the two curves obtained from the live and the dead dogs. They follow the general form of the diffusion equation quite precisely and suggest that the experimental results are reasonably valid. The reason for the difference between these two experiments may be that at death, cells swell and imbibe extracellular fluid.

There are some intriguing implications in this system. The following are some of the assumptions that must be made for a system like this.

1. The ependyma is completely permeable to the inulin.
2. Capillary membranes are impermeable to the inulin.
3. Inulin diffuses freely in the extracellular space.

4. There is no bulk flow of the solvent within the brain during the experiment.
5. There is no mixing of the solvent within the brain during the experiment.
6. The extracellular space is homogeneous in any region of the brain.
7. Inulin remains extracellular.
8. Inulin does not bind to cell membranes.

Assumptions 1 and 2 in large measure define the system. There is no, or relatively no, barrier for the diffusion of inulin from the CSF into the brain tissue,

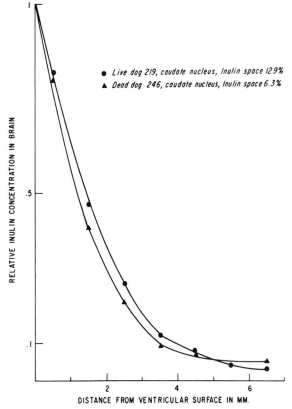

● Live dog 219, caudate nucleus, Inulin space 12.9%
▲ Dead dog 246, caudate nucleus, Inulin space 6.3%

RELATIVE INULIN CONCENTRATION IN BRAIN

DISTANCE FROM VENTRICULAR SURFACE IN MM.

Fig. 6. Inulin in brain as related to distance from ventricular surface in a live and in a dead dog.

and yet there is a very tight barrier from the brain tissue into the vascular system. The blood-brain barrier must operate in reverse. These results clearly show there is a significant extracellular space in the brain. Further, if a molecule as large as inulin can freely enter brain from CSF, then the composition of the CSF in the ventricular cavity and that of the extracellular fluid in the brain must be close.

One may say, then, that the CSF is surrounded by solid cellular barriers consisting of the choroid plexus and the investment of the capillaries of the brain, which isolate it from the blood and general circulation. The production of CSF is quite brisk and seems to be associated with carbonic anhydrase, in part. The role of (Na + K)-activated ATPase is as yet uncertain. The membranes separating spinal fluid from the general circulation are also able to extrude actively into the blood a variety of polar compounds, including weak acids and weak bases, thiocyanate, and iodide. The spinal fluid is in close contact with the cellular structure of the brain, and probably the extracellular fluid of the brain is, in fact, CSF. In terms of ionic composition, the cations, Mg, Ca, and K, are highly controlled, so that their composition in the CSF is quite constant, in spite of considerable changes in plasma concentration. The H^+ concentration of CSF is interesting, in that in metabolic acidosis, there is little effect on the H^+ concentration of CSF, but in respiratory acidosis, CSF and blood H^+ concentrations fall together. Thus, we have a system where polar compounds are not only excluded, but actively removed. We have a system where cation concentrations are highly controlled, and where pH, CO_2, and HCO_3 are controlled in a stylized fashion.

We may now consider the functions of the CSF. There are both internal CSF (ventricular fluid) and external CSF (subarachnoid fluid). We may dispose of the external CSF very rapidly by saying that it floats the brain. This is the classic function of CSF, and it obviously is important. The human brain weighs in air about 1 kg. Floating in CSF, its equivalent weight would be 50 g. Brain tissue is soft and easily damaged, and there is an obvious advantage to this system of a floating suspension.

There have been few attempts to suggest the function of the internal CSF. I would like to quote a passage from an article by Robert Tschirgi (1952):

Let us first consider the purpose of a central nervous system. This organ has seemingly developed to coordinate and integrate the activity of the organism with respect to its external environment. This environment includes not only the outside world, but also the rest of the organism external to the central nervous system. The nervous system must therefore be acutely aware of both the kind and magnitude of environmental changes within and without the body, and must, furthermore, be able to set in motion the proper responses to cope with them. In order to accomplish this, the neuronal mechanisms, which are profoundly affected by slight fluctuations in the composition of their bathing fluid, require a highly stable local environment which will keep them relatively immune from otherwise disastrous shifts in blood solutes. From this standpoint, the blood-brain barrier may be thought of as a second-order homeostatic mechanism for maintaining a central neuronal milieu more constant than is possible by the blood alone.[1]

In the discussion following this presentation of Dr. Tschirgi, this concept was described as "dream-like." I think it is clear now that he presented a

[1] S. Cobb, ed., *The Biology of Mental Health and Disease* (New York: P. B. Hoeber, 1952). P. 43. Used by permission.

valid function of the CSF. The consistency of the concentration of the major cations obviously has distinct advantages in stabilizing the excitability of the central nervous system. The second line of defense provided by the choroid plexus and the blood-brain barrier must be useful.

Now a second function of the CSF is becoming apparent. This is involved with the implications concerning the control of respiration. For a long time, it has been known that the effect of CO_2 on respiration has been large, while the effect of injected HCl has been small. If one assumes now that the receptors for the control for respiration by changes in pH and CO_2 lie within the brain and are exposed to a fluid similar to CSF, this becomes somewhat more understandable. Injection of HCl causes almost no change in composition of CSF and, therefore, almost no change in the central control of respiration. An increase in CO_2 however, causes a striking change in the H^+ and CO_2 concentrations in the CSF and considerable change in respiration. Many of the older concepts of the control of respiration may have to be revised on the basis of the H^+ and CO_2 concentration of CSF. Research in this area is moving very rapidly (Katz *et al.*, 1963; Severinghouse *et al.*, 1963).

There is a third function of the CSF: as an escape channel for polar metabolites of neuronal metabolism. This is the most speculative of the three proposed here. The results with the inulin perfusion of the ventriculocisternal system have shown that the blood-brain barrier works both ways, in that inulin is barred from diffusing through the capillaries of the brain into the blood. Thus, any polar metabolite of neuronal metabolism similarly would have difficulty diffusing back into the blood stream and would tend to accumulate within the brain substance. It can, however, diffuse in the other direction, towards the CSF. Once it enters the CSF, it is removed either by an active-transport mechanism or by bulk flow. The complex of the CSF and its associated membranes seems to be an ideal one to flush out the brain of all such polar nondiffusible metabolites.

If this is coupled with the barrier aspect, that of preventing the access, from the blood stream, of polar compounds, it appears that this also represents a second line of defense.

REFERENCES

Bekaert, J., and G. Demeester. 1952. *Arch. Intern. Physiol.* 60: 172.

Davson, H. 1960. In *Handbook of Physiology*, ed. J. Field. Washington: Am. Physiol. Soc. Sect. 1, Neurophysiology 3: 1761.

Davson, H., and M. Pollay. 1963. *J. Physiol. (London)* 167: 239.

Friedman, S. B., W. G. Austen, R. E. Rieselback, J. B. Block, and D. P. Rall. 1963. *Proc. Soc. Exptl. Biol. Med.* 114: 801.

Held, D., V. Fencl, and J. R. Pappenheimer. 1963. *Federation Proc.* 22: 332.

Katz, R. L., S. H. Ngai, G. G. Nahas, and S. C. Wang. 1963. *Am. J. Physiol.* 204: 867.

Maren, T. H., and B. Robinson. 1960. *Bull. Johns Hopkins Hosp.* 106: 1.

Oppelt, W., I. McIntyre, and D. P. Rall. 1963a. *Am. J. Physiol.* 205: 959.

Oppelt, W., E. S. Owens, and D. P. Rall. 1963b. *Life Sciences* No. 8: 599.

Oppelt, W., C. S. Patlak, and D. P. Rall. 1964. *Am. J. Physiol.* In press.

Pappenheimer, J. R., S. R. Heisey, and E. F. Jordan. 1961. *Am. J. Physiol.* 200: 1.

Pollay, M., and H. Davson. 1963. *Brain* 86: 137.

Rall, D. P., and W. Sheldon. 1961. *Biochem. Pharmacol.* 11: 169.

Rall, D. P., and C. G. Zubrod. 1962. *Ann. Rev. Pharmacol.* 2: 109.

Rall, D. P., W. Oppelt, and C. S. Patlak. 1962. *Life Sciences* No. 2: 43.

Rall, D. P., J. S. Stabenau, and C. G. Zubrod. 1958. *J. Pharmacol.* 125: 185.

Robin, E., R. Whaley, and G. Crump. 1958. *J. Appl. Physiol.* 13: 385.

Schanker, L. S. 1962. *Pharmacol. Rev.* 14: 501.

Schanker, L. S., L. D. Prockop, J. Schou, and P. Sisodia. 1962. *Life Sciences* No. 10: 515.

Severinghouse, J. W., R. A. Mitchell, B. Richardson, and M. Singer. 1963. *Federation Proc.* 22: 223.

Streicher, E. 1961. *Am. J. Physiol.* 201: 334.

Tschirgi, R. D. 1952. In *The Biology of Mental Health and Disease,* ed. S. Cobb. New York: P. B. Hoeber. P. 43.

Tschirgi, R. D., R. W. Frost, and J. L. Taylor. 1954. *Proc. Soc. Exptl. Biol. Med.* 87: 373.

Van Harreveld, A., N. K. Hooper, and J. T. Cusick. 1961. *Am. J. Physiol.* 201: 139.

Vates, T. S., Jr., and S. L. Bonting. 1963. *Federation Proc.* 22: 213.

Welch, K., and V. Friedman. 1960. *Brain* 83: 454.

Wislocki, G. B., and A. J. Ladman. 1958. In *The Cerebrospinal Fluid,* ed. G. E. W. Wolstenholme and M. O'Connor. Boston: Little, Brown & Co.

Index